Hell Is Above Us

The Epic Race to the Top of Fumu, the World's Tallest Mountain

By Lord Kenneth Tersely

With foreword by Jonathan Bloom, Ph.D.

"Hell Is Above Us: The Epic Race to the Top of Fumu, the World's Tallest Mountain"

By Lord Kenneth Tersely

With Foreword by Jonathan Bloom, Ph.D.

Cover art by Heather Kern

Cover design by Jonathan Bloom

Fumu map by Jonathan Bloom

Author photos by Doug Zacker / Zacker Images

ISBN 978-0-615-50934-1

This book is dedicated to Tricia, Ruby, and Jesse.

Thank you for being patient while my mind passed this
rather large and oddly-shaped stone.

Table of Contents

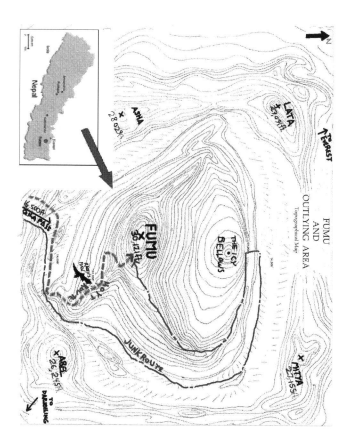

FUMU
AND
OUTLYING AREA

Topographical Map

Nepal

ASMA
28,029ft

LATA
3,60ft

FOREST

FUMU
30,121ft

THE ICY
BELLOWS

JUNK ROUTE

ABEL
26,245ft

MITA
27,155ft

TO
DARJEELING

Timeline

~200 million years B.C.	India breaks off from Pangaea.
Shortly thereafter	India returns to Pangaea, the line of impact becoming a volcanic range.
~100 million years B.C.	The volcanic range cools and becomes the Himalaya. One mountain does not cool.
1802	The Great Trigonometric Survey of India begins. Chomolungma (Everest) is estimated to be the tallest mountain in the world. Fumu is later "cheated" due to the use of a different measuring instrument built by Meriwether Albright (Eng.). In a fit of grief over the death of his daughter, Albright intentionally manufactured thousands of under-estimating survey tools ("I was subtracting out from the world what was lost" he said after his subsequent arrest).
1881	George Malick (Eng.) almost reaches the top of Fumu. High-altitude cannibals and small volcanic eruptions kill most of his party.
1910	Josef Bruner (Ger.) reaches the Eastern Ridge of Fumu before getting blown off by high winds.
Winter, 1935	William Hoyt and Aaron Junk meet and promptly beat each other senseless.
Winter, 1935	Hoyt and Junk place a wager on the likelihood of Junk, a non-climber at this point, traversing the Presidential Range in New Hampshire. The unclear outcome causes their hatred to

amplify.

1935 – 1941	Hoyt and Junk race each other to the summits of nine different mountains.
1937	Wolfgang Rauff (Ger.) reaches what is now known as "Rauff's Maw" on Fumu. Every man on the trip is lost other than the Sherpa.
September, 1939	Zachary Hoover and Sherpa Chhiri Tendi almost reach the summit of Fumu. Hoover is killed in a fiery cataclysm. Chhiri lives to share their discovery: Fumu is taller than Everest.
September, 1939	Junk and Hoyt race each other to the top of Everest. The competition is ruined when a British Spitfire Mark I flying over "The Hump" from India to China crashes into Everest's Western Ridge.
May–December, 1941	**The Fumu expeditions and their spectacular disasters transpire.**
1955	Lord Kenneth Tersely writes *Hell Is Above Us*.

Foreword

Hell Is Above Us was not on the shelves of my local library in Maplewood, New Jersey. It was wedged in *between* the stacks, about two feet in and only inches from the floor. A well-aimed morning sunbeam lit up the book just as I wandered past looking for any printed material to read on my day off. I knelt down, made a reach and it came loose without a struggle. Brushing the dust and human hair from its green, jacketless binding, I reviewed the title and author. Both were unknown to me. An inspection of the inside back cover showed that no one had checked it out since 1962, almost fifty years before the writing of this foreword. How sad. Whoever Kenneth Tersely was, he had probably put his heart and soul into writing these pages and now here they were, forgotten and covered in mouse excrement. My curiosity was nothing more than a spark at that point but it was enough for me to take the book over to a nearby carrel for a quick review.

The next ten hours in that carrel proved to be a life-changing experience for me. By the time I was leaving the library that evening, my stomach was empty, my wife had left ten unrequited voicemails on my phone, and the sun which had exposed the book to me in the first place was already gone.

What was it about the book that had caused me to burn through it in one day? For one thing, it certainly was *not* the writing. Full of labored metaphors and dated, racist terms, I often found myself fighting through the language instead of being carried along by it. Tersely's wielding of the Queen's English reflected the pompous, defensive tone of an empire recently relieved of its dominance. The style may have worked in 1955 when it was published but it certainly doesn't stand up to 2010 standards.

My intense experience also had nothing to do with the two men who are the focus of the book, William Hoyt and Aaron Junk. Certainly their actions were brave and their adventures breathtaking, but Hoyt and Junk seemed like horrible people; aggressively male and endlessly shadow-boxing their respective parent issues. If they were transported to the current year, I could easily see myself crossing the street to avoid them.

No. What stopped me cold was the sheer audacity of the book's central conceit. Did Kenneth Tersely really expect us to believe there is a mountain – a *volcano* no less - taller than Everest? And yet, as I devoured the book - each page being more exciting than its predecessor - I was slowly won over. By the end I was convinced Fumu is the tallest mountain in the world, the truth about it had been ignored due to the tyranny of flawed science, and two relatively unknown climbers – outsiders to the climbing elite for various reasons - had raced to be the first to reach its summit.

Believe me when I say I'm not a man easily swayed, especially when it comes to something as fundamental as "the tallest mountain in the world". There are some facts I almost refuse to question outright. For example, June follows May. Squares have four sides. Any number divided by itself equals one. These facts build our universe and are immovable. But recently, astronomers told us Pluto was, in fact, not a planet at all. How could that be? The nine heavenly bodies of our solar system are actually eight? The impact of this edict was incalculable to me. If such a basic building block of our universe could be wrong, then what else could be brought into question? Would the sun not rise over adult non-fiction at the library tomorrow but instead over the children's section? Would George Washington turn out to have been the second President of the United States?

Now along comes Kenneth Tersely to tell us all Everest is not the "third pole." Some volcano called Fumu is taller. As far as hard sells go, that had to be the hardest. But in the end, using the testimonials of mountaineers both living and dead, scientific data from respected sources, and the fruits of his own scholarly research, he convinced me. As Tersely makes clear in the chapter entitled "Fumu and the Dividing Engine" William Everest mismeasured Fumu and that flawed finding stuck. No one wants to challenge the tyranny of Science. Not even if *the evidence of their eyes refutes it.* How many climbers on Mount Everest's highest reaches saw Fumu in the distance, and how many of them chose to ignore the fact that Fumu looked to be of equal height if not taller than the mountain upon which they stood? All of those otherwise intelligent people denied the obvious truth just because of some charismatic blowhard's flawed discovery more than a century ago.

Thank heavens the individuals in this book accepted the truth; and thank heavens Tersely documented those individuals and spread the gospel of Fumu; and finally, thank heavens there exist a handful of people – like you – willing to read his words with an open mind. Tersely certainly did not convince his contemporaries in 1955. Although he had already written and published two well-received accounts of his personal climbing experiences (*High Camp on Aconcagua* and *Dancing with The Ogre*) and written hundreds of excellent articles on mountain climbing for British and American papers, almost no one was willing to believe or support the obsessively investigated claims he put forward in his draft of *Hell Is Above Us.* There was also the fact that Tersely was in and out of hospitals during the writing of the book. Was the ailment physical or psychological? No one but his family knew and his family never spoke of it. This led to even more rumors that he was mentally unstable and Fumu was nothing more than a castle in the sky built by a lost dreamer.

Upon release, *Hell Is Above Us* hit British bookstores with a dull thud. Utterly humiliated, the man never wrote again. From then until his death from a heart attack in 1972, Tersely stayed mostly in his London flat, rarely venturing out for a paper or tea. The experience of writing about Fumu had turned an adventurous man into a shut-in.

This new edition of *Hell Is Above Us* provides a fresh opportunity for the world to read and accept the truth. The evidence is here, in your hands. So please, sit back and enjoy the adventure. I think you may join Kenneth Tersely and me in our conviction. But there is an even more important reason for you to believe in Fumu. To reuse George Mallory's famous quip: "Because it is there."

Jonathan Bloom, Ph.D.
President, Fumu Truth Movement, New Jersey Chapter
FumuTruth.org
February 21, 2012

HELL IS ABOVE US

"I embrace hardship and privation with ecstatic delight; I want everything that the world holds; I would go to prison or to the scaffold for the sake of the experience. I have never grown out of the infantile belief that the universe was made for me to suck."

-Aleister Crowley

Prelude: September 1ˢᵗ, 1939

The following rather nasty affair was described to me by a Sherpa named Chhiri Tendi. He would later play a role in the tale that is the subject of this book, but the words below tell of an earlier expedition up the beast they call Fumu. Women - and men of questionable fortitude - are advised to read no further:

The rest of the team remained at lower camps as planned, leaving Zachary Hoover and me to summit Fumu together. My excitement was so great at this point it was almost shameful to me, and I was sure sahib Hoover's spirits were in a similar state. Our ascent had been uneventful and rapid so far that day. It was September 1st, 1939 and the sky was cloudless across Nepal. The air was cold, dry, and like it usually is in the icy mountains, scentless. The weather had played along well since the beginning of the month; the cold had been tolerable and the wind mild enough to avoid any tragic tumbles over cliff edges. The only unpleasant characteristic of the place was the noise coming from above us. Stampedes of sound shook the Earth, rumbled the gut, and the sent the testicles into hiding. It was the sound of lava, steam, and smoke being wretched up by the mountain we planned to conquer that very day.

When he got into a rhythm, this young daredevil Hoover was known not to break it. He was thrilled with the pace of our ascent and did not want to slow things down for any reason at all, not even to keep measurements like altitude and barometric pressure. Without these measurements, all the two of us knew about our location was that we required supplemental oxygen and the peak – eternally hidden in a black cloud – was just above us.

I was climbing in back, not because I'm slow, but because I take the safety of my Western customers seriously. I never wanted Hoover to be out of my sight. Whenever a customer is missing, even for a fraction of a moment, I get a stomach cramp and sweat starts to bead on my brow. Ask anyone; that sense of responsibility along with my disarming sense of humor makes me stand out. If these qualities weren't enough to draw others near, I'm also physically impressive. I'm tall for my people in Thame, Nepal, and taller even than Hoover. Some would say that I'm handsome – so handsome, in fact, I have a knife wound in my lower-left back, put there by a man who feared the wives of our village, including his own, were too infatuated with me. Many of the wives are infatuated with me. But it has nothing to do with my looks. It has to do with me being a cut-up and the fact that my dancing is so exceptional it gets every woman in the room pregnant.

Since breaking camp that morning, we had been hiking on a gradual rise that was surrounded by gentle inclines on both sides. It was completely safe, non-technical climbing. We were also hiking along a northeastern face so some morning sun reached us.

At about 11am, Hoover rounded a corner that brought us to a due-north-facing wall of ice. Our wide path turned into an icy precipice slightly narrower than our backpacks. The sun disappeared. The wall over our heads rose and disappeared into the dark cloud above us and the same wall beneath our boots dropped about eight hundred feet to the volcano's vast, extinct throat. Using ice picks and moving very slowly, we proceeded out into the shade of the monstrous cliff. The only sound was the high wind and the irregular rhythm of nearby eruptions.

Each step was calculated and then re-calculated. As footfalls came down, strength of the ice was tested. Body weight gradually shifted to favor crampons on the leading foot. Then the process would start again. Every other forward movement was accompanied by a piton driven into the wall next to us, a carabiner pulled through the piton's eye hole, a rope pulled through the carabiner, and finally the rope secured to our respective belts. We moved forward with the sluggishness of hour hands. Hoover may have been a daredevil, but he was able to attain patience at moments like this and focus obsessively on details. He saw the possibility of death even through the rolling boil of his youth.

We agreed to stop and take a break when the ledge took a gentle turn to the left. The turn proved difficult because the icy wall sloped slightly outward as it rose over the ledge, forcing us to lean into the vast nothingness of space. When we finally stopped, I was about four yards behind Hoover. I took off my mitts and oxygen mask for a moment and began to eat a piece of frozen bread I had stored in my pocket. My stomach was grumbling and I devoured the food quickly despite its unsavory state. It fought my teeth every step of the way and cracked into pieces too large to swallow. Finishing the morsel, I noticed that the world around me was spinning. I also noticed the sound of my own gasping. My chest felt as if it was full of broken glass, shards pressing against muscle with each inhalation. If I didn't breathe canned air again soon, I would collapse. The mask was in my mitts when I notice an unusual look on Hoover's face. His own mask temporarily resting on the top of his head, Hoover's mouth was open, his icy brow was furrowed, and his eyes were squinting and gazing out at a point on the horizon. I looked out to see the source of Hoover's confusion.

It was Everest. We were staring at her southern face, reflecting the morning sun so brightly it looked as if the mountain was emitting light. I could make out the Khumbu Icefall just above Base Camp, the saddle of the South Kol, and the dreaded step just below the summit that would later be named for the Brit Edmund Hillary. I estimated Everest was roughly fifty miles away, which is a small distance when talking on a Himalayan scale. I felt like I could practically reach out and touch it.

But I could tell that it was not Everest's beauty or proximity that held my sahib's attention. What made both of our minds completely rearrange was the fact that we seemed to be looking down at Everest. How could that be?

"Im-ossible," Hoover said (The letter p is difficult to pronounce when your lips are frozen). "A trick of the eye. We're not even into the cloud of this -ountain yet. I think we just need to -ut our -asks -ack on."

I agreed and raced to introduce oxygen back into my lungs. When the abundant air did pour down my throat, the uncertainty did not go away. Everest still appeared to be slightly below us. On Hoover's command, we decided to ignore what we had seen. The naked eye is not a reliable tool for such a task.

As if on cue, an American military plane flew at eye level over the ridge we just ascended, likely on its way from India to China ("Over the hump" as the Brits would later call it when the war came). The roar of its engines could not be heard until it cleared the ridge, but once it did clear the ridge it was all we could hear. The plane was not in good shape. Fumu had apparently spit a vast amount of lava at its left wing and now the entire aircraft was wobbling. Hoover and I watched as it pitched and rolled off into the distant blue, trailing black smoke and gradually losing altitude. We watched for several minutes, mute. Then we saw the plane make contact with the Hillary Step on Everest and spin off behind the mountain, out of sight.

Consider that one more time: The plane passes us at eye level, loses altitude for fifty miles, and then hits Mount Everest near its summit. How could this be, unless...unless what? Unless my parents had been wrong. Unless the elders of our village had been wrong. Unless my sahibs had been wrong. Unless every goddamned person who now lived had been wrong. Everest was not the tallest mountain on the planet. Understanding flooded over me, but I did not feel excitement or joy. I felt burdened.

Hoover and I were now sole keepers of a fact that the rest of the world needed to know but would not care to know.

Hoover spoke.

"Chhiri. Did you see that? The air-lane. It. We're..."

Those rich, eloquent words would be Hoover's last. The cliff next to him shot out a high-pressured, horizontal geyser of black smoke and ash, which cleanly detached and jettisoned Hoover's head far out into the rarefied Himalayan atmosphere. His corpse remained tied to the wall. I did not have time or breath to scream before the wall around the steam exploded into a flood of lava, louder than anything I had heard up to that point. It removed Hoover's body from the ledge and created a hole in the ice wall about the size of a train tunnel. As the ice evaporated, the hole grew larger, quickly. I had to backtrack to get away from the ever-growing danger, but now I had an additional handicap. Somehow, the hemp rope attaching me to Hoover managed not to break, which spoke well of the rope manufacturers, but put me in an unpleasant situation. Hoover's headless body was hanging four yards below me, on fire.

For a moment, I felt myself give up. I stopped moving and shut my eyes tightly. There was no way a person can live through such a scenario. Hoover's corpse was pulling me off the ledge as if asking me to join the dead. I was attached to the wall, but the presence of the lava flow was causing the air to warm up and the ice screws in the wall to lose their purchase. I was suffocating, my hyperventilation being arrested by my regulated oxygen supply.

Raw emotion was quickly tamed by reason. You see, I have a family, and I wished to return home to see my wife, son, and daughter. I decided that my only option was to cut the rope that attached me to Hoover and the wall, discard my equipment except for some food and water, and run for safety.

Things became more complicated before I could execute my plan, as several yards down, the tank of compressed oxygen that was still attached to Hoover's body exploded, obliterating what was left of Hoover, as well as the part of the ledge upon which I was standing. Now I was hanging by my waist, and the ice screws that held me were popping out of the melting ice wall one by one, each dropping me down further. I looked around helplessly at the scene of destruction. The lava flow had subsided somewhat, the hole now billowing black smoke and still growing larger. The ledge above me was totally gone. Hanging from my rope, I felt like an abandoned marionette.

Finally, I caught a lucky break. When Hoover's oxygen tank exploded, it gouged out a man-sized part of the cliff right near me, complete with flat ledge and depth for a backpack. I patiently began to swing over to the absence, digging my crampons into the ice wall and "running" along the cliff. My toes ached of cold so much that this maneuver caused me to grit my teeth and tear up. Once I'd gathered enough momentum, I was able to land on the newly-formed shelf, gather my wits, and plan my next steps.

After about an hour of catching what little breath was available to me, I removed my backpack and stuffed my pockets with food and water. I then managed to rappel down to a nearly horizontal couloir below me that lead back to the ridge where the day had begun. The rappel was treacherous because I was low on oxygen, and the experience an hour previous had placed me in a state of shock.

Over the course of the day, I descended to the nearest camp, Camp Four, with almost no equipment. Each breath felt pointless. Just a lot of pain in my chest and no pay-off. Movement had to be slow, even though my mind kept urging me to hurry before frostbite, hypothermia, or hypoxia finished me off. When I reached the camp, I collapsed into my tent and slept for an entire day. My dreams were full of death and fire. After

- 20 -

eating a meal the next morning, I descended to Camp Three, where several more members of the expedition were waiting. I shared with other expedition members the news of Hoover's grim demise and the failure to reach the top. Camp after camp we descended, gathering more men and equipment. The team members at Base Camp were waiting as the miserable line of souls came down from the mountain. "A funeral march" as one climber put it.

Chhiri Tendi then went home to his village and basked in the presence of his wife and children. To this day, he has not shared the details of what happened on the mountain with them.

The Sherpa is now 51-years-old. He has been kind enough to share all of these recollections with me even though his countenance betrays a man who would prefer to remain in the present. He stares down at the cup in his hand. It seems as if he is seeing something much grander – like Everest from the ledge, moments before the world went mad. "To use the language of your country," he says to me "it was a total *cock-up* at thirty-thousand feet. I'm lucky to be here telling you about it."

"Lucky" was indeed the word for it, given that after the Hoover expedition, Chhiri Tendi was not done with Fumu. Nor was Fumu done with him.

PART ONE: BEFORE THE ASCENT

Chapter One: The Eight-Man Rhubarb

"Few people can be happy unless they hate some other person, nation, or creed."

-Bertrand Russell

Aaron Junk and William Hoyt loathed each other before they had even exchanged a single word. Looking back at the relationship between the two rivals, it seems that their hatred went to some microscopic substrate, as if their genetic compositions were designed solely for mutual destruction. Without each other for the first half of their respective lives, Junk and Hoyt were not complete as human beings. This all changed when they accidentally met on a snowy Boston night in 1935 and wasted no time getting into a rather nasty argle bargle that would portend the events of the next six years.

Junk was drinking with his old friend Patrick McGee and one other man named Simon Phelps at the Beacon Hill Tavern. According to The Boston Globe clipping recalling the trouble, William Hoyt and his party sauntered into the bar at approximately ten at night. They were returning from a three-day traverse of the Presidential Mountain Range in New Hampshire. Most of Hoyt's group was already drunk from visiting other public houses in the area and from consuming cordials in the car. We can be sure Hoyt himself was not drunk, as the rather pious man never let alcohol pass his lips. On the topic of drink, he once said, "I may as well heat my head and strike it with a blacksmith's hammer, forming it into the shape of an ass."

The Globe article does not specify who started the fight, nor does it say anything about the cause, but only states that an "eight-man rhubarb" broke out in the bar and quickly moved to a back alley. By the time it was over, five men went to jail and three others went to the hospital.

If William Hoyt's life were boiled down to a simple sheet of facts, it would betray a pleasant enough American fellow. In his prime during the 1920's and 1930's, he worked effectively as the president of his own bread manufacturing company. He helped out every weekend at his local church. He was a husband and father of two. And of course he was a mountaineer.

However, festering within and between these facts lay another detail that was hardly subjective: William Hoyt was an asocial bore with a bad temper. He was perfunctory and pedantic with a tendency to snap at anyone who disagreed with him about anything. He felt comfortable reimagining his own mistakes as the mistakes of others, and he could not brook the mistakes of others. His temper was notorious among his co-workers, fellow climbers, and even his church. This unpleasant disposition might have been tolerable to others had it been paired with an equally adorable side; a Twain-ish wit perhaps, or the occasional glimpse of nurturance. But that was not the case. He was uninteresting. Hoyt remained quiet no matter where he was. His one-word responses to people's questions hardly counted for conversation and so those who knew him avoided the situation entirely. When it came to climbing, his personality was a serious and even dangerous liability. Many of his best climbs were ones he did alone.

These unpleasant traits roamed the world inside a human vessel uniquely built for great physical accomplishments. At six-foot-three and roughly thirteen stone, Hoyt was slim but powerful. Even at the time of the Fumu ascent, one year past the age of fifty, Hoyt was in better shape than most twenty-one-year-olds. Da Vinci himself could not have devised a machine better equipped for crawling up mountains. He had long limbs and a heart that beat as slowly as a hibernating bear's. When most climbers were halfway up the Avalanche Gulch route of Mount Shasta in California, Hoyt was waiting at the summit, making coffee. He had been climbing for thirty years when Fumu came into his life, and it showed. His face was thick and tough and wrinkled beyond his age. There were white splotches around his nose and forehead where frostbite had won, and a small scar on his temple where skin cancer had lost. But the overall effect was rugged and handsome. He also framed this beaten-up visage with perfectly-cut, slicked-back brown hair – a well-manicured lawn around an old landmark war cannon.

In a letter to his new friend Calvin Coolidge, Aaron Junk recounted the events at the Beacon Hill Tavern in elaborate detail. He, McGee, and Phelps sat at the end of the bar near the entrance. A group of five men came through the door. They were filthy and red from exposure to the sun. But they were also overjoyed and boisterous.

"This Hoyt guy and his group strutted into the tavern like an ostentation of peacocks," Junk writes, "as if this place and the women inside were their property. They spoke loudly and relentlessly. They drank a lot and flirted with every woman present, from the young bride of a local councilman to the seventy-year-old barmaid. They bought drinks for individuals they didn't know, but then mixed the kind gesture with snide comments. 'Barkeep! A scotch for the Harvard man' they'd yell as they bought a drink for Petey, the half-crazed old lush in the corner. 'Barkeep! A brandy for Sarah Bernhardt' as they bought a drink for Pearl, a morbidly fat woman who had been a fixture at the tavern for decades." So it seems that Hoyt's team fouled the room with their cheek. Then Junk's memoir turns specifically to Hoyt. "But in the center of this fool-storm there was an eye – a man who said nothing. I appreciated him the least. He sipped tonic water with a face wreathed in silent smugness, offending my sensibilities more than his colleagues who actually spoke."

Junk was not the kind of man to ignore the people or situations that rubbed him the wrong way. He could not simply move to another pub or go home. Junk had to approach Hoyt and his colleagues. His plan was not necessarily to start a fight, but instead to test these strangers. "They were either going to become my good friends or they were going to be brought low."

It seemed that no matter how much he tried to leave his hardscrabble upbringing behind, Aaron Junk returned to it every day. Between fits of tending to his business concerns – legitimate and otherwise – Junk waded waist-deep in ponies, women, and scotch. He enjoyed attending parties of all sorts but did not approve unless they turned into full-fledged bacchanals. To a New York Times reporter, he once claimed, "It's not a party until all of the bodily fluids have made an appearance." As for mountaineering, it came for him late in life, long after the vices of adolescent city living took root. But even then, climbing would never become spiritually cleansing for him. The mountains would become yet another environment full of fresh wagering opportunities.

Answers to the question "Who is Aaron Junk" resemble those of the fabled blind men describing an elephant; the explanations vary wildly depending on where one is touching the beast. He was a rapscallion masquerading as a society man. He was a jester as serious as a heart attack. Those who wished to define him by his line of work were no better off. Was he a professional gambler, Wall Street investor, or the owner of department stores and commercial real estate holdings? The answer was "yes." The man's role on this Earth was inscrutable. Ludwig Wittgenstein famously argued that the word "game" has no definition. He could just have easily argued his point using the example of Aaron Junk.

Aaron was not a big man, but his charisma and stentorian voice made him seem much taller. He had a habit of standing very close to people and looking them directly in the eye while speaking, never breaking his gaze. Most listeners found it terrifying but exhilarating. He slapped people on the back and laughed at everything they said, as if each person who spoke to him uttered the quips of Moliere. When Aaron spoke, despite his close proximity to the listener, he spoke with the gut-vibrating alto of a cello. He would occasionally pull his listener in even closer, bring the volume of his voice down to a faint whisper, and speak to the person like he were passing along the true name of God, even if he were just recommending the fish pasties in the next room. Being around Aaron Junk made people feel important.

Aaron loved to be seen. He attended every event in his hometown of Boston, or if the event was far-flung, he would use his wealth to get there. He went to business colleague's daughter's weddings in California. He attended after-parties for New York plays. Aaron was at the ribbon-cutting for any new building wings that may have appeared at Harvard (often with his name attached) even though he never attended Harvard. Once in a while, he chartered a sea excursion to Bermuda to drink rum with the locals. The man was peripatetic nearly to the point of omnipresence.

Leaving McGee and Phelps at the end of the bar, Junk approached Hoyt's group. He struck up small talk, asking the men where they had come from. Hoyt finally spoke. His responses were single-word sentences.

"Presidentials"

...in response to the question of where they had been.

"Yes"

...to the question of whether they had been successful in their attempt. And according to Junk, Hoyt avoided making eye contact the whole time he was answering. He looked at any other possible thing in the room except the person who was addressing him. This enraged Junk.

Junk offered Hoyt a drink in celebration of Hoyt's success in a last-ditch attempt to make peace. According to Junk, Hoyt responded to the offer by taking the drink and placing it on the bar without a sip. He then uttered the following words: "Proverbs...'Stay away from drunks. Their eyes are bloodshot and they have bruises that could have been avoided.'" Junk responded with a punch to Hoyt's jaw. The blow removed Hoyt from his stool and landed him on the floor. One might have expected the other men from Hoyt's party to descend on Junk and beat him mercilessly. But as had always been the case, Hoyt had not made very good friends with those around him. Now it seems that his bible quotation had offended the inebriated sensibilities of the climbers who had come into the bar with him. They had had quite enough of their tough and humourless leader. Junk's assault satisfied them deeply. They paused for a few moments after the blow before cheering and hitting mugs together.

Hoyt rose slowly from the bar floor, wiping blood off of his lip with his sleeve. Junk's chums Phelps and McGee sauntered over. Now seven men stood around Hoyt and laughed uproariously. According to some bystanders at the bar, Hoyt started to chuckle as well, raising his shoulders, hands upturned as if to say, "Oh bother! You got me!" The palm of the right upturned hand suddenly jerked forward and hit Phelps in the nose. Phelps reeled backward in a spray of blood, falling and hitting his head on a barstool. He was out cold. Hoyt must have seen the elephantine Phelps as literally the biggest threat and wanted to remove him from the equation. McGee and Junk moved quickly, taking Hoyt by the arms and collar and walking him outside and into a back alley. Hoyt's party, now having turned on him, followed along with a hunger for vengeance in their eyes.

What happened in the alley is less clear. All Junk recalled was that Hoyt actually fought back despite the odds, knocking down two people before he himself took a punch. The police arrived at that point and drove everyone down to the precinct except Phelps and the two others Hoyt had beaten down. They had to wait for an ambulance

As if they had wanted some entertainment, the police at the precinct put Junk and Hoyt in holding cells across from one another. Junk simply stared at Hoyt for hours and Hoyt stared at the floor. The latter must have been in shock over his fate. The inside of a jail was alien to him. Certainly, he had seen businessmen arrested before - the bread business was quite cut-throat and illegal dealings occurred every so often – but Hoyt was not like that, nor was he a lowlife like the man in the cell across from him. He prided himself on being the opposite of these types. He wanted to be good with God's Law and good with Man's law, not festering in a jail cell redolent of urine and teeming with future denizens of Hell's fire.

Junk on the other hand had seen the inside of a jail before, once for gambling and another time for counterfeiting, the latter charge being one he contested until the end. "I don't deal in bunko," he swore to the papers on more than one occasion. "After my dad killed himself" Junk once said to the New York Times, "my mom worked her keister off raising me in a one-room tenement, washing and folding other people's laundry. She raised me to take care of myself, but not to break the law." Per his mother's wishes, Junk tried – and sometimes failed - to stay legitimate. He had moved further and further away from floating craps games (where Junk had met McGee) and was more involved in legal dealings like land and retail. But Junk knew that the nature of his circumstance - the streets he grew up on, his earlier careers choices - required occasional violations of his mother's code.

The silence in the jail lasted for hours. Finally, one of Junk's ex-wives came and posted bail for him and his familiars. Hoyt would have to wait until his wife Wizzy could wire money to the Boston police from New

York City. According to a *Boston American* interview with Junk, Hoyt finally came alive in the last few moments before Junk was released.

Junk recalled: "He started yelling at me, calling me names that would make a hooker blush. My response was to bad-mouth his hobby of mountain climbing. I think I called it "the business of goats." How was I to know at the time that those were the exact words his dad used to say to dissuade his kid from climbing? All I know is that the words seemed to set off an explosion in his head. He started trying to grab at me through the bars. He was screaming for my neck. *'Give me his neck! Officers, give me just a moment with his neck!'* There was spittle on his lip. He was temporarily nuts. I continued anyway, saying if ants could climb then what's the big deal? His so-called accomplishments were not worthy of praise."

Hoyt regained his composure enough to insult Junk, saying if Junk tried to traverse New Hampshire's Presidential range in winter, his remains would be food for bears come spring.

The gambler in Junk awoke. As he was walking out, he turned to Hoyt and bet him one hundred thousand dollars he could traverse the Presidentials, and he invited Hoyt to join him on the trip. He added, "And spare me any hot air from Proverbs about the evils of gambling. Are you in or not?"

Hoyt must have been temporarily detached from his good senses, and in some sort of rage fugue, as he accepted the bet.

Chapter Two: The Presidentials

Hoyt had contacted Junk through the mails only three days after the Beacon Hill incident, specifying a long weekend for a climb in the White Mountains. The date was only two months off. Hoyt's need for revenge must have been like thirst for water: immediate satiety was a matter of life or death.

The press had a heyday. In a battle over honor, two wealthy society men had landed in jail. Now they were settling the score through the new, manly endeavor of mountaineering.

Aaron Junk had no idea what "the Presidentials" were, nor did he know a thing about hiking mountains. Querying friends, acquaintances, and business associates reaped nothing. No one knew about the relatively nascent field of recreational climbing. He checked with connections in Europe. It turned out an Austrian woman he had courted came from a family of climbers. Junk traveled to Vienna and consulted with her father, an elderly gentlemen who had climbed in the Alps for decades but now suffered from dementia. It was difficult for Junk to separate sound advice from gibberish. Clearly, a coat made of women's hair was not preferable to gabardine in combating the elements, but the man said other things that were less easy to dismiss. Would a climb in the Presidentials really require crampons – spikes attached to one's shoes for ice climbing? Would it really get down to thirty degrees below zero at night?

Upon returning to the States, Junk also traveled up to New Hampshire to see what lay ahead. He spoke to people in bars and restaurants. He spoke to the innkeeper where he stayed. A bleak picture was painted by the local commoners: Although the traverse was relatively simple for experienced climbers, it was no stroll through the Boston Gardens. A first-time climber should not be attempting this trek.

The Presidential Range is made up of a chain of peaks in the White Mountains named after various presidents of the United States. Among them are Mount Jefferson, Mount Adams, Mount Quincy Adams, and Mount Madison. The Traverse is a twenty-mile trail passing by a subset of those Presidential peaks, including Mount Washington, the tallest peak in the American Northeast.

The hike is not technical. No special climbing equipment is required except for crampons. An ice-climbing axe should be brought along in case of emergencies, but generally is not needed. After the initial ascent from the trailhead to the top of Mount Madison, the climb mostly follows ridgelines which also make for relatively easy hiking.

However, one cannot quantify the difficulty of an expedition purely by enumerating its technical challenges. Although her height pales in comparison to peaks in the Pacific Northwest, the Alps, and the Himalaya, Mount Washington is known to have an erratic temperament. Loose snow up to one's chest can make for excruciatingly slow progress. Storms and high winds arise out of nowhere. The highest wind speed ever recorded on Earth was at the summit of Mount Washington, which rises to an impressive height of 6,288 feet. Deaths occur on its faces and ridges regularly, especially in winter.

Junk drove to the trailhead and viewed the mountains from the road. Walking in about a half-mile, he found the snow to be deep, at times up to his waist. At eleven in the morning, he estimated the temperature to be about twenty degrees, and that was with no wind at an elevation of only one thousand feet. There would be no backing out of this. In his forty-five years, he had never backed out of anything, and that would certainly not change when the stakes were this high. The money was irrelevant, as his dignity was on the line.

Over the next two months, Junk had two goals: Exercise obsessively and learn everything there was to know about William Hoyt. The former was no problem. Junk made constant trips to the Blue Hills Reservation outside of Boston, running through the woods with weights strapped to his back. He also spent time in the local gymnasiums. Constant walking and avoidance of a desk job had kept Junk fit his entire life. The bigger challenge would be overcoming the alien terrain that was the wilderness. But Junk made quick business of this by purchasing a tent and camping out at night in the woods. The transition was painless, actually pleasurable. He took a shine to the smell of pine trees and the sighting of a snow owl. He was escaping the cold calculus of business life and the right angles of the South End. Best of all, this "escape route" did not take him through drinking benders or other games of chance.

As for his other goal of brushing up on William Hoyt, Junk read through every magazine article and newspaper society page he could get his hands on that made even a passing reference to the sourpuss. Junk also interrogated any acquaintance at social functions who had spent even a fleeting moment with Hoyt. Not surprisingly, Junk was disgusted by the picture these sources painted. Being born into wealth was already enough to leave Junk seething. But making the package ever more distasteful was the fact that Hoyt was a teetotaler and notoriously bad in social situations. As a last strike against him, Hoyt was religious and quite active in his church. As one article put it, Hoyt "was deeply invested in his walk with Christ." If there was one thing Junk could not brook, it was avid churchgoers. After years of business dealings with the ostensibly pious, Junk had grown sick of the hypocrisy of his clientele.[1] For weekends in his youth he would see these devout souls in their Sunday best; yet they were

---

[1] As youths, Junk and McGee had run a rather successful small business selling Coca Cola outside of their neighborhood church when Sunday services let out. They pitched the drink as a balm for hangovers.

the same drunks, charlatans, and hussies he would see reeling about the night before. Junk did not know Hoyt's sins, but he was sure they were profound if the man was "deeply invested in his walk with Christ."

The one unassailable part of Hoyt's background was his mountaineering abilities. At forty-four, Hoyt had already climbed the Matterhorn, the Eiger, the Dolomites, Mount Rainier, and was planning his first trip to the Himalaya, where he was going to lead an American team to the top of Nanga Parbat. Fellow climbers described him as a woefully dull man, but unrivaled in his climbing expertise. Junk, the man who always gambled the well-researched odds had clearly gotten sloppy and placed an enormous bet without doing his homework.

Junk's research suggested that William Hoyt had taken up climbing at university, while on vacation in the Alps with his lady friend Wizzy Dodge. That new avocation came to a quick end when Hoyt's father, Spalding, forbid his son from ever climbing again. The younger Hoyt "felt like a window had opened up for a brief moment and then promptly slammed shut." While it had been open he had seen a universe much like this one, with the major exception being that it was vertical instead of horizontal. It rose to glorious heights and ranged in atmospheres, unlike the present world which made only lateral changes that meant nothing. The window had not only closed in front of him, but the shades had been drawn. No light shown through. The father had essentially told the son he was not allowed to live.

William realized he simply could not face the future without his new-found hobby. But at the same time, he could not disobey his father. No choice remained but to lead a double life. He would lie to his father, promising to never climb again. But behind his father's back he would continue. William graduated from college, got a small flat in Manhattan, and worked for Spalding. But all he cared about was going up more mountains. Climbing became a "repetition compulsion" – something forbidden and taboo that he could not stop. Alcoholics kept whiskey in jars under the floorboards. Compulsive gamblers visited underground poker games on their lunch breaks. William Hoyt secretly went climbing on the weekends. Along with Wizzy, he took on the Catskills, the Adirondacks, the White Mountains, and the Green Mountains. Every time he went, he would take bigger and bigger risks, as if he wanted to get caught. Afterwards, he would "ride home in my horse-drawn carriage, still hungry for more and filled with a growing sense of shame as I reentered this horizontal world."

The single-day climbs were also becoming less interesting to him. He wanted to climb higher than a day would take him. He had read of American and British teams climbing to unprecedented heights in the Andes and the Himalaya. Only a few years previous, the British occultist Aleister Crowley had made an attempt on Kanchenjunga, the third highest peak in the world (as far as the world knew at the time). Crowley had gotten to about 20,000 feet before an avalanche wiped out much of his party and he was forced to turn around. "I dreamed of challenges like these," William wrote, "but knew there would be no way to hide them from father."

If William had some deep urge to get caught, then his urge was about to be fulfilled. One summer afternoon while climbing Smuggler's Notch in Vermont with three former classmates from Yale, William damaged himself terribly after falling twenty feet onto mossy rock. He was tied to a board and gently lowered off the notch wall with an ornate system of ropes and pulleys. He was then taken to Vermont State Hospital in Waterbury to recover from a broken arm, another broken rib, and multiple lacerations to the neck and scalp (he had landed on a raccoon).

William's father was at a garden party held by New York Governor William Sulzer when he received word of his son's folly. According to other party attendees, the usually-reserved man spat out his lemonade, cursed loudly, and punched a hole through his straw boater. After apologizing profusely to the governor for his outburst, Spalding travelled to Vermont to visit his son at the hospital. His intent was not to comfort William.

Spalding cut his first-born son out of his will, fired him from his job at the family business, and, after the hospital bills were paid off, had no intention of funding William any further in life. William may very well have been hurt by this turn of events, but he must have also felt liberated, fearing the day his father would discover his hidden life, but unconsciously willing the event for several years. Now the storm had passed, the stale humidity of sameness had broken, and he was free.

On the day of the traverse, rain fell steadily and the temperature was unseasonably warm. Early March in New Hampshire was still winter, but this year was different. A front from the south had made its way to New England one week earlier and still stubbornly held its ground.

The uncomfortable reunion at the trailhead took place just before lunch on Friday, March 1st. The two men started fighting almost immediately. Hoyt stated his concern about the weather. Such warmth could bring on avalanches. In addition, they would be soaked early on, and once the temperature dropped with higher elevation and the approach of evening, everything they carried and wore would turn to ice. Junk would have none of it. They were going to make the trip regardless of weather. What Hoyt saw as a well-reasoned, conservative decision on his part, Junk saw as cowardice. In a letter to his mate McGee, Junk wrote, "I was hell bent, and told Hoyt in no uncertain terms, 'One hundred thousand dollars says we walk today.'" In an effort to assist Junk in getting everything he deserved, Hoyt agreed to proceed.

Back in 1919, after decades of living just slightly better than street urchins, Junk and McGee hit the financial mother lode. The money they were about to make would go on to take care of them for years to come. Even the Fumu ascent, still but a dot on his horizon, impossibly orthogonal to their lives in 1919, would be funded by events that were about to transpire.

Patrick McGee was friends with a healthy number of Boston police officers, some because he grew up with them and others because he bribed them to stay away from his crap games. Through McGee, Junk had also befriended many officers over the years. These friendships were actually the means by which Junk and McGee avoided the Draft. When soldiers came for recruits, local police would "arrest" the two men for preposterous crimes (One form read "Practicing magic without a license"), and the soldiers would opt to look elsewhere for men to send to Europe.

The city of Boston was going through a terrible crisis with its police force. The police were underpaid and required to work under abominable working conditions. When the police tried to unionize, the commissioner, mayor, and governor pushed back. Many officers were fired for trying to organize.

Junk was born a calculator of situations, and this time he foresaw that the police debacle was going to get worse before it got better. He knew the hearts of the police officers, and from the newspapers, he felt he knew the hearts of Commissioner Curtis, Mayor Peters, and Governor Coolidge. All parties were bullheaded and had serious investments in the outcome. Junk understood – as if it were written on parchment – that this was going to end up with the police striking and the local government unprepared to do anything about it.

Junk acted quickly. He remembered the names of the wealthy families to whom he had sold soda in front of the church during leaner times. He went door to door, visiting them in their homes on Beacon Hill and outlying areas. He let them know things were about to get scary in their fair town. He let them know if the police did stop working and chaos ensued, chances were high the wealthy would be targeted. Their houses burned, their women raped, their children taken from them, and their own lives snuffed out. Junk also let them know that for a daily fee, he could ensure their safety with his own security force until such a time the conflict had subsided. He ensured them this was not like mafia security. Signing up was optional, and they could stop paying at any time.

It is a testament to Junk's amazing way with people that almost every family he visited took him up on the offer. Each paid him tens of thousands of dollars for protection from the riotous hoards. They signed a contract and in return were handed a piece of paper with details about the paramilitary officer who would be summoned to their house if a strike should occur. His new customers went on to tell friends about Junk's, and those people immediately came looking for protection.

On the evening of September 9th, as Junk predicted, the city descended into madness. The police went on strike, and the local and state governments were not able to replace the officers until the next day. Throughout the evening, rule of law was suspended. Violence broke out in every corner of the city. Windows were smashed, people were assaulted, and fires were started.

This is where McGee and his connections came in. Very quietly, out of the picket lines, several hundred striking officers disappeared into the night. They individually arrived at homes with well-manicured lawns and at perfectly maintained row houses. Greeted graciously by the people inside, maybe offered a sandwich or a cup of coffee, these officers then went about the business of vigilantly standing guard outside of their employers' homes, waiting to bash in the skulls of any rioters who chose to target their charge.

The officers were getting paid only slightly more than the city paid them, which was fine given the city had no intention of paying them during a strike anyway. Junk and McGee had little overhead to worry about. Most of the revenue went right into their pockets. Between the times Junk started selling the security services until the evening of the infamous Boston Police Strike – a period of about two weeks – historians estimate Junk and McGee pulled in almost one million dollars in pure profit.

Then Junk and McGee took their profits and bet it all - and considerably more - on the Cincinnati Reds in the infamous 1919 World Series. A friend of Junk's, the infamous Nicky Arnstein, had let him know "the fix was in" and the heavily favored White Sox planned to throw the game. Exactly one month to the day after the police strike, Junk turned one million dollars into tens of millions of dollars.

Junk and McGee were now major players in Boston. They ran legitimate business and they ran the streets between them. They drank watered down ale in the seediest dives in South Boston, and they drank the finest single malt scotch at private functions along The Commons. They had connections high and low, among public officials and private businessmen. Junk especially made waves because of his impressive social gifts. McGee often chose to lay low and attend to business. Junk was the face of their power. Everyone knew him. It would not be an exaggeration to say that by the opening of the 1920's, Aaron Junk *owned* the city of Boston.

On the trail, Hoyt and Junk did not speak to each other. Progress was slow. Snow and slush reached to their belts. They were soaked to the bone, making everything heavier. Even good friends would have kept conversation to a minimum in such conditions. Every bit of energy was focused on moving forward.

As they ascended, the weather improved. The rain let up. The sun shined. But the temperature dropped and the wind picked up behind the departing front. The sun was setting when they reached the top of Mount Madison, and they set up camp in brutal conditions.

In the night, the wind continued to pick up outside of their tents. Junk was introduced to a kind of cold he had never known before; the kind in which every muscle goes into a state of total rigor. As Hoyt had predicted, everything was frozen, including the wool hat Junk wore on his head as he searched in vain for dreams in his sleeping bag.

It was then things got worse. Junk's tent, which was also frozen after sitting wet in his backpack on the ascent, succumbed to the ravaging wind. It did not rip. "In its frozen state, the roof actually cracked and then rose up like a drawbridge. I was suddenly looking at the tops of aspens framing a starry sky." Humility had not been in Junk's lexicon until that night. He simply had no alternative but to hop over to Hoyt's tent in his sleeping bag and beg for entry. The two men spent the rest of the night in the same tent, which potentially kept them alive. Both Hoyt and Junk would return from the trip with advanced frostbite on their toes. Hoyt would lose one to amputation.

Having been cut off by his father, William Hoyt had no home, no finances, and no family. Wizzy's parents were fond of the young man and agreed to take him in for a few months or until he was back on his feet and Wizzy herself did not hesitate to pay for everything using her parents' vast coal fortune. Over the course of the next two years, Hoyt would marry Wizzy, enroll at Columbia Business School, have two sons, and sign up for his first mountain-climbing expedition. World War I was visited upon the United States, but thanks to climbing injuries it passed William quietly by. While colleagues fought and died in European trenches, William started up his own business concern, Daily Bread, with a loan from the Dodge family.

He competed directly with the Hoyt Bread Company, the business of his own father. With his well-honed business acumen, William succeeded in routing the old man at his own game.

The competition only lasted a few months. Spalding Hoyt died of acute constipation in 1920. His constipation had been so acute in fact that it attracted the attention of doctors around the world. The blockage backed up to his duodenum, the valve below the stomach. The case was infamous in medical circles. Many of the groundbreaking methods the doctors used to understand Spalding's condition would go on to inform the methods used today for studying the physics of automobile traffic patterns.

William and his brother Randolph attended Spalding's funeral, but spent most of their time ensuring their mother Maddy – who had gone quite mad with early onset dementia - did not blurt out comments about Woodrow Wilson's secret life as a vampire. Like Maddy, William was not in a mental state that allowed him to shed tears at the passing of Spalding. "I was certainly full of emotion, but the emotion did not have a name. My heartbeat, breathing, and thinking were rapid. My face was warm. That is all I could say about it."

Now the millionaire bread maker took on climbing with an insatiable zeal. He went on to not only climb Mount Rainier but to forge his own route, now named after him, halfway between the Fuhrer Finger Route and the Ingraham Headwall Variation. He took on McKinley. He traveled to Europe, the war now over, and completed the first known solo ascent of Monteviso in the Italian Alps. He was the talk of the climbing communities on two continents. His reputation for adventure also penetrated financial and social circles. People did not much like to be in his company as it was much like to trying to strike up conversation with an empty hat, but they made sure to be seen with him anyway. A few minutes of miserable dialogue – or monologue as the case often turned out to be -

were a small price to pay for a photo opportunity with the world's greatest mountain climber.

Now a mother, Wizzy could not and did not want to join her husband on his climbs. William's time with Wizzy and the children diminished. She begged him to save the climbing for a time when the children would be older, but he could not oblige. The weight of his own father was gone. He did not want it to be immediately replaced with his family. "Please do not play that role in my life," he once asked her. Out of deep love for her husband, Wizzy Hoyt – the woman who had run topless through Times Square, sprayed Calvin Coolidge with seltzer, and climbed many portions of the Pyrenees large men feared – acquiesced and stayed at home with her children while William climbed the world.

To be sure, William Hoyt was living out his dream. He had no idea a man was out there waiting to turn his dream into the kind of stinking, violent hallucination one experiences at the height of sepsis.

Junk hiked in front. They were now completing the main portion of the Presidential traverse which occurred on Saturday. Aside from suffering through the bodily harm they had received the night before, the day went quite well. The weather was cold but otherwise harmless. Junk showed himself to be fast and fearless. Deep snow, sheer ice, and nerve-wracking heights seemed to have little effect on him. He actually basked in it. Hoyt had to concede the glorified street urchin was a good match for him in terms of speed. "We would get separated by at most a few hundred feet, but then he would catch up within a few minutes." After a day of solid hiking, they dug bivouacs and settled in for the night. Although cold, the situation was not nearly as bad as the night before. Their clothing had dried and the snow caves kept them relatively warm. Also, Mount Pierce is not as tall as Mount Madison where they had camped the night before, so the temperature remained slightly higher.

The final day of the trip had the potential to be short, painless, and possibly even pleasant. They simply needed to descend Mount Pierce and both men would have cars waiting for them, one driven by Wizzy, the other by McGee. As they descended, the two actually made some small talk. "I remember we discussed the delightfully sunny weather, New Hampshire history, and that socialist cripple Roosevelt," recalled Hoyt. "I would not go so far as to say we experienced a moment of liking each other, but for a short while, we felt our adversarial relationship may not be worth it." These were surprising words from Hoyt given that in roughly two hours – should events continue unabated - he was going to be relieved of one hundred thousand dollars.

Some time between that brief dialogue and the end of the trail, they became separated. Hoyt arrived at the trailhead but Junk did not. Whether Hoyt deliberately sped ahead is unknown to this day. Whatever the reason, Junk became lost in the woods with only a half-mile left. "I wandered like the Hebrews of old. There was no sign of a trail, a road, a human. I couldn't follow any tracks because the low-lying area had flooded due to warm weather. The ground was slush, mud, and tiny rivers of run-off."

Junk was lost for several hours. When Hoyt and a team of local police found him, the sun was going down and Junk had already set up his ripped tent and was trying to start a fire with wet tinder. He was seething; convinced Hoyt had ditched him intentionally. "Junk said nothing to me, only to the police. I knew what he was thinking, and I was appalled. My parents raised me properly. Risking another man's life in order to save oneself money is not what humans do. The man got lost due to his own sloth."

Nonetheless, the possibility did exist that Hoyt abandoned his foe unconsciously. One hundred thousand dollars is a lot of money by today's standards, but in the 1930's, in the middle of the Great Depression, one hundred thousand dollars meant considerably more.   Hoyt may have allowed himself to pick up speed at the end using some alternative reasoning, like "This is the final sprint." That reasoning could work as an alibi when speaking to others and when carrying on an internal dialogue. And that is the alibi he used.

When the party of police and climbers arrived at the road, Junk finally asked Hoyt about delivery of his winnings. Hoyt said there would be no money because Junk did not traverse the Presidentials successfully. He got lost and required aid to get out.   Junk responded - loudly - that he was standing at the end of the trail at that very moment. No one had driven him there. No one had carried him. He had used his feet to go from one end of the trail to the other. The sheriff asked both the men to calm down, but it was no use. Hoyt yelled that the "Presidential Traverse" was the name of a trail and Junk had lost the trail, requiring the assistance of others to save him. What's more, no one had shaken on the bet. They had both been confined to jail cells when the agreement had been made. "You lose, Aaron Junk. You lose."

Holding a crampon in his left hand, spikes out, Junk ran at Hoyt. He took one swipe at his target, but Hoyt was ready. "I grabbed the arm that held the crampon," Hoyt said. "I then employed a move I had learned on a trip to the Orient. I turned around - the attacker now behind me – while putting the offending arm over my shoulder, elbow down. Pulling the arm downward and bending my back, the victim has no choice but to heave himself over me, in essence flipping himself. The alternative is to suffer a broken arm." Junk was no exception from the laws of physics. He was lifted up over Hoyt and ended up on his back, looking up at his foe. But he was quickly on his feet, fighting again.

The police descended. Had the two men stopped fighting right then, they would have simply been sent their separate directions. But the fight continued and the police had to struggle to pull the two apart. One officer received a misguided punch to the side of the head. For a second time, Hoyt and Junk spent an evening staring at each other from separate jail cells.

Upon his release, Junk returned to find his business concerns were suffering from neglect due to his absence and McGee's lack of intelligence. The experience of the past several days had also left him rather uncomfortable physically. But that was not the worst of it. At the Beacon Hill Tavern the first night home, Junk received the word his mother had died. The nightly beatings he had received as a youth were now definitively over, but then again so was the unspoken love and pride Junk had to believe were there in the meals she prepared and shelter she provided. Now he would never know.

Despite these horrible circumstances, Junk seemed in good spirits to those around him. Mountain climbing had come into his life. He wanted to do something like it again. Nay, he *had* to do something like it again. In what form, he did not know. He was above being a common bridge builder. But he would find some way and some excuse to scurry up things. Even after only one experience, Aaron felt climbing was not a metaphor for something else. Everything else in his life was a metaphor for climbing. Strip the poetry of the world away, and there was simply up, down, back, forth, left and right. Upward and forward were good. Everything else was pointless. He did not yet know how, but Aaron was destined to go upward and forward.

Interlude: August 23rd, 1937

The Nazis loved to climb. In the time leading up to World War II, Nazis and Nazi sympathizers flocked to the climbing clubs of Germany and Austria. Germany had enjoyed a rich tradition of mountaineering before and after the war. But during the 1930's and 1940's the ranks of these fine mountaineers were tainted with others who espoused fascist, racist rhetoric.

In 1933, the Nazis took power in Germany, smothering opposing leftist, socialist sentiments with brute force. At the time, Europe was between wars, but Hitler still had something to prove to the outside world. As the author Jonathan Neale points out in his book *Tigers of the Snow*, climbing was a perfect means by which the Nazi party could show the world the dominance of the Aryan race. They may not have beaten the British during World War I, but they could do one better and conquer Mother Nature herself. Clive Steinkraus, an SS soldier and avid climber, proposed another likely reason for the Nazi tendency to climb: "There are fewer Jews at high altitudes. They seem to be partial to city life and journeys of introspection. That is fine. It gives us a chance to escape to a place pure, white, and free from usury."

Whatever the reason, either for pride or prejudice or both, the Nazi government funded several expeditions in the Alps and also the Himalaya. Neither the Germans nor the British had yet succeeded in topping any of the "eight thousanders" (mountains in the Himalayan chain higher than eight thousand meters). The Germans did have a glorious success in the Alps under their belts - Andreas Heckmair's incredible 1938 ascent of the Eiger's north face - but especially under Hitler, they felt they needed to reach the highest points on Earth before their British counterparts. During the time of Nazi rule, Germany made multiple attempts at Nanga Parbat, a mountain thought to be the 9th tallest in the world, in 1934, 1937, 1938, and 1939. The 1939 expedition included Heinrich Harrer, the German climber who wrote the book *Seven Years in Tibet.* The attempts at Nanga Parbat all ended in failure and in the last case, the incarceration of the climbers by the British.

Nanga Parbat was a regular target for Germany because it was one of the few eight thousanders to which they had access. The French and British controlled most of Asia, so mountains like Everest and Kanchenjunga were out of their reach. Nanga Parbat is in the far western end of the Himalayan chain and was therefore easier for them to access.

Hitler was not satisfied with climbing the ninth tallest mountain in the world. He wanted Germany to conquer the biggest ones, even if they were deep inside enemy territory. To this end, the Nazis planned covert expeditions into India, Nepal and Tibet. One such expedition was led by a man named Wolfgang Rauff, a powerful banker from Berlin. Rauff - raised in Ernstthal, Schönburgische Rezessherrschaften, Kingdom of Saxony - was an aggressive nationalist who had served in the First World War. Jealous of the younger men who were fighting on the front lines of the latest world war, Rauff carried a gun everywhere he went, even on climbing expeditions, in the hopes of running into the enemy.

A party of eight men led by Rauff made a push to climb Fumu in the summer of 1937.[2] The expedition was bold for two reasons. Firstly, Fumu was already known to kill more climbers than it spared. Secondly, the mountain was inside Nepal, a nation surrounded on all sides by realms of aggressive "sub-humans." Getting there was half of the challenge. The party had to leverage the chaos of Stalin's purges, the Moslem uprising in

---

[2] Although believed to be the tallest, Everest was not attempted. There was simply too much traffic on the mountain, almost guaranteeing the Germans would be discovered by unfriendly parties and potentially arrested upon descent. They may also have been attracted to Fumu because it was known to be more lethal than the "taller" Everest.

Sinkiang, and the Sino-British border disputes in Tibet to create a smokescreen for their protracted, tedious trek to Fumu. They made the trip of several thousand miles with minimal equipment using any means at their disposal including cars, boats, and the vegetable carts of local farmers.

At that time, no one had even come close to reaching the top of Fumu, let alone making it past ten thousand feet. The mountain has few possible approaches, and the approaches that do exist are deathtraps. Starting at eleven thousand feet and rising to twelve thousand feet, the mountain is almost completely ringed by ever-shifting scree. This precipitous steep of rubble endlessly changes shape due to activity from above, volcanic and otherwise. Rauff's was the first recorded team to get above the scree without losing a single soul. They were certain once that obstacle had been surmounted, the remaining trip would be relatively easy.

Climbing any mountain over ten thousand feet requires a rigorous regimen of altitude acclimatization. Acclimatization is required so that climbers can adapt to changing atmospheric conditions as gradually as possible. To this end, once past ten thousand feet, climbers will ascend roughly one thousand feet *and then climb back down* to sleep. They may repeat the process more than once before ascending further. As difficult as this process may sound, it is the better option when compared to altitude sickness. In its mildest form, sufferers may just experience a headache. But in its most severe form, a person can die a painful death. Despite this risk, Rauff and his team chose not to down-climb the scree. Altitude sickness seemed like a better fate than being crushed in a landslide. Rauff's team would begin the acclimatization process above the scree.

They took what is known as the southern route, or "Malick's route," named after the first known man to attempt Fumu back in 1881. Malick's route was generally considered preferable to the northern route because of its proximity to the one pass into the Qila Sanctuary, even though the northern route was less technically challenging. If one chose to take the northern route, he would have to prepare for an extra several days hike around the base of the mountain. With an endeavor that already strained the limits of Man, few people in their right mind made that choice.

The next several days went well for Rauff's party. From the scree, the eighteen small objects moved up the southern face of Fumu to their third camp, slowly but consistently. They down-climbed the next day with no incidents, and on the third day they climbed back up even faster than before. The outlook for the next few days was even more positive. They would be ascending and descending vast fields of snow and ice that gradually rose up to the intended Camps Four and Five. These fields were not very steep and as wide as London's Trafalgar Square.

The weather was also in their favour. Other than the constant grim cloud at the summit, the blue of the sky was uninterrupted in all directions. The southern exposure, mild winds, and blazing sun reflecting off snowpack likely put the temperature somewhere around forty degrees Fahrenheit. Most of the men were shirtless.

According to Nima Sonam, one of the nine Sherpa who survived the events of that day, Rauff was walking in front, untethered. Rauff had felt on such an easy pitch, there was little need to be tied to the other men. Lobsang Tenjing, another Sherpa who was very interested in currying favor from any "white eyes" who hired him, walked in front with Rauff. He too walked without a rope. The two chatted away about politics, women, and the best places in Berlin to get a custom-made, high-quality backpack. Rauff fancied himself an expert on such topics. The other six Germans climbed in a straight line behind Rauff and Lobsang Tenjing, all tied off. They had given themselves about ten feet of rope between climbers, but climbed much closer to each other than that. The nine other Sherpa brought up the rear, also unfettered by the rope.

The warm weather put everyone in good spirits. Despite the thin air, the Germans began singing, most likely the infamous songs written for the National Socialist German Workers' Party. Nima Sonam knew enough German to catch the gist of the lyrics. "They sang songs praising their leader, condemning outsiders, and glorifying the brotherhood among Aryan men," he remembers. "It goes without saying they did not ask us to sing along." The Sherpa could only assume they were not included in the "brotherhood." Lobsang Tenjing was making every effort to defy the tradition and break through to their world. But everyone knew that when a climb was over, the old boundaries between "coolie" and "sahib" – regardless of the sahib's origin – rose back up to a great height.

Below the singing, another sound began to rise, tuneless and terrible. The men stopped their revelry one by one as it reached their ears. A cracking sound. All eighteen souls stopped in their tracks and remained motionless. Whatever was cracking was enormous, the sound coming from directly below and also echoing from afar. And in another moment, it simply stopped.

The men looked at each other, shaken. Rauff laughed to break the tension. After some time, the other Germans laughed as well. The Sherpa did not. The whole team began to walk again. Rauff broke into the first line of *Das Lied der Deutschen* when the Earth opened up beneath them. The sound must have been deafening as ice chunks the size of city row houses separated from each other and fell. What had a moment ago been a featureless field of ice and snow now looked like an enormous cat's eye - white on both sides with a long black slit up the middle, roughly fifty feet wide. The men on the rope were draped across the slit, with Rauff and Lobsang Tenjing holding onto the man at the front, and the nine Sherpa holding onto the man at the end. The ones in the middle flailed their arms and legs over the chasm and yelled for help.

Rauff was slipping and his backpack was ripping open. Oxygen tanks, cooker parts, cups, and the like fell out and rolled over the edge of the chasm. "I did not hear the sound of these things hitting the bottom," Nima Sonam recalls. "That may have been because of the screaming, or it may have been because the bottom was very far away."

Rauff yelled for everyone to keep quiet. Although straining to hold the rope, he needed a moment to think. Complete silence fell over the group, even those hanging in mid-air. The situation was problematic. The weight of the tethered men was being shared by the people standing on both sides of the chasm. Neither side could safely let go without placing all of the weight on the men on the other side. Also, if either side let go, the tethered man closest to them would fall and swing in a fifty foot arc – a fatal fall without question.

The man in the middle of the rope was an older climber named Dieter Hofstadter. Rauff called to him, telling him to take out a knife and cut through the hemp of the rope above him. In this way, the fall would be minimized for all of the hanging men, and the weight would be minimized for those holding the rope on land. But Dieter was helpless. He could not manage his knife with shaking hands, nor could he reach up to cut the rope. It was only a matter of seconds before he had dropped the knife.

They sat there for what must have seemed like an eternity, trying to consider a way out of this vexation. Rauff and Lobsang Tenjing would certainly have been growing exhausted quickly. In his stubbornness and desperation, Rauff demanded the Sherpa on the other side let go. He refused to be directly responsible for the deaths of any men on his expedition, and he was certain once the men on the rope were vertical, they could use their spikes and the pickaxes in their belt to take hold of the ice, thereby removing the burden of their weight from him and Lobsang Tenjing. The Sherpa on the other side were incredulous, as was the man the Sherpa were holding, a young typeface designer from Munich named

Hermann Shultz – the person who would take the fifty-foot fall if Rauff had his way. Shultz yelled for Rauff to be a true leader and take the difficult step of letting go. Rauff refused angrily. Everyone was now yelling.

Having reached his limit, Rauff drew the pistol he kept tucked into his belt. He fired directly at the Sherpa on the other side. He was too focused on holding onto his climber and fired wildly, missing the Sherpa entirely. The Sherpa did not lose their grip on Shultz for even a moment.

Rauff's desperate act could not have failed more miserably. The sound of the gunshot loosened whatever ground was beneath him. The cat's eye dilated wider. Rauff and Lobsang Tenjing fell, pulling every last tethered man with them into the bowels of the mountain, screaming for their lives the whole way down. The remaining Sherpa looked down in shock at the massive opening below them. It was no crevasse. It was an entirely new feature in the topography of the mountain. The snowfield they had been walking on less than twenty minutes earlier had apparently been a frozen roof – one hundred feet thick - over a concave face between major buttresses. The roof may have been weakening and cracking for some time, but the warm weather and Nazi mirth had been enough to break it open. The southern route to the summit now had a major hurdle added to it. Ever since the Sherpa returned to tell of the disaster, western climbers have called the area "Rauff's Maw." But the Sherpa use another name for it. They call it "The Cat's Eye."

Chapter Three: The Stakes Keep Climbing

Madison Square Garden Bowl was abuzz on the evening of October 12th, 1936. "Gentleman" Dan Smith was taking on "Swarthy" Vin Piano in a boxing match for the heavyweight championship title. Smith had not lost a fight yet. Nor had Piano. Anyone who could get in to see the fight had done so. At ringside were notable names like Myrna Loy, Gary Cooper, and oddly enough, Carl Jung, who happened to be visiting the states to give a series of lectures at Yale. Sitting next to Myrna Loy - and certainly more interested in Myrna Loy than the title bout - was Aaron Junk. Almost a year had passed since the Presidentials, and Junk was rather silent about the whole affair. Perhaps he shared his thoughts about that disaster with McGee, but talking to McGee was as secretive as talking to himself.

Piano laid out Smith in one round. The crowd's disappointment was palpable. People booed and threw their cigar stubs. Some of the bolder crowd members were heard to yell, "The fix is in!" directly at Piano. To his credit, Piano blew kisses to the crowd and exited the ring with his new outsized, impractical belt.

The newspapers were also let down. They had hoped to write about "The Fight of the Century" only to have one man turn the other into haggis in seconds. Writers turned to the celebrities in the crowd, asking for their take on the evening's events, hoping for some new angle. Most of the interviewees had little to say, except perhaps that "the fight was a disappointment" – not what one would call a "unique take."

Then the press turned to Junk. After a year of relative silence, the man was on fire. This may have been partly due to the fact that he had thousands of dollars riding on Piano. "Piano was the better man! He won fair and square. Although I wouldn't bet on him against some of the palookas I grew up with." This got a laugh from the crowd. "You may have noticed Piano favors his right arm, and gives off the impression he is a righty. In fact, Piano is a southpaw. The opponent begins to follow a false premise. Then out of nowhere, the left arm approaches and makes contact like a hod of bricks. The secret to winning, you see, is holding your cards close and then playing them at the right moment."

The opening was obvious. "So when are you going to play your cards, Mr. Junk?" This got a big laugh as well. Even from Junk.

"Good question. I see my pal William Hoyt is not here tonight. I guess he gets nauseous at the idea of two real men fighting fair." More laughs. "So why don't you, the esteemed members of the Fourth Estate pass this message along to him." Pens went to paper. "I am actually appreciative, William Hoyt, that you got me into the mountains. Climbing has become a late-found love of mine. I can think of no better escape from city life than to grab a rope and ascend toward the Heavens. But my appreciation ends there. William Hoyt, you are no more than a glorified bounder. Your piety is false. Your behaviour in New Hampshire was far from saintliness. It was devious. Underhanded. I know racetrack touts of better character. Mark my words. No matter what mountain you choose to climb, I will climb it too, but faster. No matter what route you choose up that mountain, I will show that route to be for novices. If you climb a ridge, I will climb a face. If you climb a face, I will climb a steeper face. The history of mountaineering will forget you. Your pride will be broken moments after it's puffed up. You are nothing, Hoyt. And you will be less than nothing when this is all done."

A writer from The Sun, in an obvious attempt to lighten the mood back up: "Mr. Junk, can't you guys just settle this quickly so we in the press can all just move on? There is an election to cover, you know?"

"Hmm. Maybe I'll suggest pistols at dawn. Or instead of pistols, maybe I'll be chivalrous and suggest silver spoons. I've heard Hoyt's pretty handy with those!" The crowd broke out in laughter, as did Junk.

It was true William Hoyt was not present that night. However, William's wife Wizzy was not only present - having a night out with her father - she was standing almost on top of Junk. Having never met the woman and only viewing one or two photographs of her, Junk had no idea that she was in attendance.

After the tirade and jokes at her husband's expense, Wizzy had two options. One was to spill a drink on Junk and the other was to slap him. As evidenced in the photos from that night, Wizzy chose to do both. The photo in the New York Times shows a man's face in profile, still recoiling from a strike to the cheek, eyes squinted and mouth off at an angle that would be impossible without external help. The long hair that crowns his bald head is fanning out in all directions. Closer inspection reveals droplets of liquid jumping from his hair into space. Wizzy's vodka stinger.

"I was angry, but I knew better than to get into a shouting match with a woman, let alone strike one," said Junk in his journals. "I would handle this the right way. You do not hurt a woman. You hurt a woman's man."

The society pages again were going wild. A staid, mountaineering New York bread magnate and a Boston urchin turned playboy were out for each other's blood. The story tapped into issues of new versus old wealth, city pride, and that uniquely American lust for any story other than one's own. Over drinks at the Algonquin, in the cheap seats at Fenway Park, in the offices of senators, and on the floors of shirt factories, the well-heeled and the baseborn alike prattled on about what would happen next. "Is one of them going to kill the other?" "I know William, and he has never been this out of sorts." "Are the likes of those two maroons able to strike a bargain?" "I saw Aaron at last night's performance of 'The Mountebanks.'

He promised me Hoyt would pay for withholding the New Hampshire money." No one could talk about anything else.

Cole Porter even wrote a song about the rivalry called "Snow-Blind Fury." It was never published nor was it performed for the general public, but he banged it out on the piano at any little get together to which he happened to be invited. Given that he was Cole Porter, he was invited to many. His friends learned it and their friends learned it, and it made the rounds at cocktail parties across the country. Although they never heard it firsthand, Hoyt and Junk both knew of it by word of mouth. They likely did not approve given the playful, mocking nature of the music and lyrics. An example:

> *"Climbing in the air*
> *shouldn't cause this much ado,*
> *Just ask the window wipers*
> *high above Park Avenue.*
> *The Southey with the mouth he's*
> *sparring with the pompous saint.*
> *I swear a pair of mountain lions*
> *would show much more restraint.*
> *An Eskimo gal once told me*
> *after a night of rubbing noses,*
> *Those mountains hold no answers*
> *unless your mama named you Moses. "*

William Hoyt had no time to care about such things. He quietly split his time between his family, his church, his job, and climbing. Granted his mother was still very much alive and crazy and living at the state hospital. Visits to her were no stroll along the Coney Island boardwalk, but they were only once or twice a year as of late.

He was getting older and he knew it. This drove him to climb harder and faster. He signed on for American expeditions to Mount McKinley, Petit Dru in the Alps, Aconcagua in the Andes, and even Mount Everest. Between 1936 and the 1939, Hoyt estimated he was part of nine expeditions. He was the expedition leader on many of them.

Nine expeditions in three years may seem like an idyllic fate for the likes of William Hoyt. But the situation was far from good. He was literally being stalked by Aaron Junk. Of the nine Hoyt expeditions during the late 1930's, Junk ran simultaneous expeditions at the same mountains on the last five of them.

The first stalking incident was harmless. Autumn of 1937, Hoyt and a small team climbed Mount McKinley in Alaska with little drama. The weather was favorable, the terrain forgiving, and the team worked together flawlessly. Everyone made it to the top unscathed. The down-climbing was also by the book. But as they started to descend, another party was coming up. The proper etiquette at such a moment is to stop and speak at least briefly to the like-minded people who have chosen such a similar path in life, both literally and figuratively. Despite his difficulties with interaction, Hoyt had every intention of striking up a conversation. But when the approaching team leader removed his goggles, Hoyt yelled back to his men "Carry on!" Hoyt began to walk again, as did his team. He didn't say another word on the descent. "I can tell when William is angry," recalled Douglas Astor, a regular member of Hoyt's expeditions. "It is usually not in his words. His mouth is closed and he moves his lower jaw around as if he's chewing on something tough, stringy, and unwilling to break. That day on McKinley was a perfect example." Junk's presence on the mountain was clearly no coincidence, and it enraged Hoyt. But he had every reason to believe this experience was a one-time thing. True, Junk had told the press he intended to climb every mountain Hoyt climbed, *but not at the same time.* If he had known this would continue, his anger would have been exponentially greater.

Hoyt would not actually *see* Junk again on the subsequent expeditions, but he would always find out sooner or later that "this new shadow I cast, darker than the absence of light" was nearby. On the next climb, Hoyt made it to the top of Mount Rainier solo. Not only did he make it solo, but he did so in record time following the route that was his namesake. Hoyt returned home to New York full of pride. He celebrated with Wizzy and his sons at Delmonico's in Lower Manhattan, ordering the largest steak on the menu. At that dinner, he ran into H. Adams Carter, a world-class mountaineer in his own right. It was unlike Hoyt to brag about his climbing successes, let alone even talk about them. But he was giddy, and shared his good news with Carter. Being a gentleman, Carter congratulated him, but also let him know Aaron Junk was at Rainier at the same time as Hoyt. Although he had not set any record in terms of ascent, Junk had taken a route along the Russell Cliff in the north, and had done it solo. No one had ever climbed Rainier via the Russell Cliff before. Everyone considered it a path of too much resistance. Put simply, Junk had just established himself in the climbing community as a force to be reckoned with. His name was known before, but more as a curiosity for pestering Hoyt. Now he had shown himself to be worthy of praise in his own right while also stealing Hoyt's thunder. Now Hoyt's new Rainier record was not of much interest to anyone. If a god performs a miracle, people yawn. Junk on the other hand was a human, and he had just turned water into wine.

On three subsequent expeditions, Hoyt would return home to news of Junk's ongoing, obsessive retribution. He also found out Junk was taking pains to begin his ascents on the same day as Hoyt, because his plans were evolving, and soon he hoped to reach the top of each mountain *before* Hoyt. With this knowledge, Hoyt started secretly setting out a day earlier or later. But Junk was ahead of him. With the exception of Hoyt's solo efforts, Junk began paying off members of Hoyt's teams to send him word, usually through phone calls. When his spies were unable to slip away, they would pass notes to people around them – usually with money inside - telling them to place the phone call. They would receive more money later if the call was indeed placed.

The turning point came three expeditions later. Hoyt was climbing Aiguille de la Grande Sassière in the Graian Alps. The ascent was extremely difficult. One man, Charles Pickwick of Fairfax, Virginia, died when a bolt broke and he fell several hundred feet. Hoyt was devastated. No one had ever died on one of his expeditions. In fact, Hoyt had never seen anyone die before, on or off a mountain. "That was simply the most sobering experience of my life. Before your very eyes, a person goes from man to meat. I was thankful Wizzy did not have to witness such horror." But as is often the case, the expedition continued despite death. There was no joy in the climb any more, only silence and determination.

On the final morning of the ascent, three team members including Hoyt had a go at the peak. A few hundred feet away from their goal, they noticed an object waiting for them at the very top. It was a flag; not the flag of a nation, nor the flag of any other organized institution. It was the flag of an individual, an unstable individual. It was constructed out of a woman's white petticoat flying from a metal tent pole. Painted in large black letters on the petticoat were the words: "YOU LOSE, FAGGOT."

Junk could not have picked a worse moment to insult his nemesis, given the tragic events that had so recently befallen Hoyt's team. Hoyt later wrote in his journal:

"My actions at that moment were deplorable. I wish I could divorce myself from the memory. I pulled out the flag, yelled like a man scorched by fire, and threw the abomination at my fellow mountaineers. I am a man

of few words, and the words I do employ are of the kind one could safely wield around tots. But at that moment, at the top of Aguille, I let out a stream of ribaldry so tawdry, I was tempted to wash out my own mouth that evening. By my rage-fueled account, Junk was the offspring of a she-dog who had sexual relations with the mother of the selfsame she-dog."

Subsequent expeditions continued along the same trajectory. Hoyt would climb, making every attempt to conceal his plans, but Junk would climb and beat Hoyt to the summit. The only variation was the writing on the flag. One time it read "$100,000?" Another time "PRIG." And another time, in smaller letters "Fat is the head that wears the crown."

At about that time, Ovaltine, the producer of sweet breakfast drinks, in association with the American Alpine Club, were sponsoring an American team to ascend Nanda Devi in India. The Ovaltine people were growing frustrated with their sponsorship of the *Little Orphan Annie* radio program. According to an internal memo, the company felt "Advertising during *Little Orphan Annie* is bringing us a narrow audience of kids, their moms, and fairies." They wanted to sell their drink to men, and they planned to pitch Ovaltine as a healthy drink for rugged, active outdoorsmen. This was one of the first marketing campaigns of its kind, jumping off of the billboards and out of the radio sponsorships and into newsreels and morning papers. The Ovaltine people were excited beyond all measure and promoted the trip heavily. William Hoyt was their first choice when selecting a team of explorers to represent their product. Hoyt accepted graciously.

Aaron Junk could never have gotten that kind of backing from Ovaltine or any other establishment because, although he was now seen as a legitimate climber, his seedy history and unpredictable behaviour were seen as too much of a liability. Granted, even Hoyt now had two arrests to his name, but most people saw those indiscretions as provoked. Junk's reputation was, in contrast, toxic. A company like, say, Woolworth would not put their brand in the hands of a man who might break all records of mountaineering one day, and then be arrested for whoring the next. Junk had no choice but to sponsor his own team if he wished to dog Hoyt at every turn. Both Hoyt and Junk set out for India by way of London on the same day, March 13 of 1939, with the goal of dominating Nanda Devi. British climbers Bill Tilman and Eric Shipton had already reached the top, but no American had yet to even enter the sanctuary.

Nanda Devi stands 25,642 feet tall. That certainly does not make it the tallest mountain in the world. It is not even the tallest in India. But Nanda Devi is brutal. Even the most experienced climber on Earth must first get to a mountain before climbing it, and that's where Nanda Devi has you. She is almost impossible to reach. Ringed by a series of other mountains, including her smaller sister, Nanda Devi East, the lowest passes into her sanctuary require an ascent to 18,000 feet. Once over the top of those passes, there is a good likelihood the way will be impassible due to serac-laced glaciers standing between you and the mountain. The only entry point not requiring a grueling climb is through the Rishi Gorge, a raging river flanked by sheer walls on both sides. Nanda Devi is, in short, an imposing giant guarded by multiple lines of defense.

Hoyt and Junk were both ready to take on this amazing challenge, and take on each other. But sadly, neither one even made it to India. Everyone to the man on Hoyt's steamer got food poisoning. Turning around in the Red Sea, the team vomited its way back to Toulon. The illness had nothing to do with Ovaltine, but the unlucky sponsors had to spend months proving as much. Only two days after Hoyt's ship headed home, Junk's ship was stopped by Burmese pirates who were nice enough not to kill the passengers, but only to loot them of everything on their ship save some tins of pemmican. "They were the most civilized men I had met since leaving

London," recalled Junk. "It turned out the lead pirate and I shared a favorite watering hole in Bermuda. They even shared a glass of brandy with the captain and me before demanding the removal of our clothing and shoving off." The party returned home in their underwear, the taste of lost adventure bitter on their tongues.

The foiled expedition would prove to be a mere grazing of a hedgerow in a much longer steeplechase. For our heroes were to return to the Himalaya soon enough, and when they did, Nanga Parbat and its missed opportunities would be overshadowed by much larger obstacles on the horizon.

Chapter Four: Fumu and the Dividing Engine

The mountains of the Himalayan chain tend to have origin stories, and more often than not these stories are based in Sanskrit literature, Indian dynasties, or colourful tales of Hindu gods. Nanda Devi got its name from a princess of the Chanda dynasty who narrowly escaped a murder attempt. The mountains that tightly ring Nanda Devi are guards protecting her from further attack. Annapurna is the Hindu goddess of food. Chomolungma, the local name for Mount Everest and its surrounding area, is a Bon god who can suffuse kindness and empathy at one moment and then turn angry due to the smallest slight. The peak of Harmukh is believed by Kashmiris to be the home of Shiva. If the peak can be seen from a nearby village, then it is believed the snakes of that village will be rendered harmless.

But no single mythology like these exists for Mount Fumu. Or more precisely, there are as many Fumu mythologies as there are people in Asia. One Sherpa will tell you that Fumu was the name of a Hindu god who slaughtered his own children to show allegiance to Vishnu. Another Sherpa will tell you Fumu was the name of Chomolungma's daughter who is also the mother of Lhotse. Ask a citizen of Darjeeling and they may tell you Fumu was the name of a 19th century European explorer who snuck into Nepal and crawled out of the woods one year later, bloody, screaming tales of a mountain haunted by spirits of strange women looking for their children in the night.

One gets the feeling after asking several hundred people for the story of Fumu that there is something intentional in the discrepancies, and that the variation comes not from miscommunication, but from obfuscation. It is as if there is a true story to be told about the mountain and its moniker, and that everyone in India, Nepal, and Tibet know the story, but we who come from far away are not meant to know anything about it. It is not for us.

The only theme that seems to run through all of the stories, as barebones as it may be, is that of a strained relationship between a parent and a child. Anyone who has attempted to climb atop Fumu's haunches and witnessed the horrors of her retaliations can understand from whence this recurring idea may have come.

Roughly 200 million years before the birth of Our Lord, the surface of the Earth was comprised of ocean and a single, monolithic landmass called Pangaea. As with all things, Pangaea began to fall apart. Slabs of earth broke from one another and wandered in random directions. Then in an act that could be seen as tectonic separation anxiety, the slab that would later become modern-day India returned to Pangaea 150 million years ago. The reunion was not peaceful. To this day, the Indian plate and the Asian plate are in the process of colliding violently. Rock meets rock with nowhere to go but up. As this conflict plays out at an excruciatingly slow clip, the mountains we call the Himalaya continue to grow. The process has slowed down somewhat as time has passed, and what used to be a chain of active volcanoes has cooled and become snow-capped peaks. However, one peak remains volcanically active.

Fumu is a strange volcano. What is left of the enormous main vent has been dormant for eons and has become dead and icy. The magma chamber beneath her has spent most of its contents and the ground above collapsed downward. An unusually large crater was formed around the huge dead vent by the collapse, what geologists call a caldera. There is a small hole in the ice at the bottom of Fumu's caldera where the vent is; in the winter it is about the size of a corpulent man's waist, and in the summer it becomes the size of a traditional 42-foot circus ring. The hole has been deemed "The Oculus" by explorers. A blasting sub-zero wind seems to rise out of the Oculus and blow up the walls of the caldera's bowl on all sides. The wind has been known to throw equipment and unsuspecting humans off of their perch along the caldera's lip. It is because of this ever-blowing arctic menace that the caldera – the four-mile-in-diameter bowl around the Oculus - has been given the name "The Icy Bellows."

Randy Felcher, an Earth scientist from the University of Bedlam, believes that Mount Fumu was once three times her current size. According to Felcher's theory, two-thirds of her width was blown off sideways about 50 million years ago by a pyroclastic event that plunged the Earth into a volcanic winter likely lasting for decades. The angled eruption explains why the lip of the Icy Bellows is not consistent in altitude all the way around; the eruption did not do a clean job of severing off the top of the mountain. The current summit of Fumu is actually the southernmost point on the lip. But then the lip erratically drops from its greatest height of approximately 30,121 feet down to its lowest point of 18,330 feet in the north. When one looks south at Fumu from Everest, one sees the peak in the distance with two ridges fanning out from it to the east and to the west. As they fan out, they begin to bend toward you and downward. Then like a pair of curved staircases, the ridges turn back towards each other, and ultimately meet once more at the bottom to create the lowest point on the lip of the Icy Bellows. Many Nepalese Sherpa who have traveled in the high elevations north of Fumu have called the mountain "The Childless Mother," with the summit as her smoky head and the two descending ridges as cradling arms holding nothing at all.

Although the main vent between the ridges has long been dead, that does not mean Fumu is dormant. Small eruptions like the one that killed Zachary Hoover continue to occur from smaller vents along the ridgelines and especially at the summit. If the mountain were momentarily transparent, you would be able to see vents wending their way to and fro but always upward, some reaching the surface and others coming to *cul de sacs* of high pressure. Some of the vents reaching for the surface look bloody, swollen with lava, almost living, like leaves of red chard. Others carry only steam, water, and gases such as carbon dioxide and hydrochloric acid. Others hold nothing at all but darkness. The old main dead vent is one such dark route, but near the new summit, hundreds of smaller vents continue to pump hot magma, posing countless threats to climbers.

It is hard to think of a better metaphor for strength and immobility than a mountain. But in the case of Fumu, the metaphor breaks. Fumu is in motion from bottom to top. Running down between the spurs near her base are glaciers that can be heard by the human ear as they plod downward. Creaks and loud snapping sounds echo through crevasses, often accompanied by the sound of ponderous ice chunks dropping into subterranean water. Between the glaciers and at approximately the same elevation (10,000-12,000 feet) is the scree. Needless to say, the scree is no monument to stability. New chunks of fresh lava rock and pulverized granite from the summit tumble down the mountain to feed its size every day. And every day, older rocks tumble off of it into the glaciers to be slowly pulverized into oblivion. Above the scree one comes to the two main ridges on the north rising up to the summit on the south. The Icy Bellows between the ridges includes ever-moving snowdrifts, sloshing slowly from east to west like cold broth in a bowl on a boat in rough seas.

On the other side of the summit, the South Face, opposite the Bellows, the mountain above the scree is comprised of snowfields. Climbing these is not difficult, except where the fields are interrupted by steep rock cliffs. And then there is Rauff's Maw, cleaving the route of the doomed Rauff expedition. That route started at the bottom in the southeast and zigzagged up to meet the Eastern Ridge just before the summit. The fate of the Rauff expedition makes it clear that this part of the mountain is also not at rest.

Finally, there is the summit. So busy is this part of Fumu that it cannot be seen through plumes of grey and black smoke.

Getting close enough to study the mountain has always been a source of difficulty. Forgetting the brutal challenges one must face in order to climb her, simply getting to Base Camp is nearly impossible. Like Nanda Devi, Fumu is ringed by four smaller but by no means small mountains. Most Europeans and Americans still call these mountains by the labels bestowed upon them by the Great Trigonometric Survey – H57, H58, H62, and H63 – but the locals call them Mitya, Abel, Lata, and Asha. Their names are as mysterious as that of Fumu. No in-depth investigation has been pursued. Each of the four peaks soars to heights ranging from 26,000 to 28,000 feet. They are connected by wall-like passes reaching more than two thirds of the peaks' heights. Seen from nearby mountains like Ama Dablam, the effect on the human eye is that of looking at a castle or fort built for gods. This may be why the entire area is locally referred to as *Qila*, the Urdu word for 'fort.' The four peaks are the towers and the ridges that connect them are the outer curtain walls. The problem with this castle is that there is no portcullis. The only way a human can even consider reasonably entering Qila is over a sixteen-thousand foot pass on the southern perimeter, aptly called the Qila Pass (also known as the Fumuri La to locals). The pass is shaped like a giant shoehorn, wide at the bottom, narrow at the top, and concave toward its center line the entirety of its length. It starts off gradually, never exceeding a forty-five degree angle; then it steepens, and by the top it takes the form of a chute rising consistently at sixty degrees. That pitch would be very possible for most technical climbers except the fifty-foot wide chute is made entirely of amethyst. The rare version of amethyst called ametrine is beautiful to behold. It is purple like most amethyst, but because of heating from volcanic activity, it is streaked with glittering yellow. In addition to being beautiful, the bumpy face is very hard and devoid of cracks. There is no purchase for climbing equipment. Countless men have tumbled to their deaths, tenderized while they fall on rough, rare stone, their twisted bodies reflecting in brilliant colours from the gemstone wall. Climbers who have gotten over the pass have usually done so by moving at a sloth-like pace and by being lucky. Needless to say, Qila Pass is usually the first filter of climbers making their way to the top of Fumu.

Measuring Fumu has been a source of much tension ever since the first summit attempt was made in 1881. At that time, it was given short shrift for a variety of reasons and assumed to be almost one thousand feet shorter than Everest. It was not until Hoover's fateful summit attempt of 1939 that people started learning what many had already felt might be true – that Fumu was the tallest mountain in the world. But before the Hoover expedition, people did what they often do to understand their world: Rely on the word of experts who may or may not know what the bloody hell they are talking about.

The experts in this case were geodesists, people who study the size and shape of the Earth. Fumu was first measured by geodesists who cared little about its height. They were in the middle of much larger projects at the time and the measurement of the Himalaya was of secondary importance.

William Lambton of Yorkshire had been in India since the turn of the 19th Century trying to figure out nothing less than the shape of the Earth. Other geodesists had recently completed an assessment of shape in the Arctic Circle and at one point on the equator. They had surmised the Earth was an "oblate spheroid." In other words, the world is not round as many had assumed, but rather shaped like a grapefruit; flattened at the poles and sticking out further at the equator. Lambton wished to supplement these findings by continuing the measurements in a small region of India called Mysore.

The British liked the idea of measuring India. It was, after all, their spoils, and it would be nice to know the size of the prize. The Raj could only be strengthened by this knowledge. Therefore, Lambton was pushed to measure more than just Mysore. Soon he had minions reporting to him and the Great Trigonometric Survey of India had begun.

Lambton's plan was to survey a straight line up the sub-continent along the Great Indian Arc of the Meridian and another line across the sub-continent from Mangalore to Madras. The north-south line along the Great Arc would ultimately end up covering 1,600 miles from Cape Comorin in the south to Mussoorie in the north, and would take 47 years and untold lives to complete. Off of the Great Trigonometric Survey would sprout countless secondary series by other surveyors, until almost all of India and modern-day Pakistan were shackled under a chain of triangles.

At its core, the survey method used by Lambton was nothing more than very basic trigonometry. Hold three flags up in different locations, creating a triangle (These were big triangles. Many were several miles along the hypotenuse). Measure the distance between any two of the three flags - A and B - using something like a chain, giving you length of side AB. This is your baseline. From A and B, get a site line of the third flag - C - and calculate the angles of those site lines from the baseline. You can then use that data to calculate the length of AC and BC, and the angle of the third corner C. *Viola.* The whole triangle of land has been measured! Now you can start a new triangle using one of the sides of the triangle you just measured.

Of course, that description only details measurements on a horizontal plane, like a map. But heights of locations needed to be recorded as well. This also required basic trigonometry, but with the added challenge that one of the corners of the triangle was inevitably hidden under the earth because no ground is perfectly flat. Start by planting a flag at sea level – corner A. Go to some nearby high point and plant another flag – corner B, again connected by a chain. Calculate the angle from straight vertical at the high point B and the angle from straight horizontal at the low point A. This gives you the other two sides of the right triangle, and thus the height of the second point. As one moves up from sea level to mountainous ranges, one just keeps adding and adding elevations, triangle by triangle.

Based on the description just given, the reader may be led to think a trigonometric survey of India was technically simple but repetitive, as if the surveyors were machines, running basic calculations over and over again. But nothing could be further from the truth. Lambton, and later George Everest after Lambton's death, faced untold challenges while measuring the sub-continent and it was these challenges that would ultimately lead to the faulty measurement of Fumu.

First there are the challenges inherent to trigonometric surveying. Take even the basic notion of measuring altitude from "sea level." Do you start your measurement at the high tide mark, the low tide mark, or an average of the two? How do you ensure other surveyors running secondary series are doing it the same way?

There is also the issue of the Earth being an oblate spheroid. When calculating the vertical triangles, you must take into account the curvature of the Earth. Even if the effect is tiny for a single triangle, less than an inch perhaps, the error will be compounded as you tack on more triangles, Altitude measurements will soon be out of whack. So if the world is not a perfect sphere, what formula can you use reliably?

When you look over an expansive vista at mountains or other large objects in the distance, what you are seeing is actually bent by water in the atmosphere, much like looking at a fish in a fish bowl. This phenomenon is called *refraction*. Surveyors trying to get a site line on distant objects are not immune to refraction, so every calculation must take it into account.

Even more possible error is introduced into the surveyor's calculation by variations in climate. If you used a 2,000-foot steel chain to measure the side of a triangle on a hot, humid Monday, and then re-measured on Tuesday when it was cooler and drier, you would find the location of your flags had moved slightly. Not only would the chain have shortened, but your other instruments for measurement, like theodolites and levels, would have changed as well. Surveyors have discovered calculations that can account for climate changes, but then how do you ensure your thermometers are accurate, especially if you are using more than one?

Lambton and Everest faced all of these challenges inherent to the science of trigonometric surveying. But they also faced hurdles specific to early 19th Century India. For example, the best time for measurement was in the weather that accompanied the monsoon season. But of course, the monsoon season is also a high point for malaria and cholera. The two diseases wiped out innumerable porters and researchers on the survey. Lambton found elephants were best equipped to carry all of the equipment required for the survey, but because of their size, elephants were injured more often by the stretches of dense jungle. Cultural problems sprouted up in many remote regions of the sub-continent; Lambton was more than once accused by local leaders of spying on women-folk and turning objects and people upside-down with his inverting telescope lens. Measurements in these situations often had to be done on the run or skipped entirely.

With the survey going on more than forty years, it finally hit the border of Nepal and could go no further because Kathmandu barred outsiders. The closest researchers could get to the distant Himalaya was the kingdom of Sikkim about one hundred miles to the east of the largest mountains in the chain. Therefore, measurement of the distant Himalaya was terribly hindered. Estimates became looser. Everest was initially underestimated and mistaken to be shorter than Kanchenjunga just because the latter was closer. Fumu was not even seen from distant Darjeeling for some time. It was not until the last researchers were packing up that Fumu would be noticed and then underestimated. The mountain simply does not stand out from any side until you are at the base of it. There are too many tall mountains surrounding it, obscuring all but its smoky summit. When a patch of snow near the top does peek out, other proximal peaks make its height less noticeable. When the fattest man in the world spends time with the second and third fattest men in the world, he does not stand out. So it went with Fumu. Social scientists might say the mountain's measurement was thrown off by an optical illusion. Locals might say the mountain protected itself from notice with visual trickery. Regardless of one's explanation, when Fumu finally did get measured on literally the last day of The Great Trigonometric Survey, it came in at a paltry 28,250 feet.

Clearly, the measurement of Fumu was problematic. But with all of the challenges the surveyors faced in accurately measuring India and ultimately the Himalaya of Nepal, surely the problems would have applied equally to *all* of the Himalayan measurements, not just to Fumu. In other words, if Fumu was given short shrift, would not Everest and all of the other Nepalese Himalaya have been given the same poor treatment equally? Was not error rampant consistently?

Indeed, that argument would be legitimate. Based on all of the points raised so far, one could still say Fumu is not the tallest mountain in the world. The mountains may have all been mismeasured the same way; Fumu because its peak was obscured, Everest because of its distance from the surveyors, and so forth. However, one last gaff occurred that must be mentioned in any discussion of Fumu – a gaff that likely stole the crown from her head and placed it illegitimately on Mount Everest...

All men see the world through the filter of their work. The banker looks at the trees in a park in summer and cannot help but see the colour of American currency. The priest looks at the same trees and sees the craftsmanship of Jehovah. Even the chef taking an evening stroll may delight in the similarity of shape between the outline of the oaks and his famous popovers. Meriwether Albright of Coventry, England was no different. He was an engineer who built instruments used for measurement. In the trees, Albright would see twigs as units of branches, branches as units of boughs, and boughs as units of the main trunk. He would notice how the trees were clearly planted to form a line with each sapling separated from its neighbors by eight feet, but he would also see that human error had been introduced into the calculations. Simply put, Meriwether Albright saw the world in increments.

Others might look upon that as quite cold and empty. Not Albright. He was a deeply religious man, and as he saw it, he was measuring God's miracles. "I felt every day like I was a millionaire counting his money...and I was," he wrote many years later. "I was drowning in the riches bestowed upon me by the Lord, and I wanted to put them in order."

Albright was an obsessive artisan, leaving his neglected old cottage seven days a week at six o'clock in the morning to tinker in his workshop that lay on the other side of his unploughed fields. On a given dark winter morning, he would likely enter the small single room, light the lamps and a fire for the kettle, let the aroma of the grease, paraffin, and hay invade his nostrils, and then let his eyes pan across the shining brass and steel. The objects he discerned in that dim light ranged in size from flat, one-foot rulers to clocks six feet in diameter. Albright would then spend the day fabricating and hammering metal, running and re-running objects through the dividing engine, calibrating springs, oiling gears, and punctuating the whole process with sips of tea.

He was known throughout Europe for his precision. No matter what instrument he was building – clock, compass, yardstick – Albright was unrivaled. When it came to clocks for example, many people including the employs of the Greenwich Observatory felt Albright had surpassed even the Swiss. He received letters from railroad concerns in Russia asking for his services. Despite bad blood between England and France, Parisian builders and architects wrote to him for help. Albright had to turn down most of the requests because he was already too busy. Friends urged him to expand his business; hire employees, build a factory, and retire on his wealth. Other businesses in Coventry goaded him as well. Any successful business in Coventry could prove beneficial to other businesses in the area. But Albright refused. He truly did not care about wealth. He liked the peace and quiet of his workshop. All that mattered to him were the creation of his objects, the goal of precise measurement, and love of God. But even more than all of this, there was spending time with his daughter, Katherine.

At the age of six, Katherine Albright was tall for her age. Other girls in town called her "Giantess." As awkward as she may have felt, she was also a beauty, with long black curls and big hazel eyes. "Her eyebrows were permanently fixed in a position of skepticism, one raised slightly higher than the other," Albright once wrote. "This gave her a very hard but intelligent look." She was an artist. She spent countless hours before bed painting still lifes and portraits of herself and her father. Her hands were constantly covered in oil paint which ultimately found its way to the furniture and walls. Meriwether loved that kind of mess generated by creativity.

Katherine did not have much time for other children, favouring the company of her father, and Meriwether would not have it any other way. His wife had died giving birth to Katherine, and with the help of local friends, he had raised her to schooling age. Now he took care of Katherine by himself, and he reveled in it. If Meriwether was not in his workshop, then he and Katherine were strolling through town or taking hikes along the river or attending church together. She was only six, but Meriwether confided in her constantly. He also let her help him in the workshop when school was out. "I remember speaking to her very early on about the importance of what we do and the magnificence of His wonders." Albright wrote in prison years later. "I told her the volume of a drop of dew, the seconds in a minute, the furlongs in a mile, each was a glimmering tile in a giant mosaic. If we can only quantify the tiles, and look at them from afar, the mosaic will show us the Face of God."

Then Katherine became ill. No one is sure what illness she had, but all signs point to consumption. She could not get up in the morning. Already thin, she began to waste away. Her skin became pale and her breaths became short. The coughing fits were relentless. "The single raised eyebrow lowered, removing the unique character that was Katherine. Her eyelids were half-moons and she stared at nothing. Then she was dead."

Meriwether stayed in his home for months, unable to even visit his workshop. He did not attend church. When he did start venturing outside, locals saw him ambling slowly, head down, mumbling to himself in a voice on the verge of tears.

A neighbor who had helped Albright raise Katherine finally visited him and begged him to return to work. She felt it would help him heal. "'Look again to God's miracles' she said to me. I took her advice. I went back to the workshop and began to tinker again."

But something had snapped in Albright's head. He could not see the reason for measuring the world anymore because the magic that used to cover every thing like gossamer was gone. He did work, but his production rate was dangerously slow. Customers complained. The world was growing, commerce was on the march, and the need for Albright's instruments was greater than ever.

Then Albright came up with the solution to his problem. God's miracles were still there to be understood, but the miracles were now severely lessened by the removal of Katherine. And so he would continue to build the tools that measure the world, but he would subtract out what was lost. He took his old dividing engine – the machine that standardizes measurements on all measuring instruments - out back and destroyed it with endless blows from a mallet. Then he began building another one, with each notch on the wheel slightly further away from its neighbor than it should be. All measurements arising from the dividing engine would be smaller. The value of Katherine was removed from every inch, every second, and every degree.

It took only a few months before the effects of Albright's deeds were felt. Every object that had been built using his tools was slightly off. In his home town of Coventry, the new church clock struck midnight at eleven twenty-five in the evening, and then earlier on each subsequent night. The locals were bewildered. Then the effects of Albright's new dividing engine escalated tragically. A train derailed near Kiev. The roof of a factory collapsed in Brussels. As far away as Santa Fe, a small battalion of the Armies of the West were overwhelmed by Navajo fighters because their guns jammed. All told, seventy-seven people had died as a direct result of Albright's "recalibrations." As Albright put it in his writings, "The removal of Katherine compounded, removing other souls from the Earth. If I had gone on in my profession, I would have had to continually make the increments on the dividing engine smaller and smaller for the ever-increasing loss of souls."

Albright would not have the chance to recalibrate again. Local authorities from all affected countries quickly narrowed down the cause of the calamities. The British government sent in the police and had Albright arrested on murder charges. Formal documents suggest Albright did not put up a fight. He was sent to prison for life although the death penalty had been seriously considered.

When the end came only two years into his sentence, prison guards found Albright resting peacefully on the floor, dead from a heart attack. In his folded hands was clutched the one object they allowed him to bring into prison – a small, wrinkled self-portrait of Katherine.

Albright had been in the middle of building his lethally incorrect dividing engine when he got a letter from India. It was from George Everest, who was finishing up the last measurements of the Great Trigonometric Survey of India. Everest needed the best theodolite possible, and he needed it quickly. A theodolite is a telescope that moves in measured amounts on both vertical and horizontal axes. The device is perfect for calculating angles such as the corners of a vast triangle. Some theodolites are small, but the one used on the Great Trigonometric Survey was gigantic - a monstrosity of cast iron and brass, weighing one thousand pounds. It had to be carried across the sub-continent by twelve men. Lambton and then Everest referred to it as "The Great Theodolite." Because of accidents along the way and general wear and tear, in truth they had used several "Great Theodolites" over the decades, all built by William Cary of England. They were perfect replicas of each other, massive and meticulous. Then, near the very end of the Survey in 1847, a mudslide led to the destruction of what should have been the last theodolite of the survey.

Everest and his team had just finished measuring the enormous mountain that would later become his namesake. He had had only one patch of Himalaya left to measure – the one that included Fumu. Everest had been displeased with the size of Cary's theodolites, and hearing of Albright's nearly alchemical engineering abilities, commissioned the man to build him a smaller but precise theodolite. Albright wrote back in response to the commission saying that he had been building a theodolite already, just as a test case for his new improved process for marking notches. It had been going quite well and he would be happy to give the Survey that one. This would also mean they would have it within only a few short weeks. All they need do is wait.

When it arrived, the team was weary and ready to go home. The measurements were done quickly. Dates on records from the survey at this time fall well after the date of Albright's arrest. We can only assume Everest heard about it through the mail. Perhaps the fatigue was so great and the urge to be done so overwhelming he decided to ignore the facts of the faulty equipment in his possession. Who would really ever know or even care? Those mountains they were measuring were in the heart of Nepal, a place where no outsider was permitted. Their height would remain irrelevant. The team packed up and returned to England. After nearly half a century, the Great Trigonometric Survey of India was complete. The mountain named H24 would remain of little interest for a long time to come. It wouldn't be until the early 1880's - when a handful of risk-taking European expeditions chose to enter Nepal illegally - that Fumu would introduce herself murderously to the world of white men.

The first known expedition to Fumu was led by George Malick in 1881. He had heard rumors that Mount Everest was the tallest mountain in the world, but had also heard it could be "climbed by the Queen in a fit of somnambulism" from fellow climbers. Put another way, the mountain was tall but not challenging enough. It is true Everest's vertical rise is not very impressive. Most of its height comes from resting atop the Tibetan Plateau, like an average-sized child sitting on the shoulders of his exceptionally tall father. Malick wanted a challenge that would make England proud, so he ventured into Nepal with his team and selected the hardest mountain visible to his naked eyes.

He lost half of his team just getting over the Qila Pass and another quarter getting above the scree. The remainder of the team did surprisingly well given that there was no precedent for what they were doing. Their ascent was not only the first up Fumu, but one of the first recorded ascents up any Himalayan peak. They were groundbreakers, and they were doing quite well at it. It was not until they started approaching the smoky summit that things went pear-shaped.

Some of Malick's men claimed to hear other people lurking outside of their tents at night. Malick chalked it up to the effects of altitude on the brain. None of them were using breathing apparatuses, and no one yet knew the effects of such high altitude. "It only made sense that lack of oxygen might make a man quite daft" Malick wrote in his journal. But the altitude sickness theory failed to explain why two men were found one morning mutilated as if by animals. "Quimby's right arm was gone up to the elbow. His lower jaw was also missing. Hirst's stomach cavity had been emptied of all contents." No one ever heard a scream.

The Sherpa pleaded with Malick to end the summit attempt and return to their homes. The mountain, they claimed, was populated by cannibals. Trying to reason with them, Malick explained that the attack was most likely committed by some kind of wild animal living in the caves of the South Face. No animal could possibly live at this altitude, the Sherpa retorted, and they wished to go home. Malick ultimate decided to send the entire expedition back down aside from himself. He would have a go at the top before turning around. Off into the smoke he ascended. According to the journal found in his backpack many years later, he got lost almost immediately. He was never seen alive again. As disastrous an expedition as it was, Malick got farther up the mountain than any subsequent expedition until 1941, when Hoyt and Junk would make their own summit attempts.

Another notable attempt came in 1910, when a German team climbed Fumu from the north. The team was led by Josef Bruner, a field marshal in the German army who had an affinity for climbing mountains long before it was fashionable. Like anyone who hopes to enter the Qila Sanctuary – the domain of Fumu - they used the Qila Pass in the south, but then hiked along glaciers below the scree for four days until they were looking up at the Icy Bellows from the north. After losing two of his European team members to the scree, Bruner led the remaining team up the Eastern Ridge with the Icy Bellows to their right the whole time and the Oculus at the bottom waiting to swallow them should they fall.

Bruner was a peculiar fellow. He was "non-standard issue" as his colleagues in the military liked to say. When not in military uniform, Bruner was foppish. He would dress in the most fashionable tweeds and bowler hats of the day, and would carry around a black parasol made with the hide of an elk he had shot in the Alps. The parasol included a mahogany pole and solid gold handle. The dandy in Bruner did not disappear when tens of thousands of feet in the air scurrying up the side of a partially dead volcano in the Himalaya. After a long day of climbing, he would pitch his tent and then immediately don his best clothes and sip brandy. If the sun was out, no matter how cold, he sat in the snow with his parasol and did his brandy-sipping outside. This ritual was well known by German mountaineers and everyone found it quite charming. Bruner certainly enjoyed himself and simultaneously made a statement. "We are not animals," he once noted to the newspaper *Tagliche Detroit & Familienblatter*. "We may visit the sanctuary of animals, but we will keep our decorum no matter what the situation." This policy was all well and good until Bruner, holding tightly to his parasol on the East Ridge of Fumu, was blown hundreds of feet away from the ridge by an icy blast from the Bellows. His parasol went flat, and he fell thousands of feet to his death. The remaining team, completely terrified, made the decision to turn around and end the expedition. The Germans would not return until Rauff's expedition in 1937.

Of the eight recorded attempts to summit Fumu before 1941, all eight failed and all eight ended in multiple deaths. Most deaths on the North Face resulted from wind gusts blowing climbers off of the East and West Ridges, and most of the deaths on the South Face resulted from falls into crevasses and "cannibals." Other than Malick, and later Hoover, no one had reached the higher elevations where lava became a consideration.

Sixty years would pass after Malick's original attempt before a human being would actually stand atop Fumu, cursing the mountain's indifference between short, pained breaths.

Chapter Five: Mount Everest

Discouraged by Nanda Devi, but by no means beaten, Hoyt decided to up the stakes and make a try for Everest in September of 1939. People new to climbing in the Himalaya rarely start with Everest. But every decision Hoyt made at this point was informed by his age. Fifty was a tiger in the tall grass, lurking just out of sight. He needed to move quickly or risk never tasting the glory of the ultimate mountaineering experience.

Immediately after the stomach spasms had subsided from the previous outing, Hoyt organized the same team, received approval from the 14th Dalai Lama to enter Tibet, and secured passage on a ship to London. None of the men on Hoyt's team risked losing their jobs after leaving work on two consecutive journeys; they were all moneyed to the monocle, and could plan an infinite holiday if that was their heart's want. The climbers sponsored their own trip this time and by the end of summer, Hoyt and his team found themselves at Everest's northern Base Camp, looking up at the fabled beast.

No one had conquered Everest yet. Thought to be the tallest mountain in the world, people had certainly tried. The British had the first designs for Everest in the early 1920's. With both Poles of the Earth conquered, The United Kingdom wished to conquer "The Third Pole." But access to Everest was limited. Even though we British ruled over what is now modern-day India, Burma, Bangladesh, and Pakistan, Nepal's borders were closed. Any British expedition would have to make its way northeast to Tibet from India and then *turn almost completely around* to approach the mountain from the north.

In 1921 a young George Mallory along with Charles Howard-Bury and a large expedition of fellow Brits and Sherpa made a reconnaissance mission to the area. Mallory, like Hoyt and Junk who followed, had never climbed in the Himalaya when he set his sights on Everest. Thanks to his efforts and the rest of the team of photographers, surveyors, and botanists, the world learned much about the mountain. Most importantly for the world of mountaineering, the expedition found the best routes for reaching the base of the mountain at a point where the summit could be attempted.

The British would try for Everest seven times officially before the war began, including the tragic 1924 expedition in which Mallory and Andrew Irvine were lost near the summit. By the beginning of World War II, no one had reached the top, but many had come painfully close – some within hundreds of feet. Landslides, altitude sickness, sudden storms, and simple exhaustion ultimately took its toll on everyone. Worse still, these brave souls climbing the northern side of Everest had no idea Fumu lurked on the other side, mocking their misguided efforts to reach the top of the world. Even those who gazed upon her from near Everest's summit –because of distance and dizziness from altitude and a blind faith in their schooling - had no idea Fumu was dominant.

By late 1939, England's Royal Geographic Society was in a damned rut. They were practically drooling to get a man to the top of Everest. The defeats were bad enough, but now the Germans had designs for the Himalaya. Hitler was already out of line on the battlefields of Europe. The Brits did not want him getting the best of them in Asia as well. It would be an absolute coup to reach the top of Everest, the tallest mountain in the world (or so it was believed), before the Germans reached the top of Nanga Parbat, known to be the ninth tallest mountain at the time.

But after seven expeditions, the Royal Geographic Society, the Everest Committee, and the entire British government were sick of putting their best and brightest men in harm's way, especially when a possible war loomed. Money was not an issue at the moment, and they were willing to fund many more campaigns. But no more would they fund the high-altitude deaths of the "old-boy" network. Names like Shipton, Longland, and Wollaston would not be put at risk anymore. A decision was made to only send chimneysweeps, the Irish, and members of the dying Liberal Party.

Sir Percy Cox, secretary of the Everest Committee, received a letter from the United States at about this time. It was from Aaron Junk. In it, Junk pleaded with the committee to let him join their next expedition to Everest. He explained that American businesses and government had little interest in funding a climb at the time, and that his own funding was currently tied up in other concerns. Junk used a rather silly argument to persuade the committee to allow an outsider to tag along: "My father was a world-renowned geographer and map-maker. I believe I am well on my way to becoming his worthy successor. In addition, I am an excellent mountaineer. If you have friendships with any American mountaineer, please ask them about my abilities. I am confident they will paint an impressive picture. The United Kingdom would benefit greatly from my participation."

Cox saw right through the request, but also championed the idea of letting Junk come along. Cox wrote to a friend who was also on the committee regarding Junk's request:

"Mister Junk is under the false impression England has no access to American newspapers. I am sure all of us [on the committee] are aware of his volatile relationship with William Hoyt, and I am sure if we contacted Hoyt, we would find he too has plans for an Everest expedition in the near future. Bloody Americans. They have the civility and tact of lowland gorillas. Nonetheless, no one wants to send good men to the top of Everest right now, so I am comfortable letting Junk join the expedition scheduled for late summer. May God have mercy on my soul."

Cox lobbied hard, but almost every member to the man was opposed to Junk's inclusion on the expedition. The Royal Geographic Society took umbrage with an American – any American – taking part in an endeavor so tied up with national identity. What if Junk reached the top first? What if Junk doomed the whole enterprise? Any press-worthy actions by an American climber on a British expedition would be problematic. His success would belittle them while his failure would bring the government's judgment into question. The competition with Hoyt only compounded the problem.

Junk decided to make his case in person. He travelled to London and made a beeline for Cox's flat. After talking Cox into dinner and after countless late-night bottles of expensive California wine, Junk literally got down on bended knee. All he wanted, he explained, was to continue the work his dearly departed father could never finish. Cox stopped him from embarrassing himself further. He knew William Hoyt was also planning a trip to Everest and that Junk wanted nothing more than to beat Hoyt to the top. Cox then shared the news that Hoyt's trip was scheduled to start ten days before the British trip. Catching up would be futile. If Junk still wished to join the expedition knowing he could not compete with his nemesis, then Cox could convince the other committee members to let Junk tag along. Put another way, removing the personal competition would de-fang the American and make him more willing to play along with his fellow team members. And this knowledge would reassure the committee.

Surprisingly to Cox, Junk needed no time to deliberate. He accepted.

Aaron Junk had absolutely no intention of "tagging along" (and of course, he had no intention of making maps, a profession in which he had little interest). He intended to use his aggressive sales skills to essentially hijack the expedition. He would work his way into a leadership position and convince the team to take Everest from the south. This had three important implications. First, the south side of Everest is in forbidden Nepal, so they would have to sneak through the Kingdom undetected and still have the strength to climb the mountain. Second, no one in the mountaineering community had a good idea what the south side of Everest held in store. People who had reached the upper ridges of Everest had looked down at its southern face and so could deduce some basic things. The glimpses from above confirmed that the southern face might offer an easier route to the top. But one could not really be sure until he or she was standing at the base, looking up. The third implication, the one most important to Junk, was that taking Everest from the south would easily shave ten days off of the trek, allowing him to catch up with Hoyt. Hoyt was a rule-follower and would unquestionably approach from Tibet in the north. Getting to Tibet from Calcutta takes a long time. Getting to Nepal takes far less time because one does not need to "loop around" the Himalaya. Perhaps the two expeditions would not start ascending from their respective base camps on the exact same day, but it would damned be close.

Cox could not have predicted how his decision to send untested climbers would help Junk's cause. The leader of the team was a man named Percy Tersely, a disgraced banker from London, who had allegedly tried to embezzle one thousand dollars from his employers, the Bank of England. His plot failed when he deposited the embezzled money into a savings account under his name *in the same bank.* The barrister at his trial pointed out that the young bookworm was an avid reader of Edgar Allen Poe, and suggested Tersely was clearly trying to avoid suspicion by using a tactic learned from Poe's "The Purloined Letter." But most people following the trial felt he was just an idiot. Tersely was ultimately let go on a technicality. As a mountaineer, he was unexceptional but sufficient, having led expeditions to K2 and Annapurna that had set height records, but had not reached the summits. His acceptable climbing abilities mixed with his status as a disgraced British old boy made him a perfect candidate for expedition leader of the 1939 "disposable" attempt on Everest.

Also along for the expedition was Elihu Twist, a farmer from the town of Woking; John Browning, a former soldier on the Indian front who was discharged for frotteurism; Andrew Witherspoon, a geologist from Vauxhall; Shaun McSorley, a noted climber from Dublin; and Bruce "Tosser" Oldhusband of Coventry. They were all decent climbers, but none of them went to good schools (McSorley did not go to any) and none were members of the British Armed Forces, which could often get a man in good with the aristocracy even if he was of ill breeding. Oldhusband came from a moneyed family, but he had been cut out of the family fortune because they did not approve of his decision to become a linguist.

The Everest Committee would not spare its best men, but it would spare no expense getting this ignoble, baseborn team to the top. They would use brute force as a replacement for skill. Along for the trip would be one hundred and fifty porters, thirty more high-altitude Sherpa, three hundred and fifty pack animals, and enough food for two expeditions.

Junk's plan was set. Perfect timing and substandard cohorts. He would climb Everest at the same time as Hoyt, but would beat him to the summit using the southern route.

Hoyt's American team left The United States in early June and arrived at Base Camp almost three months later. The weather was gorgeous. The monsoon-driven storms were gone and the sun shone off of the mountain gloriously. Hoyt was especially hopeful because of the crack squad he had put together. Gil Taylor, Phillip Zeigler, Daniel Crimmins, William Webster, and Paul Fleming. All heroes in the pantheon of American mountaineering. In addition to their climbing expertise, they were also map-makers, geologists, and naturalists. To prepare Tibet for their arrival, Hoyt asked Gil Taylor, an ethnographer from the University of Chicago, to act as liaison officer and write a letter to the Tibetan government. Hoyt believed Taylor could do the best job obtaining access to the Tibetan borders due to his occupation. Taylor wrote the following:

Sirs,

The sun slowly sets on the British Crown and, moving east, begins to rise on your new better, the United States of America. Repair to your homes and don your Sunday best, for a team of sahibs arrive from the Promised Land in three months' time. We will have in tow myriad porters and countless pack mules. You will know us by the pride in our gaits. We expect every courtesy of you, anointing our feet with soothing balms and refreshing our vodka tonics with either a wedge of lemon, or a twist, depending upon our fleeting whims. Choose to ignore these words and the talons of the bald eagle will rend your great nation asunder.

Demanding tribute,

Gilford Taylor

Hoyt had been unaware up to this point that an ethnographer could be a racist. He had to follow up this letter with an immediate apology to the Dalai Lama. Hoyt claimed Taylor was "possessed by a succubus" when he wrote the missive. The High Llama, in his infinite wisdom and tolerance, welcomed the Americans graciously.

Now, three months later, they looked up at the East Rongbuk Glacier and the mountain beyond. Unbeknownst to them, Junk was making his Tibetan approach. Also hidden from Hoyt's view was another nemesis – one he did not yet know he had. Fumu.

It had taken almost two months for the British Expedition to arrive in Calcutta. On the ocean voyage, Junk had made quick friends with everyone except Tersely. Instead, he made every effort to publicly question Tersely's plans for climbing Everest. Junk never explicitly challenged the man, but he asked pointed questions and treated the answers like they were spoken by a child.

"How many men do you plan to use for the final push at the top?" would be a likely question.

"Four" was a likely response.

"Sounds like someone is not considering any backup if an initial summit attempt fails, but okay."

All of this was part of Junk's strategy. Humiliate Tersely in front of everyone and then take his authority. It seemed to be working. By the time they made Calcutta, Tersely jokes were shooting back and forth between expedition members, usually alluding to his botched embezzlement scheme. "I think Tersely has stolen my pocket watch! Why? Because it's right here in my pocket! The genius of it all!" Sometimes they took aim at the shortcomings Junk had created about Tersely out of thin air. "Tersely wants to use four pack mules for the summit attempt instead of people. But then he thought the better of it, realizing in his infinite wisdom they could not plant the Union Jack."

Things turned awkward when Tersely simply left. No one knew that the man they were taunting was a youngest sibling in the Tersely clan. He had never been taken seriously by his family, ever. But after the failed embezzlement scheme and now the mockery of his mountaineering leadership skills, he had had enough; Junk was awoken long after he had gone to bed by noises in the hotel room next to his own. In the hallway, he saw Tersely in a fit of tears walking out of their hotel and into the Calcutta night. He would not be seen again until 1975, when some extended family members happened across him, now a Moslem sheepherder near Tehran.

A solemn and ashamed team now turned to Junk, who gladly took the helm. The next day, they met their Sherpa guides, including sardar Ang Kikuli, and headed up from Calcutta to Darjeeling by train. "Change in plans" Junk announced to his team. He then convinced them, one by one, that they should not proceed up to Tibet like previous British expeditions, but instead trek into Nepal, only a few miles away. They would then hike across the Lesser Himalaya to Everest. He explained that going through Nepal offered a more direct route and, unlike England and the United States, other nations' border restrictions were merely suggestions. Easily convinced, the team hiked northwest into Nepal and straight for Everest.

They luckily experienced no run-ins at the border. The subsequent trek through the kingdom was relatively uneventful. As the hike progresses deeper into the kingdom, Junk caught his first glimpse of the Himalaya. He wrote the following letter to McGee:

"We're crossing Nepal with amazing speed. The locals have been swell and the men are growing more and more excited with each day. What's fueling that excitement is the nature of the horizon ahead of us. Only a few days ago, the reddish-purple sunset ended at a rugged line demarcating the Earth below. Now, with each passing sunset, the line takes on more character. The ruggedness gets more rugged. The sun hits the horizon earlier. Now we can clearly see the outline of Abel ahead, and behind it, the smoky one they call Fumu. Even though our elevation is still relatively low, I swear I can smell snow in the air. It's a beautiful thing when the horizon stops being a metaphor. I can literally see my future there. I only wish Dolores and you, my dear chum, were here to enjoy it."

We can assume that Dolores was a woman he was dating briefly at the time. No other record can be found of her.

When Junk and the team reached the Himalaya, their pace slowed. Oxygen had gone from a given to a luxury. They were making every effort to save their energy for Everest. No one wanted to struggle against the waning air supply until it was necessary. The team also slowed because of the majesty of the landscape. The air was still warm and fragrant here. They travelled through lush, narrow valleys full of birch, juniper, and rhododendron, broken up by clear blue rivers of icy run-off. On both sides of them, the valleys gave way to walls of rock, leading up to mountains of other-worldly proportions. Occasionally they would cross a monk or a farmer making their way to villages laying at lower climes.

Two days away from Base Camp, the team stopped in their tracks. A valley they had been hiking through opened up to a rocky field gently rising in front of them. Straight ahead, Junk saw the peak of Everest. But that was not what stopped them. To their right, due east, rose a mountain of such height, they could swear they had gone off course and were actually passing Everest. Some of the Europeans on the expedition began to press the porters, asking how they had botched things up so badly as to miss their destination. Junk shushed them. He knew the shape of Everest and whatever this mighty Goliath happened to be, it was not their destination.

One could hardly see her because she was protected on all sides by the smaller-but-still-humbling giants, Mitya, Abel, Lata, and Asha. Junk consulted the map and spoke with the porters. They explained that it was a terrible mountain called Fumu. Junk was struck with fear. He had heard of this beast and its perils. The mountains in front of it were bright white. But behind those mountains, taking up what seemed like the whole sky, were rock faces living in an entirely different weather pattern. Overcast. No sun, at least not where they could see. Near the top, just below the ash cloud, snow squalls passed across her face. There was a distant rumbling. Elihu Twist swore he saw an avalanche accompanied by black rocks come spilling out from the cloud at the top. But the others did not make it out. There was a faint smell of sulfur in the air, even at this distance.

The team was sincerely upset by the sight. "Each one to the man, including the porters, confessed later that their hearts were racing. Even in the cool air, they were sweating under their layers. Fumu was not their destination, but certainly they must have thought if Everest was taller than this giant, then Everest must be terrible indeed."

Little did anyone on Junk's expedition know that at the same moment, Zachary Hoover, Chhiri Tendi, and about twenty other men were halfway up Fumu, looking up in terror at the same landslide above them. Luckily, they were climbing along a ridge. The falling snow and rock would bank to the left and to the right of the ridge, sparing the climbers. Chhiri Tendi was up there, somewhere, trying to lighten the mood by saying the mountain's snow was looser than Mae West.

One more thing caught the attention of Junk's team. They had seen an occasional Buddhist monastery on their way. In front of them now was not one monastery, nor two nor three, but a monastery every one hundred yards or so, trailing off into the higher elevations to the northeast and into the lower elevations to the southeast. He could easily see fourteen, each one draped in colourful flags blowing in the gentle wind. The monasteries looked as if they may be ringing around Fumu. But that would be impossible, Junk must have thought. The ring would have to be hundreds of monasteries long. No white man knew of these monasteries, seeing as Nepal was forbidden to outsiders. He asked the porters about the structures. They pleaded ignorance, but Junk knew there was no way they were in the dark about such a massive architectural feat. He chose not to press it, wanting to keep the porters on his good side.

Junk wanted to understand this beautiful vision, this Shangri La. He had researched Nepal and focused on the peoples who inhabited the higher elevations in the North. In that time, he had never heard anything about this mysterious string of buildings. In a quest to learn, and to be the first white man to uncover their secrets, Junk chose to approach one of the monasteries with Oldhusband in tow. Junk wanted Oldhusband with him so Oldhusband could make some field recordings. The more research completed, the better justified their trip. He also asked Ang Kikuli, the Sherpa sardar, to join them but he refused. When pressed for a reason, Ang Kikuli responded, "Because they are unbalanced people." Apparently, the porters did know about the monasteries. "They are not Buddhists. Nor are they Hindu. Nor Jain. I do not what they are." Junk chose to let it go.

A village of small huts and penned animals had grown up in between and in front of the monasteries. The Brit and the American walked proudly and briskly past on-looking villagers. Oldhusband lugged a cylinder phonograph on his back with two cylinders tucked into a pouch on his belt and the horn held in his left hand. They approached and then ascended a long series of wooden steps, likely straining their lungs in the sparse air, At the top they opened two heavy wooden doors. The doors were massive, having the effect of making guests feel like children walking into their parents' room.

"The transition from the bright day outside to the darkness inside caused green blotches to overwhelm our fields of vision," wrote Oldhusband. "The smell inside was that of burning wood and warm milk. More colourful ceremonial banners hung from the high rafters inside. Candles dotted the room in apparently random locations. We had to plan our steps carefully."

There were dolls everywhere. Girl dolls, boy dolls and ambiguous dolls. Some dolls were big – maybe three feet tall - and incredibly detailed, with wooden hands carved to the point of detailing knuckles and freckles. Other dolls were smaller, just a collection of sticks tied together with a stone for a head. An occasional doll had hair made of grass. Oldhusband continued: "We made every effort not to step on these dolls for fear they played some sacred role in the monks' lives."

From somewhere nearby, they heard what they thought to be throat singing, low and guttural. Junk and Oldhusband's eyes finally adjusted enough to expose two monks sitting on the floor in front of them and across the room. As they moved closer, it became clear these monks were the source of the music.

Oldhusband greeted them in what he thought would be their mother tongue, Nepali. But the monks told Oldhusband not to bother. They understood the Queen's English quite well. Learning English was part of their monastic duties, they explained. Oldhusband tried to show kindness and diplomacy right away by apologizing for interrupting their singing. One of the monks said they had not been throat singing. They were simply hung over and discussing what they would have for breakfast.

"My eyes continued to adjust to the darkness and only then did I notice other people sitting around the periphery of the room," wrote Oldhusband. "They were dressed in white loincloths and all were in various states of what could only be called 'play.' Some were playing checkers. Others were drawing large, awkward pictures. Another man was playing mumblety peg with a very sharp blade. The scene put me ill-at-ease. I had no explanation for such behaviour in fully-grown men. What also struck me was their skin. These were not Nepalese men, or at least not many of them. Some looked European. Others were coloured. Another oriental. They seemed to represent all corners of the globe."

According to Oldhusband, a large door in the back of the room swung open. A tall, skinny man of unknown descent ("Tan skin. South American? Brazilian?" Oldhusband wondered in his journal) and perhaps fifty difficult years of age stood at the threshold. Running down past his shoulders were oily, matted strips of graying black hair, thinning on the top. He called out the names of the two men who had first greeted Oldhusband and Junk. "A tattletale has informed me you have both been sneaking alcohol from the villagers! Is this so?"

Neither man answered.

"Well?!"

Silence. Looks of terror.

"Fine. You do not need to answer. But be advised that you will be going to bed early tonight."

The two men began to cry.

"I was baffled. Wordless," wrote Junk in a letter to McGee. "What the hell was going on here? This made conversations I had had with drunkards in South Boston seem like arguments before the Supreme Court."

The tall skinny man now turned around to leave. Junk stopped him and asked for a moment of his time. The tall skinny man acquiesced and grudgingly invited Junk and Oldhusband to follow him.

They entered a bright room. Across from them was an enormous opening in the wall, roughly twelve feet by twelve feet. The opening overlooked Fumu and her smaller neighbors. The room did not feel particularly cold despite the giant aperture. The warmth was due to a roaring fire burning in a pit just before the opening.

"Gumdrop?" The man held out two gumdrops he had fished out of God knows where.

Junk replied. "No. Thank you. My name is Aaron Junk, and my colleague here is Mr. Bruce Oldhusband. We are from the United States and England, respectively. Can we record our conversation with you?"

"Be my guest. Would you like to hear my imitation of a duck?"

"No thank you."

"I can sing 'Anything Goes.'"

"That's quite alright."

"This is going to be a very boring recording. I have an idea. I can pretend to be The Queen and you can pretend to be the guards outside of Buckingham Palace. I do crazy things like lift up my skirt, and you try not to laugh."

"Wait."

"Tiny! Come in here please!"

"No no. Sir, this is not supposed to be a humourous recording."

One of the other men, apparently named Tiny, dressed in a loincloth like everyone else, entered the room. The skinny man immediately put Tiny in a headlock and messed up his hair. He then released Tiny from the headlock, slapped him, and kissed him full on the mouth.

"Now get out of here."

Oldhusband laughed but quickly stifled it. "Junk shot me a scathing look and so I became silent."

The skinny man watched Tiny leave the room and then turned to view his guests. "That was more of a visual joke, I guess. Not very good for a sound recording. But entertaining nonetheless, right? Absurdity tarted up with violence can be quite amusing."

Junk spoke. "Sir, not to be rude, but we wish to record you for posterity. We have come from far away, and we find you and your colleagues fascinating. I am confident others will be amazed by your existence as well. You see? We wish to document you."

"If you do not record my antics, then you are not documenting me."

"Fair enough. Then let me rephrase our intent. We wish to interview you."

The skinny man sighed and then sat on the floor. "Go ahead."

Junk sat down as well. He pulled a pad and pencil out of his jacket pocket, wiped dirt and sand off of the pad, and prepared to write. Oldhusband took the phonograph off of his back and placed it on the floor, equidistant from Junk and the skinny man but slightly off to the side. He affixed the horn to the top, attached a cylinder, and wound the phonograph's crank. The cylinder began to turn. Oldhusband gave Junk the thumb's up sign and then sat down himself. The following is the transcript of the conversation, with Oldhusband's notes in brackets:

JUNK: "What is your name."

SKINNY MAN: "I do not have a formal name, but around here, they call me Mano, which is Portuguese for 'big brother'."

JUNK: "Why 'big brother?'"

MANO: "Because I tell them what to do to be pious."

JUNK: "Piety. What religion's dogma are you following?"

MANO: "It has no name. We worship the Angry Parent, the Fire and Ice. We worship Fumu."

JUNK: "Why is she angry?"

MANO: "He is angry because his children do not live up to his expectations."

JUNK: "Wait. Is Fumu a he or a she?"

MANO: [Raises his shoulders and lower lip, as if to express befuddlement] "May I ask *you* a few questions?"

JUNK: "Of course." [Junk replies in as friendly a tone as possible even though I know he has no interest in answering questions].

MANO: "Why are you here?"

JUNK: "In Nepal?"

MANO: "Yes."

JUNK: "We are here to climb Mount Everest."

MANO: "I see. Do you plan to climb Fumu as well?"

JUNK: "No. Not this time. But perhaps in the future."

MANO: "Why would you climb her?"

JUNK: [Junk has to think about this one. He does not want to offend Mano. For all we know, the wrong answer could lead to a public garroting. My friend chooses his words carefully.] "Out of awe. Out of worship."

MANO: [Slowly shakes his head, as if disappointed with the answer.] "Singing praises is worship. A burnt offering is worship. Living humbly is worship. For me, wearing a loincloth like a nappy is worship. Climbing atop a god is not 'worship.' It is anger. It is domination. It is nonconsensual. It is forced entry. It is rape. Licorice?" [Holds out licorice]

JUNK: [Silence. He seems angry] Let's move on. Why do you believe you have the right to boss these others around if Fumu is the, as you put it, 'angry parent?'

MANO: "Because the mountain has no voice, silly. I speak her will. Sure, we play and sing, but we are good children. We treat each other with respect, say 'Please,' go to bed at eight."

JUNK: "Do you have any sacred texts?"

MANO: "Reading primers mostly."

JUNK: "Can you ever please the angry mother?"

MANO: "The angry parent?"

JUNK: "Yes."

MANO: "Yes."

JUNK: "How?"

MANO: "Um. Well, we're not sure. We just have to keep doing the best we can. Be kind. Be honest. Treat others nicely. Don't wet ourselves. You know. The basics. But we'll know when he is pleased."

JUNK: "How?"

MANO: "When she stops bringing forth magma and starts bringing forth milk."

[Silence for about twenty seconds.]

JUNK: "Do you have children?"

MANO: "Do you?"

JUNK: [Answering, but clearly not liking being asked] "No."

MANO: "So why are you waltzing all over the planet? Why aren't you at home making children? As monks of Fumu, we are sworn to celibacy. We are forbidden to have children because the act of having children stops one from being a child. But others should have them. Why else are you on this planet? Sucker?" [Holds out two lollies]

JUNK: "That's enough, Bruce."

According to Oldhusband, Junk got up and walked out without a word. Oldhusband took apart the recording equipment in silence. Mano watched while licking his lolly. Oldhusband quietly thanked Mano for his time and walked out.

Junk and his team left the circle of temples and headed for Everest. With only a few days left to reach the base, everyone was anxious, talkative and ready to begin the ascent. Junk, however, was not. He seemed to the others enraged by the interaction that had taken place at the monastery. We cannot be sure why, but the anger and accompanying silence remained until they reached Base Camp later in the week.

William Hoyt and his team arrived at the northern Base Camp at about the same time Junk was pulling away from the circle of temples. If the ascent was a competition between the two men, Hoyt's early arrival made things perfectly even. The distance between Base Camp and the summit was longer on the north side where Hoyt was climbing, which meant he would get the proper handicap.

The camp lay at the end of the Rongbuk Glacier, just south of the Rongbuk Monastery. The plan was to have all of the Americans – Hoyt, Taylor, Zeigler, Crimmins, Webster, and Fleming – as well as countless Sherpa proceed along the side of the glacier to Camps One, Two, and then Camp Three at the North Col. When the route left the glacier and started to rise dramatically along the Northern Ridge, Hoyt, Taylor, and Zeigler would continue with fifty Sherpa. The rest would remain at Camp Three as back-up. This was a classic example of "the arctic method", in which the mountain was taken by force. No climber at any altitude would have far to down-climb in order to find safety. Even the highest camp would be manned by several Sherpa, warm food, and good company. If a summit attempt went awry, the climbers could be sipping scotch and feeling superior within a few hours.

They made excellent progress along the glacier. The weather was fair and the men were in good health. Taylor even summoned the strength to sing along the way. He was a fan of British opera, especially Gilbert and Sullivan. The other climbers were treated to repeated recitals of "The Pirates of Penzance." It didn't help that Taylor was slightly inebriated; carrying a flask of Jameson everywhere he went. He did not intend to abstain from alcohol until the climbing got truly intense along the Northern Ridge. The musical entertainment did not last long. "I pulled a clump of ice from my crampons and threw it at the soused tenor" Hoyt wrote. "The stinging ice did its work and he became silent."

"When I return from my attempt at reaching the 'Third Pole,'" Aaron Junk wrote to his girlfriend of the time, "perhaps you can have some fun reaching for the Fourth, if you know what I mean." All of his writings from the expedition had this tone. One has to turn to Twist's diary to have a good idea of the events that occurred on the south side of the mountain over the next several weeks.

From the rocky, desolate southern Base Camp, Junk's team ascended and descended between the Khumbu Icefall and Camp One. Junk, Ang Kikuli, and the Europeans would blaze the trail, and then return for the rest of the Sherpa and equipment. The Icefall is not a landscape for the timid. It has the texture of parched earth if one were a small insect, with massive cracks in the ground running in every direction, some of them forty feet wide and one hundred feet deep. Ladders and ropes were set up to cross crevasses. Twist wrote, "When negotiating a homemade, quickly fashioned rope bridge over a one-hundred-foot-deep, forty-foot-wide crevasse, the saying 'Don't look down' takes on a life-or-death immediacy. Climbing up and down the Icefall over and over, one takes those words and internalizes them so they are no longer consciously repeated to oneself. They become part of the inner workings of the Soul. But I have no fear. I look down into the crevasses, and I see smiling angels looking up, their arms out, waiting to catch me. Would they catch the Sherpa if one fell? They do not look like Church of England congregants, so it is unlikely. Perhaps the elephant-headed fellow is down there too, waiting for them, but I cannot see him."

It was near the top of the Icefall where they ran into problems. No one could find John Browning. When they awoke in the morning, he was gone along with his camera equipment. He had not told anyone he would be off taking pictures, and it was essential for safety's sake that everyone be accounted for, always. Expedition members were also supposed to bring someone along should they leave the group for even a moment. The team looked around for about an hour. The camp was located within a series of shallow crevasses forming a kind of maze, so everyone needed to be careful not to get lost.

When Browning was found, he was taking pictures of himself naked. Apparently, frotteurism was not his only "hobby." Browning had misjudged the excursion to Everest, thinking it a time in the vast wilderness where he would have relative seclusion. He had clearly gambled he could get away for a short time to "commune with nature." But the gamble had failed. Despite the expansive environment, climbing expeditions can be quite claustrophobic, especially back then, with men living on top of each other for months on end. His later explanation to the barristers was that he wanted to make artistic photographs of Man in Nature, in the spirit of the American Thomas Eakins' paintings of bathers. One barrister wrote, "I do not recall any Thomas Eakins paintings that include a naked man on his back holding his legs in the air." When the team down-climbed the Icefall as part of the acclimatization process, Browning was sent back to Base Camp with a few Sherpa. He would have to wait there until the expedition was over. Now the team was one man down.

The Sherpa were in an uproar. Browning's actions were almost guaranteed to offend Chomolungma, goddess of Everest and the surrounding region. Their religion dictated piety on the mountain. There was to be no moral coarseness on an expedition. In the opinion of the Sherpa, what Browning did was the equivalent of slapping a goddess in the face. Now they only had to await her response.

"There is no air here, Wiz," William Hoyt wrote. "We are not even past the North Col, and already I feel a great weight upon my chest. Each inhalation is like going through business school again. I cannot imagine how I will feel when we ascend another several thousand feet. I am also afraid. So many men greater than I have sat here before, writing to their loved ones, only to meet icy death hours later. There is no way to know what God will deliver from on high, but I promise you, I will not be lost."

Hoyt, along with Taylor, Zeigler, and myriad Sherpa left from the North Col to Camp Four early on the morning of August 31st, wearing their breathing apparatuses. The addition of oxygen was bittersweet for the Americans. Now they could breathe easily but they also had to carry heavy tanks on their backs. For the Sherpa, the addition of oxygen was a pure victory. They had to carry fewer tanks and they could breathe easier, Sahibs be damned.

The team was plagued by bad weather almost immediately. Snow and wind bit at them each step of the way, not forceful enough to stop them entirely, but enough to slow them down. The men made it to Camp Four, exhausted and doubtful. When they awoke the next morning to take on more of the Northern Ridge, ten Sherpa said they were through. The weather and their own fatigue had gotten the best of them. Hoyt, in his usual manner, refused to let them leave. Instead of giving them a pep talk, he berated them for their "weakness." This had the wrong effect. Twenty Sherpa began down-climbing. Taylor also complained of pain in his kidneys but Hoyt would have none of it. He yelled at Taylor, saying he must continue up the mountain until death stopped him.

The three Americans and the thirty remaining Sherpa made their way toward the top of the Northern Ridge and High Camp. At that point, they planned to turn onto the Northeast Ridge which led all the way to the top. That had been the route of the British ascents of the 1920's. It was by the time of Hoyt a well-established route. But getting to the Northeast Ridge proved difficult. The storm worsened. The wind and snow was coming from the north, leaving them absolutely no protection from its wrath. More Sherpa turned back despite Hoyt's attempts to bark at them through his mask and over the wind. Shortly thereafter, Taylor tapped on Hoyt's shoulder. "I turned to look and Taylor waved goodbye," wrote Hoyt. "I ripped off my mask and cursed at him. 'You are nothing!' I yelled. 'I should have invited my mother to come. She would have made it.' Taylor held up the back of his mitten to me. I can only assume he was giving me the finger. Nonetheless, despite his protestations, he stayed with me. My belittling worked, as it often does."

After many days of negotiating the Khumbu Icefall, Junk's team made it to the Western Cwm, a relatively gentle climb leading to Camp Two. Despite its lack of technical challenge, the Western Cwm presents its own unique obstacles. One major obstacle is the heat. It catches copious amounts of sunlight during the day, so climbers spend much of their time boiling and dressed down. But Junk's team was not so lucky. The storm that was simultaneously abusing Hoyt's team on the north side of the mountain was also wreaking havoc on the southern approach. They had planned to set up Camp Two at the bottom of the Lhotse Face, but the entire team was exhausted. They set up their tents half way up the Western Cwm, nuzzled up against the rocky face that rose to the Western Ridge. The rocks protected them from the full force of the wind, and so there they stayed for two endless, dull days.

When they woke up on the next day, the air was cold and windy, but the sky was a brilliant blue. Junk was ready to go, but Twist hesitated. "I told him the Lhotse Face was a major risk. It had taken the brunt of the storm, and I was concerned an attempt on it today guaranteed an avalanche." Junk agreed that the Lhotse Face looked threatening, covered with a fresh layer of soft snow begging to drop. But now they had to come up with an alternate route. Twist suggested the Western Ridge, up a steep incline off to their left.

Oldhusband implored Twist to forget the idea. From where they stood, the Western Ridge looked serrated like a knife. Oldhusband wrote, "Training the eyes left to right, one saw step after step after step. What perils awaited us on the Western Ridge? Twist was thinking in a shortsighted manner to say the least."

The gambler in Junk once again leapt into action. Both options were perilous. The Lhotse Face was an avalanche threat, but if they were quiet about it, they could ascend the face and be out of harm's way quickly. The Western Ridge was hard to read from their vantage point, but it could be a somewhat bumpy magic carpet straight to the top of Everest. For a moment, Junk was back on the streets of South Boston and, as usual, he was going for the long shot.

Oldhusband made one last effort to convince the other men to take the Lhotse Face. In desperation, he proposed the team intentionally set off an avalanche by making a lot of noise. Junk was willing to give it one chance before committing to the enigmatic Western Ridge.

They started by screaming bloody murder. All twenty-eight Sherpa were asked to participate. But the groups' exhausted lungs were not very effective at this altitude. The resulting chorus of "yells" sounded like someone snoring into a trombone. Twist spotted a boulder about twenty feet up the rock face below the Western Ridge that looked as if it could easily be pushed down to the rocky surface below. Perhaps the sound of rock meeting rock would do the trick? He, McSorley, and several Sherpa slowly climbed up to it and began to push. To their amazement, it worked. The boulder slowly leaned away from them and then quickly dropped over the lip it had long called home, issuing a loud echoing crack as it hit limestone twenty feet down. It then broke into two massive halves, both rolling in different directions. Unfortunately, one of the halves advanced toward the group waiting at the camp, a giant coin rolling on its thin side, beginning to wobble as it lost speed. The boulder finally came to rest on Huggins' left foot.

The resulting cry from Huggins echoed up and down the Western Cwm. It was high-pitched; more of a scream than a yell. And it persisted. Huggins kept screaming and screaming, spit flying from his mouth. The yell stopped only occasionally so he could produce curse words and pleas for someone to remove the boulder from his hobbled foot. It took no less than four men to lift the boulder up an inch so Huggins could pull his foot out from under. The simple act of moving his foot must have set off a new wave of pain because Huggins increased his scream to eardrum-damaging levels.

And still the Lhotse Face remained silent. Junk decided the Western Ridge was their only chance. Huggins was to stay back with all of the

Sherpa excepting Ang Kikuli. The remainder of the expedition would ascend to the Western Ridge. They would place their final camp at the shoulder of the ridge, down-climb to continue the acclimatization process, and then return. From there, Junk, Oldhusband, Twist, and Ang Kikuli would have a go at the summit. They were getting closer to the prize, and the excitement was setting in, muffling the pain wracking their depleted bodies.

After a night of fitful sleep, Hoyt's team was now tackling the Northern Ridge at 10 a.m. on September 1st. The weather had cleared and the summit was now in view. The men could measure the distance to their prize in hundreds of feet now instead of thousands. They moved with all haste. But all of this time, of course, the air was getting thinner. It is along the Northern Ridge that the climber enters the "death zone" – the altitude at which the human body begins to deteriorate rapidly. No one can take up permanent residence there. The acclimatization process of moving up and down the mountain stops, and speed becomes of the essence.

Hoyt looked at the route lying ahead of them. Three large steps stood between them and the summit. The climbing would be quite technical and would require the team to exert more effort. Hoyt was becoming fearful they may run out of oxygen tanks. If they were willing to venture off the ridge slightly, they could perhaps avoid the steps and instead follow the massive couloir scarring the Northern Face. But the "Great Couloir" as it would come to be known was a mystery near the top. It may present a challenge dwarfing the steps of the Northern Ridge. In the end, with input from the Sherpa sardar and Zeigler, Hoyt decided to try the Great Couloir. There was a 100% chance of difficulty if they stayed on course and a 50% chance if they tried their hand at the Northern Face.

By all accounts – Hoyt's accounts, Junk's accounts, and the British military's accounts - the group walked off the ridge and onto the Northern

Face at 11:05 a.m. According to Hoyt's notes, they had not hiked twenty feet when they saw a massive fireball rise up from the Western Ridge on the far side of the North Face, followed a second later by its accompanying, deafening explosion...

It was 11 a.m. on the Western Ridge. "The world is now in view" Twist wrote from their final camp. "Before, we could only see a small slice of the surrounding mountains. Now we can see over Lhotse into Tibet, we can see the entirety of the Northern Face, and behind us we can see the familiar landscape of Nepal. Of most interest to me is that Fumu. It seems to be smoking more than it was when we passed it on the approach. We see small explosions and flecks of bright orange amid the grey smoke. Active bugger. It looks mean and enormous. I would not be surprised if someday someone judged it taller than the mountain we are now on."

The wind on the ridge was impossible. It felt strong enough to send the men airborne, hurtling them toward the Northern Face. They were making very slow progress. As planned, the Sherpa and Huggins, nursing his broken foot, had stayed behind at the camp on the Western Cwm. The remainder of Junk's team had ascended to the Western Ridge, camped out on the shoulder marking the start of the ridge, only about one hundred feet back, and now, Junk, McSorley, Twist, Oldhusband, and Ang Kikuli were hiking along its razor edge, averaging only about four steps per minute. Junk walked far in front. McSorley, Oldhusband, and Twist walked in a group about fifty feet back, all attached to a rope. Ang Kikuli took up the rear, feeling an obligation to keep an eye on the foreigners. They were known to push themselves far beyond their capabilities and "hit a wall" quite suddenly. And at 11:05, that is what happened. In an interview about the events on the Western Ridge many years later, Ang Kikuli wrote the following.

"Oldhusband went down on two knees. The rope went taut, so the others stopped. Junk also turned and watched from further up the ridge. Oldhusband turned to look down the ridge at me. I was more than willing to help him. 'Are you okay?' I yelled over the wind. But I did not expect his response. 'Carry me!' he yelled back between gasps. 'Carry me! On your back!' Like most Sherpa, I am a man of patience. But this white-eyes had passed my limit. 'No' was all I could say. He said he must get to the top. That England must get to the top. That if he did not continue, his Queen was that much less likely to get her prize. Not only was I to carry him, but I needed to beat Junk to the top. No one planned on having the American take the lead, and it was an egg in the face of England. 'Carry me!' he exclaimed once more. 'For England.' I apologized and refused. It was right about then we heard the noise."

There is no disagreement among the various parties about what happened next. A buzzing noise was heard from the south. Everyone looked up. They saw something spinning toward them through space. It spun on a vertical plane, like a circular saw but much, much larger. As it spun, smoke escaped from a single point on its perimeter, leaving a spiraling black trail through the air, originating all the way back to Fumu.

It was an airplane. Some sort of single-man fighter. The left wing was clearly damaged. The men had little time to run, nor did they have many places to run, nor did they have the energy to move quickly. The plane passed above the Hillary Step, and within moments, it made contact with the Western Ridge. As if planned by some cruel, unknowable force, the plane met the ridge at an angle practically parallel to the ridge, like a train gradually meeting up with a new track. It then proceeded to tumble like an acrobat down the ridge, not leaving it at all. Junk, who was the first in its path, had moved off the ridge just enough to avoid contact, and to avoid falling to his death, but he was close enough to receive a piece of flying shrapnel to the chest.

Oldhusband rose from his knees and tried to jump off the north side of the ridge, but his rope-mate McSorley tried jumping in the opposite direction, with Twist pulled down right in the middle. The plane hit Twist head on, killing him instantly and snapping the rope connecting the three climbers. Oldhusband fell off the ridge to his death in one direction while McSorley fell off the ridge to his death in the other direction.

Ang Kikuli watched as the plane, coming right for him, hit an upturn in the ridge (between where he and Oldhusband had had their awkward moment) and sail up into the air directly over him. It came to land on their camp, full of supplies including oxygen tanks. When it made contact with the tents, it exploded. Ang Kikuli recalls "I could feel the heat even from several hundred feet off. And the sound deafened me for days. I saw but could not hear the Lhotse Face collapse – only now - in a massive avalanche. It was an obnoxious, cruel taunt by the mountain. For Browning's nudity? For the hubris of us all? I will never know."

Junk lay on his back, looking up at black brush strokes of smoke on a deep blue sky canvas. He must have felt unbearable pain in his chest. He would later find out the shrapnel had punctured his right lung, doubling breathing difficulties brought on by high altitude.

He must have wondered how his long shot had gone so wrong. Years later, while discussing the risk involved in a business investment with the New Yorker Magazine, Junk said, "I am confident, but cautiously so. I'm older now, and I've learned you can calculate the angles to death, measuring the marigolds until you are exhausted, but there's always the unknowable." It is hard to imagine that he was not thinking of planes randomly falling out of the sky when he uttered those words.

William Hoyt saw people through the binoculars. They were strewn across the Western Ridge. Some were not moving, but others were. Up until that point, he had had no idea other people were on the mountain. He saw no flags flying over their devastated camp. They could be from anywhere. For all he knew, they could be pesky Nazis climbing in enemy territory. The States were not at war with Germany of course, but best to leave Nazis alone regardless. If this was some sort of strange military operation, and the exploding plane increased the likelihood of that, then more violence could ensue.

Nonetheless, Hoyt did not hesitate. He told the rest of his team the plans had changed. They were giving up their bid for the summit and instead being good Christians and crossing the Northern Face in order to aid those who were still alive and possibly stranded. Taylor and Zeigler urged him to reconsider; after all, there is an understanding among climbers that at high altitudes, all bets are off. If you come across a dying man, you are not expected to help him. Nonetheless, Hoyt was convinced it was God's will they forego glory and practice kindness. Even if the rescue meant they would have to abandon their other team members below and risk returning home through forbidden Nepal, they were going to do it. Those at lower camps would ultimately leave Hoyt and the others for dead and go home. They would even have a pleasant surprise when they returned to civilization and found out their team leaders were indeed alive. It would all work out. It had to.

Starting from the Great Couloir, Hoyt's men traversed the Northern Face, following one of the many coloured bands of rock cutting horizontally across. The traverse was long and risky. There was little snow or ice to give their crampons purchase. Pockets of loose scree made a slip likely, and any slip from here would almost certainly be fatal. The North Face is, after all, a mostly-featureless, steep slope dropping for over ten thousand feet. There is little to catch one's fall. Between the risk of a fall and the Death Zone atmosphere, Hoyt and the others moved at a glacial pace.

With the sun beginning to set many hours later, Hoyt approached the Western Ridge. "The scene was now quite clear," Hoyt wrote. "A person lay on the ridge. The shape of him was all wrong - a puzzle forced together incorrectly by a child's hand. I only ascertained it was human because it was adorned in climbing equipment. Any exposed skin was bone-white.

"About one hundred feet higher up the ridge, I saw a man, possibly a Sherpa, standing over another man who was holding his abdomen. The two figures looked desperate. They had likely gone for some time without supplemental oxygen. The standing man was hardly standing at all. He had to keep resting his hands on his bent knees. Occasionally, he would get the energy to wave us over."

When Hoyt finally reached the two survivors, Ang Kikuli introduced himself. He said he could not get his charge down the mountain alone. He would need help. Hoyt explained that they could help carry the man down the mountain provided there was food, air, and shelter for the northern expedition on the way down the south side of the mountain. If not, they would have to back-track to the safety of their own camps on the other side of the Northern Face. Ang Kikuli said there would be no problem once they down-climbed past the ruined High Camp. Hoyt's team could simply use the rations of the dead men. But they would need to start the down-climb immediately. The sun was setting and the nearest camp was down on the Western Cwm. Hoyt agreed and they turned to the man on the ground, calculating the best method of carrying him.

It was then the man on the ground removed his mask and goggles. "I was too tired and too shocked to become enraged," Hoyt wrote. "I saw the wincing face. I heard the pleas for help. I even heard him apologize. My response, not conscious at all mind you, was to go down on two knees, bend over, and emit sounds somewhere between laughing and crying. I had no idea what I was doing or what I was feeling. Perhaps that is what madness feels like." According to Ang Kikuli, Hoyt was looking down and was impossible to read. He put a gentle hand on Junk's leg, and then rocked back and forth.

After a few minutes, Hoyt rose and walked over to Taylor. He turned Taylor around quite roughly and began rummaging through his pack. Hoyt found what he was looking for and returned to Junk's beaten body. "Help...me....help," Junk expelled between gasps, unvoiced, merely whispered loudly, hands clutching his chest.

Hoyt took the bottle of Jameson whiskey from Taylor's pack and placed it on Junk's belly. Then he yelled, "Stay away from drunks! Their eyes are bloodshot and they have bruises that could have been avoided!" Rising from the dying man, Hoyt yelled, "Come along men! Let us continue our bid for the summit!" Turning his back on Junk, Hoyt began to march back across the northern face toward his own high camp.

Taylor and Zeigler did not follow. They had tried to convince Hoyt not to attempt a rescue in the first place, and now their leader was circling back, displaying indecision like a woman? Bah! They would have no more of it. Mutiny was afoot!

With this shocking act of disobedience, the top of Everest was lost to Hoyt. It was over. After standing motionless for some time, staring through goggles at his former expedition members and the expiring Junk, Hoyt began descending to the Western Cwm. He did not stop at that camp, for he was intent on keeping ahead of the others all the way home. Junk, living or corpse must not catch up to him. He would come down Everest alone, accompanied only by his rage.

Years later, mountaineers with backgrounds in military history would climb Everest and study the remnants of the plane that lay shredded and burnt along the Western Ridge. It turned out to be a Spitfire Mark 1, a

British fighter plane. It had been flying over "The Hump" on its way to delivering weapons to China, a nation embroiled in the Sino-Japanese War at the time. Granted, the British did not *officially* start transporting weapons to China until 1941 when the Asian theatre of World War II rose from the Pacific. But secretly, and slowly, British leaders were planning ahead, sensing Japan's threat early on. The route over the Himalaya was still fresh to most pilots, and apparently this one had flown too close to Fumu and damaged his wing.

Was it the same plane that Hoover and Chhiri Tendi had seen on the day of Hoover's beheading? We cannot be sure, but the timing is perfect.

As Hoyt and Junk climbed or were carried down Everest, the world around them was descending into fire. September 1939 saw Hitler's invasion of Poland and England's entry into the war. The Blitz would follow within a year's time. All but the Sherpa on these expeditions would have to navigate a brutal landscape to get back to their respective homes. Yet despite the world around them going to war, and despite the fact that their own nation would enter the fray in only a few years' time, Hoyt and Junk would remain indifferent. The only war that mattered to them was their own, and it was only one insult away from the final conflict.

Interlude: July 14, 1881

Roughly 25,000 up Fumu, sitting alone in his tent at Camp Five, George Malick wrote in his journal. He wrote more than usual and spent what little energy he had left on topics more expansive than the day-to-day drudgery of climbing the mountain. The lucidity of the prose suggests that he wore his oxygen mask in order to retain focus. One cannot help but read his entry on that day and think George Malick was aware of his coming demise:

I remember as a boy being on holiday with my family at Blackpool. We went there quite regularly. Specialists claimed the salt air provided therapy for my mother's manic prostration. Perhaps I was five years old. I was a small, frail child. The cold weather of England paired with my sensitivities did not permit a soak in the ocean. I spent my hours playing in the sand. I would find a stick and write messages I hoped would be read from far across the sea and across the spandrels of time by the ghost of Henry Morgan. I would let the cold waves roll in over the tops of my feet and when they rolled out, it looked as if I was moving backwards. The thrill of that sensation never wore off, no matter how many times I did it. But my greatest joy on those excursions was building castles. They were glorious structures. Ten towers. Motes. Outer walls and inner walls. Flags of seaweed. Windows crafted using the poke of a finger. To this day, those castles are the source of my greatest pride.

I recall one time, I had finished a particularly exquisite masterpiece when my father walked over to review my work, which he usually did not do. As always, I was silent in the presence of Father. He stood over me in his Sunday suit, as tall as a mountain, his eyes taking in every side, corner, stairwell, and gate. "You are not done, boy" he said through his moustache. I was confused. Clearly everything was there. I reviewed my work. Nothing was missing. I had even placed an extra gate outside of the mote. Then he explained. "What about the roads leading away from the castle? Where are you to go and how are you to get there? And while you are at it, you should start digging a hole. You will need passage to the Orient. I hear they have the world's most delectable teas."

It was at that moment I understood the heart of the Englishman. We are restless and hungry. The Englishman must expand outward. He must consume all. It is a wonder the Empire does not suffer from gout given all of our incessant gobbling. We consume and grow and then without wiping our mouths we consume and grow even more. "To Hell with that arrogant American, Thomas Payne," says the Englishman. "An island will rule all continents."

How big must we get? We consume countries, sub-continents, poles, and mountains. Is the goal to be everywhere all of the time and thereby control everything? Have we deluded ourselves into believing we are in the process of transforming into gods? We proceed as if one day, the entire world will be part of the Empire and every living person will be an Englishman; and we will have no where to go but the celestial bodies; and we will conquer them too; and then we will meet the Deity himself who will greet us by saying "How good of you to finally arrive! I have been so lonesome in my omnipotence and look forward to giving up this monotheistic rubbish. All men can be gods, from the lowly bushman to the Queen! Would you please join me in steering the Universe on its holy course to Perfection?"

Folderol.

Yet here I am, in a tent on the back of a frozen, angry giant, lacking any basic comfort, far from everything I should hold dear, all in the name of my father's – and my country's – quite mad endeavor. I act as if I have learned nothing. Once an Englishman, always an Englishman."

Two days after writing that entry, Malick looked back at his men. They would not be joining him as he walked headlong into the filthy cloud hovering and spitting ash only a few hundred feet above them. Thousands of miles they had travelled for this moment. But an unspeakable Fear, more powerful than their pride, had gotten the better of those around him. Malick wrote in his journal, "Each expedition member and each Sherpa looked back at me with an expression suggesting that they had seen a ghost." But they had not. They had seen cannibals.

Or at least they had convinced one another they had had a run-in with a herd of cannibals some time in the night. What had been done to their colleagues Quimby and Hirst was enough to make almost anyone reconsider their priorities. Down climbing only hours away from the summit seemed reasonable. Maybe home and hearth were a legitimate option after you had witnessed good Christian men torn apart by ghouls.

These people were traumatized and any debate about proceeding was unwinnable. They were going through hell. The cannibals were only one part of that hell. They were also dealing with an atmosphere simply incapable of sustaining human life. Each breath was futile and accompanied by a feeling of being buried alive. No one could think straight; moments of unwanted daydreaming were arrested by spells of total panic. And another type of hell awaited them if they continued to ascend. Ominous sounds came from the cloud. Explosions and grumblings. It stunk of chimney soot and eggs. The cloud was already causing the expedition trouble before they had even reached it, showering ash on them as they slept the night before. One ember, still glowing as it spiraled gently downward, had landed on the backpack of Coville, the man in charge of maps, setting their route home ablaze.

But Malick would not consider turning and running. He was going to the summit even if it meant going alone with no high camp full of colleagues waiting for him afterwards. He had come too far and given up too much – no, he had given up *everything* - to be here. His wife had threatened to leave him and to take his son with her should Malick decide to go on this damned expedition. It took him all of one minute after her threat to leave on the trip anyway. A volcano in the Himalaya! How could he, a man of adventure and discovery, resist such an opportunity? He would never see his wife and son again.

"I am letting my team go down," Malick continued in his writings from the night before. "They are of no use to me or their country." He waved to the men and wished them a safe descent. He then turned and began his journey to the top.

Three entries appear in his journal on July the 16th.

The first: "No air. Life not possble [sic] here. Wind is too powerful. Eruptions. No disernible [sic] top. Terrified."

The second, in all capital letters, taking up the whole page, mostly etches in the paper devoid of ink: "CANNOT FIND THE TENT"

The final, hardly legible, tearing through the page: "LOST"

Chapter Six: The Sins of the Father

It was three in the morning when Hoyt received the telephone call from the Manhattan State Hospital. When he heard Tom Frances, president of the hospital, on the other end of the line, Hoyt was sure his mother had passed on. But she had not. Frances explained that Maddy was in a "heightened emotional state" and demanded to speak to her son. It would be best if Hoyt came right away.

Hoyt drove from his brownstone on Washington Square Park up to the hospital. As he drove, his mind probably wandered to thoughts of climbing. It often did, especially after he had been away from it for some time. Two years had passed since Everest, and life had been relatively quiet. He went to work every day of the week, spent dinner with Wizzy and the children, and went to bed at nine. This routine only varied for church on Sundays. Climbing had ceased altogether, except for an occasional Sunday hike near Bear Mountain.

He had stopped climbing for three reasons. First, his body had taken a beating on Everest. He had sent his back into constant spasms because of a tiny fall on his way down to the Southern Base Camp. His anatomy had deviated in some subtle way for but a moment from its predetermined limits, and the response was extreme. He tried endless trips to chiropractors ("All of them, ultimately, quacks" according to Hoyt.), stretching exercises on the floor of his bedroom and his office, employees walking on his back, but nothing worked for more than a few days. Then a routine visit to the dermatologist for hammer toe also revealed a patch of cancerous skin on his forehead. It was removed with success but not without some unpleasant procedures. Hoyt's vision had also begun to go since the trip. He was not sure if the light in the Himalaya was any different than home, but he got headaches whenever he tried to read now, or he simply fell asleep. Old age arrives slowly and quietly for most men. In the case of Hoyt, it charged him like the Bull of Heaven did Gilgamesh.

In addition to the sub-standard condition of his body, there was the sub-standard condition of the world in 1941. Europe and Asia were already at war, and the United States was only five months away from Pearl Harbor. Fighting had closed off all four corners of the world to travel and most of the younger men who would have possibly accompanied Hoyt on an expedition were steeling themselves for looming combat.

But even more than the slow-motion collapse of his body, and even more than a world at war, there were Wizzy's pleas that kept him home. He was fifty, and as his body brittled, each climb carried more risk. Another small slip on ice could ruin him forever. Hoyt was in denial about that, but Wizzy was not. She wanted her husband around, even if their children were grown and off at college. She still loved him and wanted his company. He had to stop, or at least slow down. Otherwise, Wizzy would be at her wit's end and capable of anything.

Deep down, Hoyt likely knew he could only stop climbing for a short while. Some day, even if it killed him and his marriage, he would return to the harsh world that liberated him from his father. It brought him the greatest joy he knew. And that urge to climb was hastened by a letter he received shortly after the Everest expedition. It came from a town in Nepal called Thame, from a man named Chhiri Tendi. Chhiri Tendi had been following the climbing career of Hoyt closely, and considered him somewhat of a hero. "I have guided many men to the tops of mountains, and all of them speak of you highly" Chhiri Tendi wrote. "They say you 'have a gnat in your ass,' but you rise to peaks faster than an eagle, and your decisions are wise in times of crisis. I read about your ascent of Mont Blanc when your rope broke and you saved yourself by chimneying up a fifty-foot crevasse. Incredible. In addition to my great admiration for you,

I simultaneously share your feeling that Aaron Junk is a prick." These words must have made Hoyt cringe, not because of the bawdy language, but because he did not like to even think about Junk these days. Chhiri Tendi continued, writing that he had once felt sympathetic to Junk because they had both lost a father early in life, but he found Junk's stalking of Hoyt distasteful. "Not a good way to act" Chhiri Tendi wrote, "even if you did not have a father around to tell you right from wrong."

The letter went on to explain that, oddly enough, Chhiri Tendi was climbing in the Himalaya at the same time Hoyt was making his bid for Everest. He wrote of a fascinating and terrifying experience on the mountain they called Fumu, which lay about fifty miles southeast of Everest. Hoyt knew of it and its difficulty, but not much more. Chhiri Tendi wrote that he had almost made it to the top when his employer, a Mister Zachary Hoover had met a violent end. Chhiri Tendi himself had almost died as well. But all of this was secondary information. Chhiri Tendi wrote for another purpose.

> *"Here is the thing, Mr. Hoyt. We saw something that day just before Hoover's head went spinning off into the air. We saw Everest below us. It was below us! Fumu is taller, Mr. Hoyt! It is the tallest. I thought you might want to know that. It seems pretty important. All of your mountaineering friends know it is a difficult mountain, but they are dummies now compared to you because they do not know this juicy tidbit I just shared. The bastard is taller than Everest! I hope you will act on this information some day, and when you do, I hope you will take me along."*

> *Yours,*
> *Chhiri Tendi*

- 120 -

Hoyt was taken aback. The man writing the letter seemed legitimate. The other facts and opinions in the letter were all reasonable. Why should he doubt the Fumu information? Sure, this Tendi fellow had latched on to English curses a little too tightly, but he otherwise seemed well-grounded. "And perhaps I wanted to believe" he wrote some time later on his journey to Fumu. "I wanted to believe Everest was not the tallest mountain because it would minimize the disaster that had occurred there. And more importantly, it meant that another opportunity still existed out there for me. Retirement would have to wait but another season." Minutes after reading the letter, he almost started to pack. How could this information not be acted upon? How could an opium addict not react when learning of the existence of a thing called an "opium den?"

But Hoyt did not write back to Chhiri Tendi. He probably saw Wizzy needle-pointing in the living room, looking as domestic as a pioneer woman on the Great Plains. For Wizzy's sake, he did not act on his urges. "But I also thought to myself: 'Tell no one.' Maybe some day I would climb again, and when I did, I wanted to be the first to conquer the tallest mountain in the world."

Underneath all of these other thoughts likely swimming in William Hoyt's head that night driving to see his mother, there was definitely another thought Hoyt was intentionally *not* having. Aaron Junk and the disaster at the top of Everest must have been off-limits to Hoyt's consciousness. They would bring him too much discomfort. The amount of shame associated with that day would be too great, and the residual anger for losing the summit too vexing. In a letter of apology to fellow Everest climber Gilford Taylor one year after the accident (an apology Taylor never dignified with a response) Hoyt wrote "Memories of the summit – visible but unattained - make my eyes close tightly and my jaw clench." He was haunted. Indeed, with the Manhattan State Hospital sign in his headlights, rain coming down, William Hoyt was likely not thinking about Aaron Junk...with every fiber of his being.

"I am going to grab Hoyt by the berries and twist until he swallows his own tongue" Aaron Junk wrote to Patrick McGee while on brief holiday in the town of Truro on Cape Cod. "I am going to show him the meaning of a 'forearm shiver' but he'll only know its meaning for the fraction of a second before the bridge of his nose lodges in his God damned brain." Junk had been in this state of rage for a year. He had been capable of anger and brutality before, but it had never lasted very long, and certainly never long enough to escalate to a point where Junk considered murder a viable option. In the past, the moment his anger set in, Junk would simply hurt the offending individual, or he would whisper in McGee's ear and then McGee would hurt the offending individual. But Junk's current anger toward Hoyt was another story. After the Everest debacle, he had spent the remainder of 1939 in a hospital in Bombay and then in another in Boston, recovering from a laceration on his chest, two broken ribs, and a punctured lung. There was no chance for him to get back at the monster that had simply walked away from a dying man. Then, after leaving the hospital, there was too much publicity around the rivalry for Junk to exact revenge. Comedians in the Catskills were telling Hoyt/Junk jokes. Life Magazine ran a twenty-page article on "Infamous Rivalries Throughout History," culminating in the story of Hoyt and Junk. The English populace was able to distract itself from the war at least enough to be enraged by the inclusion of Junk on the 1939 British expedition to Everest (The consensus was that the American was the cause of the failure). If the world was caught up in their story, if every eye was trained on the two of them, Junk felt there was no way to get back at his rival with physical brutality.

Junk's letters to McGee from Cape Cod kept arriving:

Dearest McGee, my oldest friend,

Now that I am out of the hospital, I must begin hatching a plan. I am not yet sure what it will be, but I will be sure to offend every sensibility that the man has. He will be so arrested by my actions he will simply stop getting out of bed in the morning. But what should it be?

Perhaps I need to get back at him through that Jezebel Spirit he calls a wife. The one who slapped me and drenched me with her cocktail. I could flirt with her on afternoons in Washington Square Park and win her over. Perhaps that's the ticket? Or maybe his boys? I could befriend his boys at Princeton, invite them to a friendly game of poker and take them for their trust funds? No. Monetary damage is not enough. I need to ruin him spiritually, and there is no easier way to do that than through Family.

Marriage. Family. What a laugh. Why Marriage and Family? Why do it? Why do people feel their life is meaningless unless their death devastates at least one other person? I will feel more than content if I die with only you by my side, old friend.

This Hoyt thing tortures me. The young broad I brought on this vacation wants nothing more to do with me. She wants to go home. I don't blame her. I sit around in my undergarments, food in my beard, wearing only one black sock. Definitely not a good look on any man, but especially not on one who wanders around mumbling things about wrath and revenge.

Looking down on me for drinking. Judging me as not having what it takes to climb. How dare he judge me? HE IS NOT MY PARENT! If anything...

The letter ended there. Mid-sentence and without a sign off.

Hoyt likely had to go through the usual procedures to gain entrance into the hospital: signing in, identification checked, massive metal doors opening and then slamming shut behind him. As always, Frances and a nurse would escort him to Maddy's room. One can almost hear their hard rubber shoe soles clicking and echoing on long linoleum floors.

According to Hoyt's recollection to his wife (later shared by Wizzy in an interview with the author), the door to Maddy's private room opened and there stood a radiant soul. She was literally dancing; dancing in a room lit by one flickering light bulb. Dancing at four in the morning. A waltz. An imaginary partner leading. When "he" dipped her, Maddy apparently fell but got right up and laughed. When she saw William, she screamed with joy, ran over, and threw her arms around him. She then sat her son down on the bed and took a seat next to him. One of the nurses on the ward recalled the whole conversation and shared it with the author on condition of anonymity (Nurses are not supposed to share the private conversations between wards and their guests):

"William! Oh dear, dear William!"

"Hello mother."

"I'm overjoyed you've come. I have great news. I didn't want to contact you until it was official."

"Official? What are you talking about mother?"

"Are you ready? I got married!"

Hoyt apparently laughed at this comment. It was a frustrated laugh. He had been awoken in the middle of the night for this. She was happy and celebrating a delusion. For this, Frances had contacted him. Since he was there, he decided to play along.

"And who is the lucky man, mother?"

"I am not sure you could call him a man."

"What should I call him?"

"The father. The son. The holy spirit. It's Jesus, William! Jesus and I got married!"

Hoyt squirmed, followed by more forced snickers. "That is great news, mother. You have good taste. Now if you'll excuse me, I have to…"

"He's been visiting me for a while now. When he came to visit me last year out of nowhere, a dozen roses in his hand, I said 'What do you know? It's the second coming!' Oh we both laughed and laughed at that. Now almost every day he visits. And then a few weeks ago, he proposes! How could I say no?"

Hoyt leaned forward, maybe interested. Or concerned. This delusion was somewhat detailed. "So how did Jesus propose mother?"

"Like a true gentleman. He got down on one knee, took a huge rock out and asked me to marry him. Funny thing, William, throughout all my years at church, going with Spalding and you and Randolph, I learned so much about the good carpenter of Nazareth. But never in a million years would I have expected Jesus to have a Boston accent."

The nurse recalled silence. She recalled a look of concern on Maddy's face. Her son had slowly slid off the bed and onto the floor. His face was buried in his hands, his hands resting on his bent knees.

Frances broke the silence. "We're sorry, Mr. Hoyt. No one at the hospital contacted you before today because you had given us crystal clear and specific orders never to bother you about your mother unless she was visibly dying. And we felt that, given the scarcity of your visits and the regularity and kindness of Mr. Junk's visits, Maddy would be well taken care of in such a relationship. We sought legal counsel and found it was well within our rights to do what we felt was best for the patient. We…"

Frances' explanation was cut off. Hoyt the climber of incomparable speed rose to his feet in a flash and was upon Frances in a second. "Scoundrel!" yelled Hoyt. "Monster! Quack monster! How could you let such a thing happen?" Frances' answer from a moment ago was apparently insufficient, but even if he had wanted to continue his explanation, he could not because Hoyt was blocking his windpipe. The nurse recalled hitting an alarm and within moments, men in white suits were swarming around Hoyt, pulling him away from the throat of their employer. Hoyt used his powerful legs to administer two well-placed kicks to Frances' stomach and groin before being pulled from the room. His mother called after him. "Oh! I almost forgot to pass along a message from your father! He wants you to know that Jesus loves you!"

Moans were disappearing down the hall. Frances had Hoyt placed in a padded cell for more than two hours at which point he began to calm down. Then he was released, given some coffee, and set free into the cold, grey dawn.

Junk received a letter from Hoyt on May 10th, 1941. Given what Junk had just done, he was surprised the penmanship of the letter was legible and the wording clear and brief. In the letter, Hoyt requested Junk's company for tea at 2 p.m. on May 13th at Fraunces Tavern in New York City. The letter went on to read "I promise on the souls of my children that harm will come to you upon your visit to New York City." Unsure whether the leaving out of the word "no" before "harm" was a "Freudian typo" or a threat, Junk had Simon Phelps wait outside the Tavern. Hoyt simply wanted to discuss "an idea that will end this disagreement for good." He wrote "Both of us run the chance of ending up victorious, vanquished, or dead."

The afternoon of the 13th was beautiful in New York City. The weather was warm enough to permit the opening of windows, but cool enough to keep the stench of the city at bay. The stepfather and stepson met at the specified date and time. They sat across from each other at a table for two. No food or drink was had. Too much bad blood existed between them for anything to transpire other than quick, efficient conversation.

Hoyt showed Junk the letter he received from Chhiri Tendi. The Sherpa's comment about Junk being a "prick" likely caused a brief chuckle from the reader, but the subsequent information about Fumu surely gave Junk pause. Fumu was the tallest mountain on Earth? How could that be? Hoyt likely told Junk to keep the information about Fumu a secret. Many respectable climbers knew about the existence of Fumu, but as far as Hoyt could tell, none of them knew – or were willing to believe – that it was the tallest mountain in the world. For now, it was a secret to be kept between the two of them and this Chhiri Tendi fellow.

Hoyt went on to propose a contest. The idea was simple: A race to the top of Fumu, the tallest mountain in the world. The victor plants a flag with his name on it at the summit and walks away the better man. The loser returns home quietly and graciously, never to bother the other again. Both men were free to independently choose the size of their respective teams, the means of reaching the mountain, and the route up the mountain. The hope was they would not have to see each other along the way, but if they chose the same route and the same time frame, so be it. Every last penny of corporate and government funding was accounted for by the war effort so they would need to use their own money. Hoyt asked for Junk's opinion on the proposal.

According to a letter written to McGee about the lunch, Junk wrote "I was immediately thrilled by the idea, but had to remind Hoyt the world was at war. In a very un-Christian manner, Hoyt snapped back 'Fuck the world.' We would have to work around that 'snag.' He said if I wanted to wait until the War was over to make my bid for the summit, then that was my bad decision to make. As for him, packing and planning would begin the moment the lunch was over."

There was likely some hesitation remaining on the part of Junk. Could he trust this man? After all, Hoyt had not paid Junk any money at the end of the Mount Washington trip. Maybe Hoyt was concocting some scheme in which he would never actually leave the United States and just pay off some Sherpa to climb for him and plant a flag with his name at the top. Maybe Hoyt had already climbed Fumu, planted a flag there, and was now sending Junk on an excursion to inevitable defeat. Hoyt assured Junk no one had reached the top of Fumu yet and he wished to be the first. Too much personal dignity was at stake. Junk quoted Hoyt in the letter to McGee: "He said 'I am a fifty-year-old mountain climber who has never bagged a single Himalayan peak. I probably have one trip left in me, and it is going to be to the top.'" Basically, Junk was not even required. Either way, Hoyt was going to try. Hoyt finished his soliloquy by saying "We have both gone as low as we can. There is nowhere to go but up."

At this point, Junk was convinced. He apparently walked to the window and waved off Simon Phelps. Hoyt and Junk shook on the deal. Before leaving, they agreed to hide their plans from the press. One or the other would share the news with the world when they returned. If they returned.

Hoyt exited the establishment first. Junk walked outside a few moments later. Greeted by the warm spring day, Junk probably inhaled deeply and looked forward to the future. He was probably also surprised to see Hoyt standing right next to him.

"I almost forgot!" Hoyt said and then punched Junk hard in the mouth. Junk fell to the street, lips dripping blood as if to fructify the teeth he had already lost on the cobblestone. Hoyt stood over him and yelled, "That is for my mother, you ape!" He followed this declaration with a kick to Junk's stomach. Hoyt finished: "Now that we have settled this business regarding my mother, we may proceed. I will see you on the mountain, sir. May the best man win and may the Devil take the hindmost!"

Chapter Seven: "Souls at Sea" with Gary Cooper

According to records from the Criminal Investigation Division of the United States Navy, a band of pirates took everything off of the ship. Money. Communications systems. Weaponry. The weapons they stole were not those commonly found in the hands of pirates, for they boarded a battle cruiser, full of torpedoes, mines, and guns. The items would bring a high price on the black market. It would keep the pirates afloat, literally, for years to come.

The report went into more detail about the attack. At 6:10 p.m., ten miles due south of Bermuda, the *U.S.S. Stamford* approached what appeared to be a fishing trawler with the intent of boarding and confirming that the hold contained nothing but fish. At 6:15 p.m., when the *Stamford* was within a quarter mile of the fishing trawler – in fact a stolen British naval trawler - the "fishermen" fired a series of 4-inch guns that had been concealed under heaps of nets and lines. They destroyed the cruiser's radio antennae first, ensuring no military backup would arrive for some time. Taken by surprise and utterly unprepared for a gun battle, the *Stamford* started to turn to starboard, leaving its broadside exposed. The pirates took this opportunity to wipe out almost every man on the *Stamford's* portside deck in a barrage of gunfire, board in less than three minutes, tie up the remaining sailors, and take the United States for hundreds of thousands of dollars in weaponry. The *Stamford's* captain recalled the pirates being surprisingly polite in the end. "They didn't leave until they were sure all fires were out on board the *Stamford*. They claimed they didn't want any of us to die needlessly. Not bad form."

Landing in Bermuda (but steering well clear of the American bases located on British soil), we can assume that the pirates went to their favorite local haunt, "The Bloviated Mule," which was unknown to almost anyone other than the locals and a few American tourists who liked to wander from the main town of Hamilton. The pirates probably toasted everything from their fresh victory at sea to little girls (the captain's preference) to Burma, their homeland. These men were far from their country of origin, but such was the nature of their businesses. The war had provided them with more opportunities than just pirating. They smuggled weapons for Southeast Asian governments and freedom fighters alike. They did privateer work for China, attacking Japanese destroyers in the South Pacific. Business was so good and their reputation so brutal and efficient, that they began to take on work further abroad. Sensing the United States' coming involvement in the war, the Axis Powers had started to pay pirates handsomely – these pirates included - for simply creeping up on American naval ships and wreaking havoc. Tonight's marauding had been just one example of the tactics they used on the current mission.

The captain's name was Than, but no one was allowed to call him that. To remark that Than was a fan of the United States and its popular culture would be an understatement. His favorite reading material was Hollywood gossip magazines he stole off of other ships. He traded weapons and other booty for canisters of gangster films and then watched them with his own projector whenever docked at a port with an electrical outlet. So deep was his infatuation with all things American he demanded his crew call him Gary Cooper. And it was this same obsession that led him to rename his boat several years earlier from Eidolon Yacht (a Whitman poem) to *Souls at Sea*, a Gary Cooper film from 1937.

The Burmese pirate Gary Cooper had been coming to Bermuda and the Bloviated Mule for over a decade. Even before the war, back when he mostly pirated in the South Pacific, Cooper would take "holidays" to

Bermuda in order to be closer to the nation he worshipped so much. In Bermuda, he was close enough to feel America's cultural pull, but far enough away to minimize the odds of capture or death. He had never been to the United States, nor did he expect to ever get there. For hours he would sit on the docks on the western side of the island and stare longingly at the horizon, likely dreaming of President Roosevelt in a wheelchair made of pure gold, spoon-feeding caviar to Fay Wray. Both Roosevelt and Wray would be making the "come here" gesture with their index fingers. Cooper would then sigh, get up, and amble slowly back to the bar to continue his drinking, fighting and raping.

On May 18th, 1941, Cooper was approached by another salty patron of the Bloviated Mule by the name of Kevin O'Neil. He was a captain of a vessel out of Boston, illegally shipping goods to the mainland from Bermuda and the Caribbean Islands. The Hawley-Smoot Tariff had stopped all such importing in the 1930's, but O'Neil knew no other life and so he continued. That night, O'Neil sauntered over to Cooper and handed him a letter. It was from a friend of O'Neil's named Aaron Junk. Cooper spoke perfect English, but could not read it. This led to O'Neil reciting the letter to Cooper.

In the letter, Junk remembered Cooper fondly from the Nanda Devi expedition. "You were a gentleman, even when you were stealing my beloved 1903 Victrola and the crew's prized pornographic photographs. Despite the fact that you ended the Nanda Devi expedition for me, I regard you highly and consider you someone I can bring into my trust." The letter went on to offer Cooper four hundred thousand dollars to sail Junk, five other individuals, and almost one ton of mountain climbing equipment from Martha's Vineyard, Massachusetts to Calcutta in May and then back again in early December. Payment would be made in two installments; half at the beginning of the journey and the other half when Junk and team were standing safely on United States soil. "We expect to be picked up on the southeastern most point of Chappaquiddick on the evening of May 22 one hour after sunset."

Cooper had intended to track down and loot more American warships over the next few weeks, but that could wait. Germany and Italy were not paying him or his crew enough to pass up this offer. They had four days to go a long distance. Cooper gathered his men and set sail immediately.

O'Neil had phoned ahead to let Junk know that Cooper was in. Now Junk waited on South Beach on the island of Martha's Vineyard at the specified time. Although not his usual temperament, Junk must have felt deep apprehension. He was almost broke for the first time since his youth. His investments including recent wagers had not been panning out, making this an inopportune time to be heading off to Nepal. He found himself selling off many of his business concerns in order to pay the pirates, the waiting Sherpa, and several high-stakes gamblers who had gotten the better of him. Money be damned. He had to make this trip. He had to win this row, and he was willing to live off of the dole in order to make it happen.

Waiting on the beach with him was the team he had picked in a rush to accompany him to the top of the world. Each one of them was a desperate choice – another reason for Junk's likely apprehension. Any sane person was involved in the war effort or some other noble project and would immediately reject any offer to essentially drop everything and commit adventurous suicide. There had been no way for Junk to sweeten his sales pitch to these individuals. "How would you like to leave the relative safety of the American mainland to enter a Hieronymus Bosch painting come to life? Arrival at the mountain is highly unlikely, but if you do get there, success is not an option." What else could he possibly say that would not be deception? Swindling men out of the contents of their strongboxes was one thing, but Junk was not the sort of fellow to intentionally swindle men out of their lives.

After asking every able-bodied person he knew, some odd individuals agreed. First there was Joseph Cole. Cole was a top-notch climber, having scaled multiple peaks in the Swiss Alps including the Matterhorn and the Dent Blanche. Once before having been to the Himalaya, Cole had not succeeded in an attempt on K2, but that expedition had reached higher than any other up to that point. Cole was of moderate height and weight with a pairing of bright blue eyes and ink-black hair one usually finds only in the Irish. Junk had never climbed with Cole, but had heard he was in a class all of his own. When not climbing, Cole was a physicist. Since the war in Europe began, he had been doing classified work for the United States Government at Michigan State University. Recently unclassified documents from the Physics department suggest that Cole's role in the secret project had been to ascertain at what temperature the atmosphere catches fire. His written notes from that time suggest the job was too unsettling for him; they begin to digress toward irrelevant but less troubling topics such the best recipe for shepherd's pie, a half-written screenplay about a lovelorn lighthouse keeper, and so forth, until notes on actual physics end entirely. He was soon kicked out of the research project for being "unstable." Not one week after, Cole heard from Junk - only four days before the rendezvous at Chappaquiddick. Cole had nothing else to do and had no family, so the assault on Fumu made perfect sense. He grabbed his equipment and hopped on a plane for Boston right away.

Next was Frederick Morrow, a professor of Psychology at Harvard, focusing on memory. He was also an occasional gambling and climbing friend of Junk's. Morrow rarely climbed anything bigger than what could be found in the northeastern United States, although he had once successfully climbed the Maroon Bells in Colorado. The experience had been harrowing for him. He had been trapped at the top overnight by foul weather and required rescue. However, based on the regularity and technical precision of his climbs locally, his talents were unquestionable.

Also on the journey was a woman. No female had ever climbed in the Himalaya and Junk had no interest in changing that. He would never have chosen a woman for such a harrowing and manly adventure under normal circumstances, but his options were limited. Her presence on the expedition was truly one of the stranger aspects of Hoyt and Junk's story.

According to the recollection of some of Junk's old South Boston friends, approximately one week before leaving on the expedition (his friends thought he was "going to New Hampshire for a long break from gambling"), Junk had gotten an unexpected knock on his door. It was an old gambling chum by the name of Nick Fontana. Fontana entered without being invited, looked out the door and windows apprehensively, and drew the blinds without asking. He was accompanied by a small woman dressed in a man's trench coat and wearing a long blond wig covering most of her face. He guided her everywhere as if she had no sense of direction or balance. Fontana started telling Junk a long tale of gambling debts and angry mafia. They had already twice beaten up Fontana, and he had the black eye and broken thumb to prove it. "They said they're gonna kill her, Aaron" Fontana apparently yelled. "Because I'm delinquent on five measly large they're gonna kill my lady friend!" Fontana first asked for money to pay off the thugs. Junk refused because of his own financial straits. Striking out on that front, Fontana turned to his true intended request. "Hide her, Junk." Fontana himself was going to Juarez, Mexico to hide, but he suspected the mob would catch up sooner or later. He wanted this woman safe. "She's the love of my life. Hide her for me, Junk. You'll be doing something that guarantees you a place in Heaven at the same table with the Big Guy."

Fontana was asking too much. Junk explained he could not; he was going out of town for a long time and he simply could not watch this woman, whoever she was. As if not hearing him, perhaps seeing uncertainty in his eyes, Fontana hugged Junk, patted him on the shoulders, and walked out, leaving the woman behind. On his way out, he said "She speaks no English, so you'll have to talk slowly." With the exception of a prostitute from Baxter Street, Fontana was never heard from again by another living soul.

When she removed her wig, Junk saw the woman was some sort of Indian. She was also lovely. Junk wrote to his friend Simon Phelps, "I asked her very slowly what her name was. She quickly responded, in perfect English, that her name was River Leaf. I thought she didn't speak English. She explained that 'Fontana is an imbecile. I've seen him trip over a fire hydrant, stand up, and trip over it again. He thinks I don't speak English because he never speaks to me. Nor does he care." Before it was time to retire for the night, Junk was able to get out of her that she was a member of the Great Sioux Nation. As the Nation's territories disappeared in Minnesota, taken piece by piece by the "Great Father" (the United States government), her mother had asked the young girl to leave and try to make a life for herself in the white man's world. She would have more luck there. Needless to say, she did not. She got Nick Fontana. Years of suffering at the hands of belligerent providence had made this young woman as pliant as a broken horse.

Junk made River Leaf a cup of tea and prepared a bed for her. "That night, I sat in a chair across the room from her bed and watched her as she laid there, her back to me. She was probably awake and aware of my staring eyes. I was not watching her in any untoward way. I was actually looking at her in complete despair. Was I really going to ask her what I needed to ask her? Was I really so desperate to go through with this stupidity that I would invite this fainting flower into the mouth of Certain

- 135 -

Death? I could not ignore the request of a friend (maybe even a dying request?) and abandon my responsibility, but it was also mandatory that I bring my personal war with Hoyt to a conclusion. So what else could I do? The sadness and shame were overpowering."

She was indeed awake and she turned over and asked what he wanted. If it was to make love, fine. Just be quiet about it. In the moment, Junk came up with a compromise. He asked her to come with him on the journey, but she could wait safely in Darjeeling until he returned from Fumu. Again, her response was "fine."

Sitting on the Chappaquiddick shore that night was also Cranston Fenimore, a law student from Chicago. Fenimore was only twenty-five years old. By far, and to this day, he is the youngest man to ever try for the summit of Fumu. Educated overseas at Eton, Fenimore had packed a lot of climbing into those twenty-five years, three times climbing Mount McKinley before even graduating from university. The summit was reached on all three climbs. Fenimore had signed up for the army in 1940 but could not join because a serious case of tinnitus made him almost deaf in his right ear. The constant ringing impaired not only his hearing but his balance. He was fervent in his patriotism and wanted desperately to be enlisted when the inevitable call would come to ship off to Germany or Japan. But the army wanted nothing to do with him. Fenimore would have to get his excitement from climbing.

Junk had actually climbed with Fenimore on an earlier expedition in Europe. He had been impressed with the young man's abilities. When Junk made the offer to Fenimore to go off to Fumu, it was a godsend for the dejected youth. Fenimore had no wife or children yet, and he had been struggling through law school at the University of Chicago. He was a strong student, but a distracted one. Upon receiving the call from Junk, Fenimore wrote to the dean, withdrew from his classes, declared "maintenance of status" until his return, and then left Chicago. His parents were too busy in their own social affairs to care about the comings and goings of their now-grown middle son of three, and so he did not even tell them he was leaving for Nepal.

The last person waiting on the beach that night was none other than Patrick McGee. The bear of a man was quieter than usual. He was actually petrified. Junk had approached McGee before any of the other team members, almost immediately after Hoyt's proposition. Over draughts at Beacon Hill Tavern, Junk said, "I need people I can trust in a tight situation even more than I need people who can climb." McGee turned a ghostly hue. He explained he was in no kind of shape to be climbing anything. Junk responded that McGee could head off to Blue Hills Reservation every day for the subsequent week and just try to run up the mountains. It would hurt, but it *was* possible to get physically ready in seven days (of course it was not). In the debate between the two old friends it also came out that, to McGee's embarrassment, he was deathly afraid of heights. He had lived his whole life on the city streets. Boston, Providence, and occasionally New York. He explained to Junk that the highest he had ever been was Commonwealth Avenue out past Brookline. They were like brothers, but McGee pleaded with Junk not to ask for this favor. He was not a mountain climber. Junk put his hands on the giant shoulders of his oldest friend who was noticeably sweating and said, "There are people out there who beat their children yet they call themselves 'parents.' There are cretins with crooked writing and sparse vocabulary who call themselves 'writers.' So why can't you call yourself a mountain climber?"

After a long silence McGee repeated slowly and quietly, "I'm afraid of heights."

Junk responded, "I swear you'll be safe. I won't let anything happen to you. Let me speak a language you understand; I will bet you one million dollars you die on this trip." The largest wager the two had ever placed. An odd wager at that, but Junk must have felt he knew what he was doing. This man would work twice as hard if money was on the line. Of course if McGee died, he would not be able to pay out. Junk suggested McGee deposit the money into a bank account under both of their names.

Ever so slowly, McGee put out his hand. Junk shook it and then hugged his old friend.

While he waited on the shore that night with his motley team of disenfranchised adventurers, Junk must have sensed how far away his destination lay. There he was on a clear, cool New England evening, smelling salt air; watching large waves crash and roll away; feeling cool winds from the north; listening to seagulls cry out in hunger and war. How on earth could he be leaving the approaching spring for such a forbidding destination? Fumu may have been answering his question at that moment, but from so far away, Junk could not hear it.

The light of a small lantern appeared out of the dark, bobbing on the waves. One distant voice was yelling rhythmically in a foreign tongue; commands to others on a large rowboat to take strokes of the oar. Then the boat was coming over the breaking waves. A short man stood in the bow. He was a dashing oriental, dressed impeccably – but oddly - in an American naval captain's uniform. Next to him was a girl of no more than thirteen. The rowers, their backs to the shore, were shirtless and sweating. When the boat made land, the standing man jumped ashore and rushed up to the team. "Junk!" he shouted. Junk walked forward. The man saluted. Junk saluted back. Then the man shook Junk's hand formally and said in very good English, "You may remember me as Than. I am Gary Cooper now. Please address me as such. It is a pleasure to see you once again. My ship is at anchor only a few hundred yards out. My men will row you out to it. Now if you will excuse me for one moment." He walked past the

Americans and dropped to his knees. Then he lay on his stomach, face to the side, contorted in ecstasy. He slowly sifted the sand through his fingers. Craning his neck back in what appeared to be a painful position he kissed the sand beneath. For the first time in his life, he was touching America.

Morrow wrote near the beginning of his journal:

"He bounced up quickly and strode back to the group, not removing the sand still holding fast to his face. Cooper then told half of us to get on the boat. He would return momentarily for the second group and then return several more times to pick up the equipment. As part of the first group, Loading on my backpack, tent, and dried goods, I jumped aboard. My hiking boots were tied to my pack and they drove into my side. Water soaked through my loafers. The young girl looked at me, expressionless. To break the ice, I asked Cooper if this lovely girl was his daughter. Cooper looked back at me with an expression that could have set my hair on fire had it not been slick with sea water. Out of self preservation, I never said a word to the man again."

And so, on the evening of May 22nd, 1941, Junk's team left the United States on its way around the war-torn world to ascend to its loftiest perch. Some of the team would never return.

Within less than one hour on the *Souls At Sea*, a pirate was already trying to have his way with River Leaf. He pawed at her and flicked his tongue near her face. Morrow wrote, "His back was to us and he was quite tall, so we could not see River Leaf behind him." The rest of the Americans watched quietly. If they did nothing, her honor would be compromised. If they acted, they risked roughly twenty armed pirates killing them in cold blood.

As it turned out, they did not need to do anything. The randy pirate was suddenly screaming. "From behind, all we could see were his hands trembling in the air, fingers contracted into claws. He whirled around to show a gaping orifice beginning at the left shoulder and ending at the right hip. He looked down at parts of his body he had never seen before, not daring to touch for the certainty of pain beyond that which he was already experiencing. Blood was already pooling at his feet. Then he fell and never moved again."

River Leaf was brandishing a small knife she must have taken from the galley and stowed in her clothing for just such an occasion. She was standing as if ready to take on another comer. The Americans looked around silently, no doubt waiting to be murdered. But to their surprise, after a long silence, Gary Cooper laughed deeply and this made the other pirates laugh. Cooper approached River Leaf, slapped her on the back and handed her a glass of whiskey. The dead pirate was unceremoniously thrown overboard like so much jetsam and the rest of the night was spent in sloppy revelry. Junk looked at River Leaf all night as she drank deeply. Perhaps he would not have to watch over her as much as he thought.

And so the journey started off well. The Souls At Sea traveled slowly eastward across the Atlantic. The Americans busied themselves studying maps of India and Nepal, checking and re-checking their equipment, and debating strategies to surmount the Qila Pass. Fumu routes be damned; the knotty issue of the Qila Pass would have to take all of their attention or else the mountain beyond it would be irrelevant. Fenimore recommended looking for a more forgiving route on the north side of the Qila dominion, but Junk felt the gamble was too great. A hike to the north around the *outside* of Qila - to the east of Abel and Mitya - would cost them two solid weeks, and the odds were high that no easier pass would be found. No one who had tried to climb Fumu had ever come across one. They would take the Qila Pass or die trying.

As the *Souls at Sea* left the continental shelf of the Americas and the swells began to grow, the vomiting began. Those seasoned climbers who had been on ships before were better off, vomiting only when the weather got rougher. River Leaf also did relatively well. But McGee was unstoppable. He vomited throughout the day and dry-heaved throughout the night. He would sit in bed waiting for sleep to rescue him from this ceaseless universe of movement, but it rarely came. At Junk's pleading, McGee drank water constantly so as not to dehydrate. For the first time since he was about twelve years old, McGee stopped drinking alcohol entirely. Although not in much better shape, River Leaf mothered him as best she could. McGee, who had little experience writing anything, began to compose a journal, just to keep his brain busy. The sentences were childlike in their brevity, lack of capitalization, and incompleteness. "I fel (sic) teribel (sic)" he wrote. "No horizin (sic). Just waves. Where is gravutee (sic) coming from? From difrent (sic) places every momint (sic)."

The journey hit a serious snag about two weeks in. Junk had an uncanny sense of direction, and for the life of him, he could not detect any southerly tendency in the ship's course. The sun remained at their bow every morning and to their stern at sunset. This concerned him no end. Were they not going to head into the South Atlantic and make their way into the Indian Ocean around Cape Agulhas? If they were, then by now he would have surely detected some gentle turn to starboard. But none came. Junk gently prodded Cooper about the route, but Cooper always showed resistance. "Leave the route to me" Cooper would say in a patronizing voice. But Junk was persistent. He began to ask other related questions in the hopes of obtaining clues about their course. "How long do you estimate before we see the African continent on our port side?" But Cooper did not bite. "Don't you worry Mr. Junk. I will you get you to your destination."

Finally, Junk was out of patience. One evening after the crew had attained a state between drunk and asleep, Junk convinced his team member Cole to inquire about the chances of coming ashore in Liberia. "I've heard great things about the natives. Apparently they look resplendent in their colourful robes. I fancy myself a photographer and would love to take some photographs." The Americans were all at the table and they listened intently for Cooper's reply. Cooper was not fooled. After a long pause and a smile clearly designed to mask annoyance, he pushed himself away from the table and said "Fine Junk. You really want to know? No, we are not going around Cape Horn. We are going to get there by way of the Mediterranean. It is a far quicker route."

This was Junk's worst fear realized. He immediately inquired as to whether Cooper was insane. Such a route would take them within firing range of the European continent. The Straits of Gibraltar were guarded by the British, who upon detecting a ship full of pirates would show no quarter. And even on the outside chance the British missed them or decided *not* to blow them out of the water, the Germans and Vichy French were making air and sea incursions on Gibraltar regularly. Never mind the German navy controlling most of the Mediterranean that lay beyond, or the Suez Canal bordered as it was by Italian occupied territory, The Straits of Gibraltar was a death trap.

Morrow recalled in his writing that Cooper was visibly angered:

"He barked through gritted teeth 'Fear is for animals. Not men.' Junk, also angry, responded, 'My reaction is based on pure reason, not emotion. You are greatly decreasing the odds my team will make it to their destination. And besides, I see nothing manly about taking your boat straight into the devil's cloacae. It is suicide. And homicide.' Cooper stood up and yelled 'You speak of pure reason? You are a reasonable man? Look where I am taking you! You want to

arrive safely at your death. We are both suicidal and homicidal, so do not try to paint me as the madman.'

Junk tried to respond but was quickly interrupted by Cooper yelling "Enough!" and having the Americans placed in the hold, where they were to stay for one week. They would be let out after that time only if they agreed to never question the captain again.

The week in the hold was horrible for everyone. There were only two small portholes letting in natural light. The floors and walls were made of metal. There were only two chairs and no beds or cots. Wooden crates full of unknown contents shared limited space with their own climbing equipment and clothing. The remainder of the room, perhaps half of its total size, was left for them to exist. "I suspect solitary confinement is preferable to shared confinement" Morrow recalled in his writings. "We started out well, commiserating about our condition, but soon were bickering over everything; where to sleep, how best to manage the rats, and whether or not we should negotiate an early release. Our response to McGee's sickness turned from sympathy to frustration. Every wretch was met with grumblings about the stench and the need to request more cleaning supplies from the pirates."

The last thing Junk needed was a team prematurely at odds with one another before they had even reached their destination. He had a deck of cards and a pair of dice in his pocket so he organized games of chance to keep people active and friendly. River Leaf would have nothing to do with it, so she spent almost every waking hour caring for McGee, reading Morrow's research papers and Junk's copy of *Don Quixote*.

When the games of chance became tiresome and bickering began again, Junk pulled out a roughly sketched map of Fumu – copied from another roughly sketched map that had been drafted by a surviving member of Hoover's expedition. After two days of tireless discussion, interrupted only by the pirates delivering food, they believed they had a strategy for the Qila Pass. They decided they would not risk the more novice climbers' lives this early in the ascent. They would build a platform about six feet by four feet with ropes attached to all four corners. The ropes would meet each roughly six feet above the board where they would be tied off to a thicker and stronger 50-yard length of rope. Climbing ahead about 40 yards, they would have the entire 30-man Sherpa team grab the free end of the long rope and pull the rest of the team up one by one on the makeshift "lift." It would be the lift passenger's responsibility to ensure the board did not become snagged on any rocks or ice. They would have to continually push away from the mountain as the Sherpa pulled them up. The idea was imperfect, but it seemed like it would improve their odds of making it to the mountain proper.

River Leaf interrupted the men. "Your idea is broken" she said forcefully. Pointing to Junk's pad of paper, she asked "May I?" Junk handed her the pad. River Leaf liked the idea of a lift, but she recommended an alternative structure. The one the men had proposed would only work if the grade of the pass was always perfectly vertical, which it was not. Any decrease of the angle to, say, 85 degrees, would cause the lift to drag along the mountain face. Those on the lift would have to use all of their energy – like an endless push-up - to continually keep the board away from the rock face. As an alternative, River Leaf proposed more of a sleigh. The big board of the sleigh would now slide up the face. A smaller board, big enough for two people to stand on, would stick out at a ninety-degree angle from the bottom of the big board. The people on the sleigh would stand, back to the rock face, on the smaller board. Ropes would pull the big board from its "top" corners. Now the passengers of the sleigh would only need to use their strength if the big board became stuck under a protuberance in the rock face. Also, like a sleigh, they could easily fashion runners under the board to minimize the amount of surface touching the mountain.

Cole tut tutted, as if he were about to discredit the timid Indian girl's idea. But nothing came. The men were all silent. River Leaf was right. Junk gently took his pad back, thanked River Leaf, and suggested they begin discussing where to set up Base Camp beyond the Qila Pass.

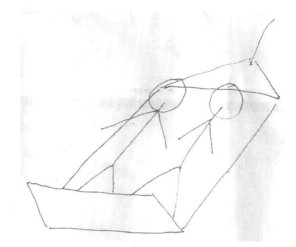

Image: River Leaf's sketch of the Qila Elevator

Near the end of the week, distant rumblings of artillery became audible in the distance. Soon they were surrounded by mortar concussions and yelling from the deck above. The ship lurched from evasive maneuvers. They heard British voices over loudspeakers coming from ahead of them, the words impossible to make out over machine gun fire. A scream was heard above them and then the sound of something the size of a person breaking the surface tension of the sea. Chaos was all around them, but impossible to see.

Gibraltar.

"Junk banged on the door, demanding exit," Morrow wrote. "No one responded. My stomach was churning and my heart was racing. I felt every minute was our last. We would meet our maker and it would be Churchill who introduced us. The distant gunfire and yells of pain from on deck continued. I kept praying the Brits would board the ship and find us captive instead of simply riddling us with bullets."

Cole wrote "Poor McGee. He lay in a corner of the room near our pile of packs and tents, curled up into a ball. Useless. River Leaf was sitting not far from McGee, but her eyes were closed and she seemed totally calm (Why the two of them ended up on this voyage is beyond me). The rest of us stood by Junk as he banged on the door and simply listened to every sound."

Running footsteps were heard on the other side of the door and then a chair being pulled out. A radio crackled to life - something they had not heard the entire time they had been at sea. A pirate's voice rose up speaking in German. None of the Americans spoke German, but they were able to make out series of numbers and letters. Perhaps coordinates. German voices responded in kind. The conversation went on for only a moment and then was over. The chair was kicked out and the footsteps ran away.

Moments later, enormous explosions were heard in the distance followed by cheering from the pirates. The explosions were followed by distant gun fire and then more explosions. The pattern continued but gradually became more distant and seemed to be coming from aft. Then there was silence save the creaking of the ship on gentle waves. Someone approached the door of the hold. The lock was turned and the door opened. Cooper stood at the threshold, a streak of blood on his shirt but otherwise quite presentable. He had his arm around the young girl who was visibly shaking. In his journal, Fenimore quoted Cooper as saying, "Gentlemen, and pretty Indian woman, welcome to the Mediterranean.

You are welcome to wander the ship again provided you keep your mouths closed."

The team exited the hold. Everything was in disarray. Life vests, ammunition shells, and blood-tainted seawater covered the floors. Furniture was knocked over. Upon reaching the deck," Morrow continued, "we hoped to be greeted by fresh Mediterranean air. But that sensation was compromised by the smell of gunpowder and burning oil. In the distance, off of the stern, we could just make out burning ships in the night."

It became clear to the Americans in that moment they were in the hands of "the enemy," although each of them had been so indifferent to the war that sides meant little. Cooper told them not to worry. He was not about to tell the Germans about the revenue-generating American cargo he had on board. He was on any side that paid him.

Quite unexpectedly, the remainder of the ocean voyage – through the Mediterranean, along the Suez Canal, down the Nile, through the Red Sea and across the Indian Ocean – was calm. German ships and planes passed quietly. The sounds of waves, seagulls, and the *Souls At Sea*'s engines dominated. The weather remained relatively calm. The air was hot, varying in humidity with each leg of the voyage, but always forgiving at night.

The Americans did not challenge Cooper's judgment after Gibraltar. With the exception of McGee and River Leaf, they spent the remaining weeks at sea planning the rendezvous with the Sherpa team in Calcutta, the land journey to Fumu, and the climb itself. River Leaf spent her time reading novels in silence. McGee wiled away the hours throwing up.

Upon passing Sri Lanka, the ship turned northward. Morrow wrote:

"On July 12, almost two months after shoving off from
New England, we sighted land off of the port side. We

smelled jasmine, chai, and smoke in the sultry atmosphere.
Small buildings began to take shape on the shore connected
by clotheslines festooned with saris. Then the Ganges Delta
was around us and we followed her for a day before a major
city was around us. We had arrived at Calcutta.

"The city before us was lovely. It writhed with activity.
With the monsoon late to arrive, the sun beat down on
children playing in the streets, stevedores unloading ships,
and even actors performing a play – a jatra *- on a distant*
outdoor stage. If these sights and sounds did not signal the
end of our sea voyage, then the scent of lemons, tubers, and
other cargo did the trick. But the commotion did not give us
the sense we were any closer to Fumu. We were even deeper
inside Humanity's belly than we had been before setting
sail!"

Less obvious to their senses was the fact the city before them was
caught in a large maelstrom trapped within an even larger maelstrom: Civil
unrest had been plaguing Calcutta for years as many Indians began to clash
with their British colonizers. Now that conflict was getting swept up in the
British engagement in World War II. Given Cooper had been in the
employ of the Axis powers, he and his ship were not welcome here at all.
But Cooper was aware and prepared. He had made some deal in advance
with local government sympathizers of Subhas Chandra Bose and the
Indian independence movement, allowing the ship, crew, and passengers
safe access to a slip. There was not a British soldier within several
hundred feet of the ship when they threw their lines to the dockworkers.
The expedition members walked off the Souls at Sea for the first time in
weeks. In the case of McGee, unlike Cooper before him, he did not care
what land he was on or who inhabited it. He was just happy to be touching

land. That feeling would quickly dwindle once the long hike to Nepal commenced.

Junk was back in the city he had last seen on the Everest voyage. It likely brought back memories of injury and defeat. This time would be different, he likely told himself. This time, the name Aaron Junk would become as holy as a prayer upon the lips of mountaineers for centuries to come. And if all went well, William Hoyt's name would be exiled to a footnote in an out-of-print book in some failed author's cellar.

Chapter Eight: The Lord High Executioner

Journal: September the 1st, 1941

I write now to you, dear Journal, because Wizzy has left me. She has grown overly concerned about the climbing, especially when it is being driven by an obsession for vengeance. She claims to still love me, and she hopes I do not die. But beyond that, she says she 'just doesn't know anymore.' She is staying with the rest of the Dodge clan on the Upper East Side. So until this business is over, it is you and me. I trust you are as good a listener as she was.

I am writing this from our camp on a moraine at the bottom of the Qila Pass, waiting for our Sherpa to arrive. Behind the pass is a mountain so menacing I cannot find the words to do it justice. Glaciers crack and grumble, rocks fall, streaks of ash hundreds of yards long taint pristine snow, overhanging limestone cliffs block routes, and above it all, a cloud looms. Its shape is impermanent but it is ever-present. We already hear distant thunder constantly. It is likely not thunder at all, but small eruptions from on high. Without a view of the peak, I cannot 'read' the mountain. It is like a giant Mohamedan woman, the cloud her veil and the volcanic explosions her ululations. Mysterious. Terrifying.

As nauseating as the future looks for my team and me, there is no turning back now. The journey to arrive here was grueling. We have crossed the Rubicon. We are going up.

Yours,

W.J.H.

The journey to get to Fumu was indeed grueling for Hoyt's team, and especially for Hoyt himself. The difficulties began right after the meeting with Junk in New York, when he had to tell Wizzy of his plans. She had tolerated the Everest expedition two years earlier, but when he told her of his plans to take on another Himalayan mountain, she raised her voice for the first time in their marriage. She called him unstable and suggested that perhaps William had inherited his mother's insanity. She said that he had lost his religion, his family, and his bearings. His need to climb and to compete with Aaron Junk were distracting him to the point where family was an afterthought. "For William" Wizzy wrote a dear friend just before the Fumu ascent, "remembering to spend time with me has become like remembering to visit his mother. Now he is planning some far-flung adventure about which I am to have no information. This can only further isolate him from his sons and me. The boys do not know their father. Before they went off to college they knew him only as some hulking figure that was sometimes in the house, mumbling at the newspaper, telling them not to slurp their soup, or snoring too loudly. Now he is someone they only see at Thanksgiving and Christmas because those holidays do not fall during his normal climbing season." The war in Europe had been a blessing for Wizzy because it kept William at home except for a few weekend excursions. But now not even a global conflagration could stop him from climbing.

Wizzy gathered up her nerve and gave Hoyt an ultimatum: Stay with her, visit the boys at college regularly and stop climbing, or continue to climb and live without her. Hoyt likely did not see this as a choice. As much as he loved her – whatever "love" was to the William Hoyt of 1941 – he had to see this competition through to its conclusion, and the conclusion was so close. It was no longer about the love of climbing. In fact, he felt he was at a place in life where perhaps he could walk away from the Thrill of the Ascent. His body was certainly telling him to rein in; that the grid of

New York City was not such a bad place to spend his time. No, it had nothing to do with climbing any more. To use his words from his Fumu journal, Hoyt said it had everything to do with "Vanity and Wrath." "I sense there is a little Gluttony in there as well, but I would be hard-pressed to explain why without sounding like some effeminate, French poet. Yes, let us leave it at Vanity and Wrath."

On the morning of May 22nd, he planned to have a moving company take him and his unwieldy climbing equipment to the airport. He would then catch an airplane for the West Coast. Once there, he was to meet up with his team and his transportation to Burma at a beach in southern California. But before this series of events could transpire, Hoyt took the time to call his mother. He dialed from an empty house. His mother answered the phone. If there was anyone who Hoyt could tell about Fumu, about its unrivaled height, he could tell his mother. She may keep the secret, but even if she did not, no one would believe her. So Hoyt told her he was off to the Himalaya one more time for the purpose of conquering the tallest mountain in the world. According to Hoyt, Maddy replied in a manner so lucid he was momentarily convinced he was speaking to the wrong person. She was, in fact, painfully lucid. "I am so sorry I was not around to soften the blow of Father. I should have been around for you when you were a little boy." Hoyt was not moved to tears by anything. Music. Death. No matter how emotional a situation, he remained as dry as fired clay. But at this sentence from his mother, he confessed to a pain in his throat. How would he have been different had she been available to him? Would he be less rigid? Would he be capable of joy? The possibilities were endless. Although he may not have felt this way, he quietly told his old mother it was quite alright and it was not her fault. Then she added a sentiment that simply embarrassed and confused William. "I should have nursed you. Then you would not be off doing these things." She then mumbled something about the "damn Gypsies" controlling the weather and hung up. That would be the last time William and his mother would ever speak to each other.

Like Junk's team, Hoyt and his men had to wait on the shore to be picked up by life boats. But in the case of Hoyt, the boats were manned by sailors from a ship captained by none other than Randolph Hoyt, William's brother.

Randolph had served valiantly during World War One. He had been captain of the *U.S.S. Impaction*, a dreadnought-style battleship supporting the Royal Navy in the North Sea. In that capacity, he had received medals from both the United States and England for tirelessly assisting in keeping the German Navy at bay. Randolph retired from the Navy in 1931, but continued his life at sea as captain of a steam schooner called the *S.S. Auxesis*, mostly shipping lumber along the West Coast. It was April 1941 when Randolph was contacted by the U.S. Navy. They met with him behind closed doors at a naval base in San Diego. According to documents released by the military after the war had ended, the meeting had included Randolph and six high-ranking officials. The officials sat on one side of the desk and Randolph on the other. They asked him if he was willing to carry out top secret activities for his country in the North Pacific that would keep the world safe for Democracy. With Europe and Asia at war and the United States on the brink, Randolph could probably think of nothing he would rather do than captain a merchant vessel. He must have heard rumblings about the "Flying Tigers," a team of American mercenaries stationed in Rangoon who were secretly aiding the Chinese in their aerial engagements against Japan. Supporting them would be a thrilling possibility. Even though the Curtiss P-40's the Tigers flew were not manufactured in the States, perhaps he would be shipping other supplies to them, like ammunition or food.

Alas, that did not turn out to be his assignment. "Captain Hoyt, have you ever heard of Operation Barrymore?" the commanders asked him. Randolph had not heard of it. The commanders went on to explain the details of the operation, one of the most unique but failed operations in American and Chinese military history. The plan, devised by General William Felcher and approved by President Roosevelt, was to put on a radio play for the enemy so convincing in its execution that the enemy would think it real and respond accordingly. Going under the assumption the enemy was listening in, all Chinese soldiers in charge of radio communications were to be given "parts" to play. These parts required them to intersperse their normal communications with occasional lines from a script written by a team of top American playwrights. The soldiers were also to be given acting lessons from Chinese *Xiangsheng* actors, American stage actors, and given direction from American directors (Although his involvement would make perfect sense after the infamy of "War of the Worlds," it has never been confirmed whether Orson Welles took some supporting part in the operation. Welles has repeatedly and adamantly denied any involvement. Given that Operation Barrymore occurred during production of *Citizen Kane*, one has no reason to question Welles on the matter). "One of our nation's most successful exports is entertainment" explained the commanders. "We might as well use it to our military advantage."

The "play" the Chinese soldiers were going to act out involved a natural disaster. During their coded communications about troop, ship, and airplane positions, the soldiers would pretend an earthquake had occurred somewhere off the coast of China. Then, moments later, they would act as if a tsunami of awesome magnitude was ravaging villages along the Chinese shoreline. Soldiers involved in the play who were along the coast in places like Shanghai would pretend to be drowned: screaming, gurgling, and then radio silence. If all went as planned, then the Japanese would be quick to evacuate their southern shores. This would leave them open to attack by air. The Chinese assisted by the Flying Tigers would then swoop in with a massive aerial assault on multiple targets, including naval ports, factories, and airfields in Nagasaki, the Ryukyu Islands, and Pusan in Japanese-occupied Korea.

"We need a top-notch captain to get all of this American talent overseas. Can we count on you?" Probably discouraged by the nature of his cargo but ever the patriot, Randolph shook their hands and swore to keep the operation his secret. There was no dotted line to sign on because the military wanted no paper trail.

About one month later, Randolph was contacted by his brother. William explained he required a ship to India for himself and his team of five other men. What perfection of timing! Yet little else about the request was perfect. Picking up stowaways during a military mission was a major security breach. Randolph could get court marshaled if anyone found out. But such was the nature of their relationship; William had lorded over his brother since childhood, fathering him when Spalding Hoyt had not been around. Fighting back was not an option. William was larger and his temper was enough to keep anyone at bay. The two siblings were no different as adults. William Hoyt made a demand and Randolph followed it without question.

Randolph left from the naval base in Los Angeles on May 23rd with ten writers, twenty-five actors, three directors and his crew of ten men on board. Before setting the *Auxesis* on a course for Burma, he reluctantly ordered his crew to drop anchor off of Cameo Cove in Corona Del Mar so they could pick up some more individuals. The passengers and crew were likely confused by this deviation. According to Randolph's ship log, he quelled their concerns by explaining the detour as "top secret."

"I said to everyone, 'These men we are picking up, they are trained killers; mercenaries being sent over enemy lines to help take back China from the Japs. They are ground support for the Flying Tigers. They are codenamed the Flightless Tigers.' I probably could have come up with a better name if I had not been put on the spot."

His explanation seemed to be enough to gain the crew's acceptance. After all, it must have been very intriguing to be making a top secret rendezvous on an already top secret mission. They picked up William, his team, and their equipment at approximately seven o'clock at night. Randolph turned the bow of the *Auxesis* into the sunset and started the journey to Rangoon.

On the journey with William Hoyt were five men. Hoyt apparently had superior luck to Junk, finding mostly master climbers who happened to be in situations allowing them to walk away from their lives for one half of a year at a moment's notice. First there was Sebastian Drake, a man who had climbed in the Himalaya more than any other person on either the Hoyt or Junk expeditions. On his list of adventures he could count Ama Dablam, Annapurna, Nanga Parbat, K2, and Everest. He had not reached the summit of any of them so his hunger for success was immense. He had no problem joining Hoyt for the expedition because his wife had passed on one year earlier and he had retired from General Motors the previous year. Being the company's top scientist, he had retired a millionaire. Drake was a short, stocky man, standing only five feet two inches, but practically as wide. He was by no means fat; Drake was simply built like an icebox. He wore spectacles no matter the situation. He was a natural-born tinkerer and since retiring he had already devised several new pieces of climbing equipment he felt would improve a man's odds of vanquishing a mountain.

The Fumu expedition provided him with a perfect opportunity to test his creations out in the field.

Also along for the journey was William Chatham, a billionaire oil baron who hardly worked at all any more. He spent most of his time adventuring; one year in the Amazon rain forest, the next in the South Pole. Joining Hoyt was simply another item to add to his list of cocktail party topics. The old boy did enjoy his alcohol and palaver. Tall and handsome for a man of advanced age, with a tan complexion and a full head of bright white hair, Chatham would hold forth at any social gathering, recounting tales of mystery and daring do at the far corners of the Earth. Without exception he was the hero of the stories he told. In one such tale, a fellow explorer is attacked by a conger eel along the Nile. It has swallowed the man's arm up to the elbow. Chatham swoops in and administers a judo chop to the eel's head. It dies instantly. The eel is now in his study acting as a pen holder.

The only issue with Chatham's yarns was that no one was ever around to corroborate them. And more than once, he had fellow explorers sign off on contracts stating they would not tell their side of the story for ten years, making Chatham's the sole account. He was able to get several book deals from this and also became a favourite subject for articles in National Geographic and Life. For the Fumu expedition, William Hoyt was confident Chatham would live up to his legend. Even if he did not and he was only one tenth the man he claimed to be, Hoyt would have a solid climber on his side. However, he would have to ignore Chatham's personality as it was quite the opposite of his own and quite similar to Aaron Junk's.

Hoyt rounded out his list of older, seasoned climbers with Oscar Wilde. Wilde had no relation to the infamous writer and was very quick to make that clear. In fact, he could not stand the writer, who he felt to be nothing more than a depraved, half-crazed libertine. Like Hoyt, Wilde was a reserved, fastidious man who felt speech is not like a case of cigarettes to be taken out and enjoyed whenever the mood strikes. Speech is more like a hammer, used only in very specific cases to perform specific tasks. These characteristics made Wilde a personal favorite of Hoyt's. The man was gigantic; six foot five and thick. His bulbous head rested on a neck like a truck tire. His fingers looked like Italian meats hanging in a butcher shop window. However, Wilde kept this large frame very still unless climbing, arms crossed while standing, or hands placed neatly on his thighs while sitting, as if posing for a family portrait. Wilde was a masterful climber, having climbed peaks on all seven continents. He was born into wealth which gave him as much time as he wanted to go off on his adventures.

Less experienced but by no means less able were Ramsey Thornton and Frederick Ferguson. These two last-minute additions to the team were brought in because, although young, they were both known as good climbers and they brought certain required expertise to the team. Referred to Hoyt by academic connections in New York City, Thornton was an assistant professor of linguistics at Columbia University, fluent in both Nepali and Tibetan. Luckily for Hoyt, Thornton happened to be on sabbatical that fall and had no problem joining the expedition to Fumu. He had no climbing experience whatsoever but he exhibited such a level of athleticism many found him off-putting, like being in the presence of a species whose actions mimicked humans but were subtly alien. He had almost gone to the Olympics for track and field in 1936 but chose not to go due to the death of both of his parents in an automobile accident. Hoyt felt such discipline of body, mind, and spirit were sufficient for the task at hand.

Ferguson was the Swiss army knife of the team. Having been promoted to Eagle Scout in his home state of Michigan at the tender age of fourteen, he was an expert at navigation, tracking sign, and general survival. He was also a doctor who in medical school had concentrated on the effects of high altitude on the human body.   Ferguson was also a disciple of John Harvey Kellogg, the famous nutritionist from his home state.   Ferguson lectured all over Michigan about the efficacy of vegetarianism, celibacy, enemas, and a treatment Ferguson invented himself called "quinine suffusion" - a process in which a patient is given gallons of tonic water both orally and otherwise for the purpose of cleansing the gastrointestinal tract. The liquid is administered until it is literally suffusing out of the patient's pores.   The process was said to promote vim as well as the "stability of intestinal flora." Kellogg himself had considered employing the procedure on visitors at his sanitarium in Battle Creek, but then decided he wanted nothing to do with it. Ferguson broke from Kellogg and patented the procedure.   So far, only one patient had died out of several thousand, although when pressed, Ferguson admitted to a handful having required a stomach pump after near-drowning.   Hoyt selected Ferguson for his medical and navigational training, and merely tolerated what he called his "dietary quackery."

It was with this team – Drake, Chatham, Wilde, Thornton, and Ferguson – that Hoyt intended to conquer the mountain, the world, and "the vermin that married my mother."

The vast majority of the oceanic journey offered delightful weather and calm water.   Seamen, thespians, and mountain climbers mingled together in relative peace.   Chatham, by far the most garrulous of the climbers, found himself drinking with the film directors and feeding lines to the actors as they rehearsed.   Drake wiled away the days at sea with the sailors on the bridge and in the engine room, inquiring about the mechanics of the ship.   Wilde stayed mostly in his berth and on deck, reading Dickens and avoiding sailors and actors alike, steadfast in his belief that both groups consisted exclusively of homosexuals who would have their way with him if given the chance.   Thornton and Ferguson spent much of their time playing cribbage and flirting with the starlets who happened to be on board (No one was certain why actresses had been recruited for the mission, but the sailors and climbers were not complaining).

Hoyt himself spent hours every day in the galley, one of the only places on the ship where he could spread out maps and books and truly study up for the journey that lay ahead. He had decided that once over the Qila Pass, they were going to take the southern route up Fumu; similar to the route the Nazi Rauff had tried a decade earlier before the mountain had swallowed his expedition whole. Hoyt was certain Junk would go for the northern route, for he was a drunken gambler, and he liked long shots. The northern route was indeed the long shot. It was harder to get to, but if one got there with enough energy and supplies, the ascent up considerably easier than the southern route. That was fine with Hoyt, who had enough confidence in himself and his team to believe the southern route "winnable."

They would set up advanced Base Camp at the southern foot of the mountain, a few longitudinal degrees east from the Qila Pass. From Base Camp, they would switchback up the scree at the southeast extreme of the mountain. Just as the Nazi Rauff had chosen to do, Hoyt made the decision beforehand that no attempt at acclimatization would occur across the scree. He did not want anyone climbing up the scree more than once. They would place Camp One at the top of it and use that as "super-advanced" Base Camp.

The next section would actually be the steepest and possibly most technically challenging part of their ascent. They would have to climb almost straight up the southern face toward the Eastern Ridge. But they would not be able to get all the way to the ridge; the final thousand feet being a sheer, featureless wall of granite and ice. Camp Two would be established when the climbing party met the bottom of the wall and from there they would climb northwest, following the wall's bottom until the wall was almost gone. They would meet Rauff's Maw along the way. No one had taken the southern route since the Rauff disaster, and so it was totally unknown to Hoyt how they were going to get around the chasm. He did not like leaving things to chance, but in this case he felt confident there would be some sort of ledge where the chasm narrows and meets the bottom of the southern face. If no such ledge existed, then they would down climb a few thousand feet along the edge of the chasm and go around it. This alternative was not optimal, but certainly possible for hearty souls such as themselves.

After Rauff's Maw, they would set up Camp Three. The wall of the southern face that would separate them from the Eastern Ridge would have dwindled to only a few hundred feet now, and its gradient drastically decreased. Their group of Sherpa would also dwindle at that point to only five and they would begin their windy route up the former face to meet the Eastern Ridge. That leg of the climb would be predominantly easy. However, the path was scarred in one place by a short but treacherous step, no more than thirty feet high but straight vertical and running almost the length of the entire southern side of the mountain. The step was bountiful with footholds, handholds, and solid ice into which to drive a pick, but it began at an elevation of 25,000 feet. At that height, with oxygen depleted and an exhausting journey behind him, a step even half as high would be demanding on a climber. Because of that, Hoyt set the same rules for the step as he did for the scree: No acclimatization. His team would go up it only once.

After they got over the step, their reward would be Camp Four and a fitful sleep before the final push for the summit. Anyone on Hoyt's team who was still physically and mentally capable was invited by him to go into the cloud and try for the top, although he demanded he be the first up. Once he had planted a flag – one with his name on it - the rest of the men were welcome to have at it. Chhiri Tendi, the sardar who he had chosen for the expedition, was required to assist Hoyt all the way to the top. For everyone else, summiting was optional.

The weather turned tragic just off the coast of the Marshall Islands. They had entered a part of the North Pacific known as "Freytag's Triangle," a rather nasty patch of ocean in which ships and planes simply went missing. William's brother Randolph wrote in his personal journal:

It had been a hot, humid, stagnant week. The world had been completely still with the Auxesis *the only thing in motion, cutting steadily through the glassy water with her engines humming at a consistent unwavering pitch. The water began to churn long before the storm was over us. Sunshine still shone through a hazy, hot sky, but the placid water that we had enjoyed for weeks became choppy. Then the ocean beneath the chop began to roil on a much larger scale. Ten foot swells caused the* Auxesis *to groan and pitch. The crew had gotten lazy over the past weeks and had stopped securing items when putting them down. Now all of those items began to fall and crash. We could just make out cumulonimbus clouds through the haze in the western sky. When they got closer, the world underneath their majestic whiteness turned completely black. I had been at sea more than half of my life and had seen some truly foul weather, but this storm looked like it was going to take the prize. Thunder and lightning could be heard over the creaking of the ship. The first gentle wind arrived off the starboard bow. Seagulls raced past us heading eastward. We were moving directly into it.*

The sun disappeared turning day to night and the wind became violent. Rain did not so much "fall" as "fire" in varying directions. Visibility dropped to zero. Randolph estimated the swells reached forty feet at the height of the storm but even at that size they could not be seen until they were already upon them.

The crew went about their business as calmly as possible, running around securing everything, minding the hull for leaks, and keeping the engines running. Randolph focused his entire being on steering the boat directly into oncoming swells. If they took one of these beasts on the beam they could capsize and sink. If they took one from behind they could broach and sink.

The climbers stayed in their hammocks trying to keep their meals down and focusing their thoughts on the fact a storm of this magnitude would not last too long. It would subside soon enough. Thornton and Ferguson, being the younger members of the expedition, had the hardest time. According to Drake, "They both looked as white and clammy as steam." The vomit came soonest for them. Hoyt, Drake, Chatham, and Wilde took longer to succumb.

By far, the strangest response to the storm came from the Hollywood denizens. According to Randolph:

> *They responded to the crisis as if scared, but the responses were 'off' for lack of a better word. The movements, facial tics, and comments were those of some alternate universe's responses to crisis. A young Fay Wray lookalike held the back of her hand to her head and then seemed to faint into a handsome actor's arms. I have seen men and women faint before and none of them put the back of their hand to their head, nor did they conveniently fall into another person's arms. The male actors started getting angry in the face of danger, yelling and throwing around the words 'damn it' a lot. Stranger yet, not a single actor I could spy was showing even*

the slightest evidence of seasickness. None vomited. None turned pale.

The actors' behaviour would have been merely an oddity to discuss at journey's end except that it escalated along with the storm and impaired Randolph's ability to control his ship. The male actors could not stand being on the periphery of the unfurling crisis. They all wanted to "save the ship."

A Clark Gable type stormed onto the bridge uninvited. He approached me at the wheel, fists clenched and yelling. He demanded I explain my 'incompetence', and then stated with the confidence of a bullfighter that he was taking charge of the ship. Without turning his head to face the two sailors behind him, he addressed them, telling them to take me to 'the brig.' The sailors saw this as mutiny and quickly subdued the lunatic with quick punches to the face. But the trouble was not over. Yet another actor came onto the bridge and did practically the same thing, except he threw in some extra gibberish about "doing it for the orphanage." Another sailor subdued him, taking him down to the hold. I was now alone. Unfortunately, another actor, entered. I could not look at him for more than a second because I was concentrating on steering the wheel and looking out for swells. Even a moment's glance showed him to be tall and built like a brick wall. His sleeves were torn off in perfect symmetry to one another, as if he did it to himself. He stared at me even though I could not look back. Then he said 'At what price your vanity, Prescott?' I had no idea what he was talking about or who Prescott was. There were no sailors left on the bridge to help me. The actor put me in a full nelson,

pulled me away from the wheel and pushed me out the door of
the bridge. I heard him say 'Jack Meachem's taking this ship to
safety.' With that he locked the door behind him and took the
wheel.

Now at the mercy of someone who clearly had no experience steering a ship or mastering the concept of 'Self', the *Auxesis* began to take swells from the side. Several sailors were lost overboard as walls of water passed across the deck. Randolph and his men banged on the windows of the bridge, trying to get this Jack Meacham – or person playing Jack Meacham - to come to his senses and open the door, but he would not. He had instead tied himself to the wheel.

William Hoyt could not stay still for long and made the decision to help his brother in any way he could. He left the other climbers, took the stairs to the deck and then climbed the stairs to the bridge.

Randolph could not afford to lose any more of his crew, lest they end up at the bottom of the Marianas Trench. He, William, and two first officers went below and came back with the first thing they could find that would end this problem. It was a movie studio light and its stand - long, heavy and made of metal. A film director saw the sailors coming up from below with the equipment and raced after them, begging them to reconsider. The light and stand were expensive and "would set Paramount back hundreds." The men ignored him. Now outside of the bridge again, William and the sailors positioned the light-stand horizontally and distributed themselves evenly along its length. On the count of three, they ran forward, and the lighting became a battering ram. Glass shattered; Randolph reached his arm through and opened the door of the bridge. Meacham, who was still lashed to the wheel, could not untie himself in time to stop the intruders. He began swinging his free arm wildly at those who were stealing his moment. William held the studio light high in the air and brought it down on Meacham's head. The actor fell to the ground and his tied arm caused the wheel to turn. Randolph untied the unconscious man and took back control of the ship.

The storm died down in an instant. Sun shone. The subsequent halting of the rain was so sudden as to be jarring. Only a gentle breeze and the swells remained. It took a little longer for the swells to go away; it would be several minutes before their peaks stayed lower than the deck. All was then calm.

Nonetheless, the damage was done. Men had died, the *Auxesis* was off course, and the compass broken. Randolph used the setting sun to steer west, but he had no idea how far north or south he was. They would simply need to hope the waves and wind had not blown them too far, and that the evening stars would be visible to help them find their way.

It was two days later when they arrived in Japan. Arrested immediately by ships off the coast of Miyazaki, all crew and passengers of the *Auxesis* were quickly rounded up and driven to a military prison miles away in Osaka. They were there for three days, given nothing to eat but water and rice. On the fourth day, things moved quickly. Randolph and a few actors who claimed to be "in charge" were taken to meet Major-General Tatsuya Ubugai of the Japanese army. Ubugai had a stern countenance with unmoving facial features save the slightest variation in lip placement when he spoke. He was tall; as tall as the Hoyt brothers who were both well over six feet. Ubugai looked to be approaching sixty-years-old, with white mustache and sagging jaw, but he stood like a man half that age. He spoke perfect English and demanded to know who they were and what they were doing off the coast of Japan. Randolph spoke for the group. He claimed they were an acting troupe, traveling to India to perform a musical. They had been blown off course by a storm, provable by the damage to the ship, and simply wished to go on their way to Bombay.

"Which musical?" asked Ubugai. Randolph, who probably knew little about musical theatre, was stumped. Luckily for him, the actors had been most impressed with his deception and one of them quickly joined in the ruse. They were performing 'The Mikado' by Gilbert and Sullivan. Ubugai seemed skeptical, but he had also heard of the opera and wished to see it for himself. He demanded the company perform the show for him that night, sung *a cappella* and without costumes.

They had three hours to prepare. Directors and actors scurried to get the show ready, teaching songs, dance numbers, and choreography to one another. Randolph sat with his brother William, watching the chaos, the two of them trying to figure out if there was some way to escape. No options came to mind. The predicament was absurd and impossible. Their only hope was that the actors pulled off the performance of a lifetime.

Apparently, that is exactly what happened. One of the stage directors on the journey named Arthur Spelke wrote in his autobiography many years later:

The audience of Japanese soldiers sat on the floor of a large room that must have been a cafeteria of some sort. When the lights went down, everyone to the man – from the sailors to the Flightless Tiger folks to the soldiers sitting on the floor – was transported to Titipu. When Nanki-Poo came on stage, we all imagined it was centuries ago and we were wandering minstrels in love. I looked around the room and saw American and Japanese laugh at the antics of the Lord High Executioner (even though the Japanese soldiers probably couldn't understand most of it). I saw tears in a soldier's eyes when he learned Yum-Yum had to be buried alive. It was a show like no other. The audience was temporarily forgetful of their lot in life and brought together

in some kind of strange union. For a short time there, we were all
Japs.

The entire audience stood and cheered for a long while. The actors and directors patted one another on the back, confident their performance had guaranteed their freedom.

About three minutes after the actors took their bows, Ubugai followed by four soldiers walked up from the darkness of the back of the room. He was not amused, rebuking his soldiers for laughing at this 'travesty.' He felt it was a mockery of his great nation. The Japanese were made to look like buffoons. Most angering to him was the music. Why, Ubugai asked, was the music full of Western tonalities if it was supposed to be Japan? The answer, he explained, was simple: The Mikado was an act of musical imperialism by the West. If Americans and the British did not attack a people brandishing one weapon, then they would attack brandishing another. Ubugai finished his scolding by saying 'none of this matters' because other events had transpired during the performance. He held up a pocket-sized book for a moment and then threw it hard at Captain Randolph Hoyt. "It was found in the hold of the *Auxesis* along with fifteen other copies," Ubugai hissed. The crew of the ship would only see later that it was an English-Chinese translation book.

Without another word, Ubugai pulled out a pistol and shot Randolph Hoyt in the chest. Ferguson wrote:

I had never heard a gun before. At the picture shows, they
sounded no louder than a pan falling to the floor. In reality, it was
deafening. My heart responded to the shock as if I were the one
being shot in the chest. I watched in horror as Randolph's left
shoulder went back at an impossible angle. Then without making
a sound, he fell to the floor. The women in the room screamed.

William, not making a noise, went down on the floor over his brother. He started shaking Randolph, and if I made out his lips correctly, he was repeating Randolph's name in a warbling whisper. There was no response because Randolph Hoyt was dead.

Ubugai did not leave after that. He looked around the room and asked in a loud voice, "Who are the mountain climbers here?" Everyone was silent. Ubugai went on to explain that he had found in the hold climbing equipment for six men. If they came forward, he made a promise he would not harm them. William Hoyt rose from the ground "tears in his eyes and staring off to nowhere" wrote Ferguson. Hoyt simply said in a shaky voice, "I am, as are five others." The five others came forward. Ubugai told the climbers to follow him. They did as they were ordered, followed by the four soldiers who were prodding them with occasional shoves from their rifles.

According to Ferguson's journal, Ubugai took the climbers to his office, a sparsely appointed space with walls of rice paper, a desk with a few framed photographs and a tea tray, and one larger table in the middle of the room. Ubugai suddenly turned gracious, pouring tea for his guests and gesturing downward toward the table sunken into the floor. While the soldiers stood in the corners of the room, the seven men sat down.

"I was once a climber, as was my father and my grandfather" explained Ubugai. "Ibuki, Shirouma, Fuji. The Ubugai family has climbed them all countless times. Many in this great nation are drawn to the sea and its life-sustaining riches. Ubugai men are different. In Japan, being different is not something that is celebrated. No, we climb despite ridicule. That is how much we crave it." Hoyt likely did not even hear the Major-General's words. "I have also been to the mainland and climbed in China before the war began. Many difficult climbs there. And after my father died, my first expedition without him was all the way to Tibet with the goal of Chomolungma, which I believe you call Everest. The ascent would have been a success, had it not been for early snow ahead of the monsoon. So you see, I know a thing or two about your world." Still, Hoyt said nothing.

Ubugai clapped his hands unexpectedly and loudly an inch away from Hoyt's face. Hoyt summoned the ability to focus on the Major-General for a moment. "Listen to me" Ubugai said very seriously. "I looked through your maps and your journals and I know you are going to a mountain called Fumu which you claim to be the tallest. Being a fellow climber, I have found it in my heart to let you go. Your brother was an enemy of Japan, as are all of those performers and their handlers. But I have no quarrel with you. You and I are brothers of the same adventurous family! You clearly talked your way onto that ship with no intention of wrongdoing against the Japanese Empire. So you are free to go on your way. That is not all. I am prepared to airlift you to your destination. We can fly over Nepal at night and you can parachute down. We will airdrop your equipment as well."

The Americans, with the exception of Hoyt, looked at each other, eyes wide and disbelieving. Ferguson wrote that the feeling at the moment was "as if a growling dog, baring its teeth inches from your face had suddenly started panting and licking."

However, Ubugai was not finished speaking. "As the American expression goes, 'Too good to be true'. Yes? Indeed it *is* too good to be true. You see, I require something in return." Ubugai then stood up and growled "Yuudai," causing the prisoners to flinch because they did not know what the word meant. One of the soldiers in the corners of the room came quickly forward. The soldier bowed to the Major-General. Ubugai put his arm on the soldier's shoulder. This man was only slightly shorter than Ubugai and had a similar look to him only many years younger. Both of their noses were rather pronounced for Japanese, and the two were strikingly handsome. Yuudai stood at attention, looking ahead while his father continued to talk. The father explained that his climbing days were well behind him, and then paused as if he were holding back tears. Three generations of Ubugai men, he continued, had climbed and enjoyed considerable success. Yuudai represented the next generation. He had a moderate amount of climbing experience and was smarter than most.

Ubugai sat back down and looked directly at the catatonic Hoyt, who did not return his gaze. He looked at him for a very long time and then presented his demands. "You must bring my son with you to this Fumu and I fully expect he will accompany you all the way to the top. Once he arrives there, he will plant our nation's flag alongside yours." Yuudai's stare broke for one shocked moment, his eyes darting over to his father's. Then the old man continued. "I will have mercenaries retrieve him - dead or alive - on the docks of Calcutta at nine pm on the first of November."

The prisoners did not know how to respond. His demand was, on its surface, not too difficult to meet. However, the moment one scraped back the rind, one was greeted with several problems. To begin, Yuudai was Japanese, and therefore anathema in the mind of the 1940's American. The United States had not yet experienced the tragedy of Pearl Harbor, but it was already wary of the Japanese. They had aligned with Nazi Germany and were hell-bent on conquest. Although these Americans had little involvement or interest in the war, they were not fools. They likely knew consorting with the enemy in any way could threaten their futures once they returned to the States, no matter how hard they tried to cover up where they had been. Yuudai's nationality also posed another problem. The members of a climbing expedition needed to work together like a family of acrobats, each one placing their life in the hands of the others. Trust was of the utmost importance. "How," Ferguson wrote, "will the team be able to work with this man, let alone look at him if he is an enemy of our nation?" What is more, this man's father had just killed Hoyt's brother. How in the blazes would the two ever be able to work together? It is not out of the realm of possibility that some of the Americans were already considering abandoning Yuudai the moment the planes dropped them in Nepal. However, the Major-General had made it clear that Yuudai was *one of them*: A climber. There was an unspoken code among climbers that they look out for one another. William Hoyt had broken that code once before on Everest, and was not likely to do it again. No, Yuudai would not be abandoned.

Ubugai looked at them for a long time in the silence. "So? Do you agree or do I kill you all?" Hoyt was still silent. Wilde, who was unofficially second in command, agreed to the offer. This apparently made Hoyt look up at Wilde, but only for a moment. He was then back to staring at nothing. The Major-General smiled and, in a Western gesture, put out his hand which Wilde shook heartily without a moment's hesitation. He then bowed, and knowing a little about Japanese culture, Wilde bowed lower.

Then Wilde had a moment of concern. "The Sherpa" he said. They were planning on meeting their Sherpa and porters in Rangoon. How would they handle this problem? Ubugai told them not to worry. He would send soldiers out to the mainland who would pass the information along to spies. The spies in turn would catch up with the Sherpa in Rangoon and let them know where to meet Hoyt and his men. The major-general continued, "My soldiers will leave with the message this very evening and the Sherpa will know within twenty-four hours. You may have to wait several weeks for the Sherpa to arrive at Fumu, but they will arrive."

The climbers were released long before dawn on the fourth day of their captivity. As they walked out of the giant cell, they looked back at the sailors, actors, writers, and directors. Ubugai had made it clear that the sailors were officially prisoners of war. They would not be going anywhere. Ubugai also pointed out that because the sailors' mission had been secretive, the United States could not loudly respond to this as an act of war. The actors, writers, and directors were more of an issue. The burden of keeping all of them imprisoned was more than Ubugai wished to take on, not to mention their histrionics got on his nerves. They would be released in a few months and placed on the *Auxesis*.

However, in the months before they were let go, Ubugai chose to take advantage of the presence of the entertainers. Along with the best writers and actors in Japanese *Shingeki* theatre, Ubugai decided to give the Chinese a taste of their own medicine. Japanese soldiers in charge of sending messages via radio were given scripts and acting lessons. They could not use the "tsunami play" because the Chinese would be aware of the ruse and ignore it. Therefore, Ubugai himself oversaw the creation of a new script, one in which the United States unleashed a surprise attack upon Japan using a phalanx of "giant, amphibious war machines." Each treaded behemoth was a thousand feet high and covered with spinning cannons, flamethrowers, and catapults throwing containers of mustard gas. The machines had risen from the depths of the North Pacific and had cut a swath of destruction across the island. The radio men speaking the information over the radio were sure to use voices laced with panic and terror. They shook as they read their lines into the microphones. They pleaded with others to check on their families in their homes towns. They cried openly. Then they continued the charade through choked up voices: Based on (completely fabricated) radio transmissions they had picked up from the United States, the Japanese found out the killing machines were "out of control and on a rampage." According to calculations from headquarters, some said, the "now master-less machines would reach China and begin wreaking havoc within six hours."

After an hour of radio silence from Chinese forces, the following transcribed transmission was picked up by Japanese radio men in Kyoto [translated from Chinese]:

Japanese curs. What did you do with the money? [silence] What did you do with the money? [silence] What did you do with the money? [silence] What did you do with the money?

This was repeated hundreds of times until one hour later:

The money your mother gave you for acting lessons.

Operation Barrymore and its Japanese "counter-play" were both disasters. Serving no more purpose, the American actors, writers, and directors were released. Of course, given that the sailors of the *Auxesis* were being held captive (they would not be released until 1945), the entertainers would need to sail the ship back to America themselves. Ultimately, they did get back to America, pulling off possibly the greatest "performance" of their lives: Negotiating the storms and swells of the tumultuous Pacific and returning home to tell the tale.

Fifteen years have now passed since the botching of Operation Barrymore. The American government's gag order on the operation and its subsequent fallout has finally been lifted. Of the twenty-five actors, actresses, writers, and directors on board the *Auxesis* on that fateful journey, twenty-five are preparing to publish their own accounts. Reviewing the manuscripts, one does not see a single mention of the mountain climbers who passed through their lives, shared life-altering trauma, and then moved on.

The climbers were taken by jeeps to an airfield outside of the village of their imprisonment. Yuudai sat next to Hoyt in the first jeep. Nothing is known about that short ride, but one can only imagine they said nothing to each other and likely avoided eye contact entirely.

The team boarded a cargo plane that carried them over the Sea of Japan, over the hostile enemy territory of inland China and India, and now was crossing over into Nepal. Fumu was getting closer. It was practically on the horizon now. Months of preparation, perils, and death were behind them. Now the Goal was approaching. It was so close but still slightly distorted, just as the oxygen-rich sky awaits beyond the rippling water's surface after a dive into deep water. Ferguson wrote: "I could not stand the suspense any longer. Enough already! This has gone on too long. Get us to the damned mountain!" He would have his wish soon enough.

Inside the plane, Yuudai approached Hoyt. He sat next to him. Over the hoarse roar of the engines, he apologized to Hoyt. He apologized for the actions of his father. His father was a hard man who did not suffer any challenge to himself or his country. The choice between killing or imprisoning the captain of an enemy ship was no choice at all. Death was mandatory. Yuudai leaned closer until he was apparently an inch from Hoyt's ear. "I am not my father" he said.

Hoyt's fog dissipated instantaneously at this utterance. He turned and looked directly at Yuudai without blinking. "Rubbish. What exception are you? I am my father. Chatham over there is his father. We are all but vessels of our parents' will, and we can no more change that than we can tear off our own skin. Now go and have a seat, yellow scoundrel!" Yuudai returned to his seat, saying no more for the rest of the journey. Hoyt returned to his fog. Ferguson wrote that everyone who could hear the conversation had put their heads down in order to avoid the awkwardness. How could the expedition go well when such animosity existed between team members?

Before Hoyt's first official entry in his journal on September 1 - the one in which he addressed the journal itself and told of the long hard journey to arrive at Fumu – Hoyt had entered a more "unofficial" entry, one having no date. However, it was clearly written somewhere between meeting Yuudai and reaching the base of Qila. Hoyt wrote: "My brother is dead. This Yuudai character seems to think I am mad at him. I am not. I am not even mad at his father. What these Japs do not realize is that this is all the fault of another man. He shoulders responsibility for the series of disasters that have befallen me. His name is Aaron Junk, My Stepfather. My Nemesis. For his undoing, I have forsaken my family. The battle will commence soon."

At approximately four in the morning on August 20th, Hoyt and his men jumped into the unbroken darkness of low cloud cover. Ferguson wrote later from Base Camp that he had been terrified during the airdrop. No one on the expedition, including Yuudai, had ever skydived. They had all been reluctant before the plane door opened and the deafening wind and engine throb had greeted them. Now they were dropping. Despite his experience with death-defying adventures, Ferguson said that the feeling in his stomach from freefall and the stinging cold on his face had made him cry for a moment.

While still in the clouds, the monstrous mountain to their north could not be sensed. When they descended below the ceiling and pulled their ripcords, things changed. Their descent had instantaneously slowed and they could take in the world around them. The rushing sounds of airplane engines and freefall had dissipated. Now something otherworldly took their place. It seemed to be coming from several miles away, but had the structure of thunder claps occurring right outside one's window during a summer storm. Gun fire perhaps? Had they dropped into a war zone? Visually, the world was still dark save one patch of sky. The patch looked like a fireworks display as it might appear on an overcast night; misty tendrils of light dispersing in myriad directions from central points. The colors of these fireworks did not vary. They remained constantly orange.

After but a few seconds, all became clear in the minds of these adventurers. There were no fireworks. There was no war zone. They were hearing and seeing Fumu expel its boiling innards in short, explosive bursts from random locations clustered miles in the air around the summit. Then as the men descended further, Qila Pass rose up in their fields of vision and blocked their view of the Vast Inevitable. With a heavy grunt and a few hurried steps over rocky terrain, Hoyt and his men had arrived at their destination.

Upon lighting his torch in the frozen darkness, the first thing he saw was corpses. These were souls who had lost their lives falling down the Qila Pass. Most of them looked to have been exposed to the elements for years. The exception was the one at Hoyt's feet, the one strapped mysteriously to a large plank of cracked wood. He appeared to be only about one week dead. And his face was familiar.

PART TWO: THE ASCENT

Chapter Nine: The Qila Pass

Almost one month earlier on July 12th, Junk and team had picked up their five high-altitude Sherpa, the remaining twenty-five Sherpa, and sixty porters in Calcutta. Headed by the sardar Pasang Dolma, the five high altitude Sherpa were well-seasoned and game for the summit. Junk had paid top dollar for the best. If his support was going to be a small group by traditional climbing standards, he wanted that support to be of the best quality. Pasang Dolma was well-known and well-respected. He had an uncanny ability for finding the best routes up mountains upon which he had never trod before, and he also had a knack for surviving terrible conditions. Climbing with George Mallory many years earlier on Annapurna, he had survived an avalanche while all others around him had been lost. Junk did not know the other four high altitude Sherpa, but he trusted Pasang Dolma's ability to choose good men.

The trip by train to Darjeeling had been drenched in monsoon rains but otherwise pleasant. An unexpected and wonderful coincidence occurred when they stepped off the train. They ran into none other than Gilford Taylor and Philip Zeigler, the men who had climbed with Hoyt on Everest and found the bruised and bloodied Junk on the Western Ridge. At that time, Taylor and Zeigler had bonded with Junk over their disdain for Hoyt. Now here they were at the Darjeeling Station. They had been living in the Indian city of Shillong ever since the Everest climb, rich American expatriates who wanted nothing more than to spend their wealth hiking around the Himalaya and climbing whenever the opportunity arose. Of course, the war had put a damper on their plans. There were no expeditions on which they could tag along. On this particular morning, they were returning from a hike around the base of Kanchenjunga. There had been no ascent, just hiking and camping at the bottom. That had left Taylor and Zeigler thirsting for an adventure. Junk did not hesitate to invite them on the expedition to Fumu. The team would have to collect more supplies in Darjeeling before setting out on the hike to Qila Pass, but that would be no problem. Supplies were relatively cheap there, and adding two able-bodied men to his anemic group was worth anything to Junk at this point.

The night before setting out for Fumu, Junk approached River Leaf and asked her to continue with the expedition. He had been impressed with her recommendations for fashioning a device for pulling men and supplies up the Qila pass, a device they had come to call "the Qila elevator." He had been equally impressed with her gutting of a pirate. She clearly had the tough core and keen intellect required for the Fumu ascent. In her usual, passive style, River Leaf agreed without an argument. Junk provided her with the equipment she would need and went the extra several steps to ensure maximum comfort for the small squaw, even procuring for her two sleeping bags in case one got wet.

Junk was beginning to feel confident about the ascent. His team had just expanded by three people, all of whom were strong and bright. He did not suspect Hoyt would have a much better group. Junk celebrated the night before they left Darjeeling by drinking gin and tonics, gambling deep into the evening with McGee, Morrow, Cole, and Fenimore, and then bedding the wife of a British soldier visiting from Vauxhall. One of the porters commented to McGee, "Sahib can't control pants." This rather primitive comment was unfortunately true. Junk could no more control his lust for women than he could his lust for money and alcohol. But he was more than happy to begin his hike with no sleep and a blinding hangover. It was a feeling he had known since his youth. It was as familiar and as comforting to him as the sound of the radiator pipes banging to life on a cold winter night in his childhood bedroom.

By eight the following morning, they had collected the "Qila elevator" which Junk had commissioned from a local carpenter upon arrival in the city. It was beautiful; its oak planks planed and nailed together just as River Leaf had specified. With the elevator placed on the backs of several porters, they set out for the mountain. Eight American climbers, thirty Sherpa (five of them high-altitude), sixty porters, and a subcommittee of yaks moved slowly through the lush and lovely foothills of the Himalaya.

Three weeks later, the environment had grown rockier and the air thinner. The team's endurance was being tested well before they even arrived at the mountain. Blisters sprung from heels anew. Sunburn set in. Gastrointestinal tracts made the unpleasant adaption to new foods and water sources. A sting in the lungs became as omnipresent as the music of the spheres. Only Taylor, Zeigler, and the coolies were spared.

When they reached the monasteries ringing Fumu, they found them to be empty. There was no sign of any people or their livestock. Doors were closed and windows covered with blankets. Junk was mildly disappointed according to Morrow's notes. He had not expected to see Mano because the expedition was approaching the southernmost portion of the ring instead of the west, but he had hoped to at least run into some of Mano's cracked colleagues. He vaguely remembered being annoyed by Mano, but also fascinated. Unsure what to do, he left a note for the man-children, assuming they could read and would not scribble over it. The note, according to Morrow, was a simple salutation, no more.

As they set out for the mountain again, Morrow wrote:

"I could have sworn I saw one of the high altitude Sherpa, a short, crooked employ of Pasang Dolma's, spit on the monastery. I know Junk saw it as well because he turned to me with a questioning look. Sherpa tend to be very kind, gentle souls. Thus it was hard to understand why he

would do such a nasty thing. We were unsure whether the Sherpa spoke English and we were in no mood to turn sour a relationship with someone who might save our life soon, so we chose to ignore the act."

While Hoyt was still fumbling across the globe, Aaron Junk and his team were looking up at the Qila Pass. Its beauty was undeniable, but so was its treachery. Morrow wrote that God must have had a moment of true inspiration when cobbling together this landscape, but He must have been collaborating with a similarly inspired Lucifer. The three thousand foot amethyst incline before them was a deep, gorgeous purple picking up yellow, sparkling highlights whenever sunlight rose over the horizon. The face was rugged, with surfaces changing angles in haphazard directions. Upon closer inspection, between the angles, the surface was smooth and flawless, leaving no room for handholds or the hammering in of pitons.

Strewn about the base of this gorgeous spectacle was a generous smattering of decayed corpses clothed in mountain climbing apparel; fools like themselves who had chosen to enter Qila of their own free will to conquer the Monster inside (Such thoughts made Junk agree with his fellow climber Cole, the physicist, that free will was an illusion. Determinism made the pile of carnage before them easier to grasp). Most of the corpses were broken apart, with arms far from torsos and heads. This grotesque detail pointed to a crucial fact about the pass: It gets harder as it gets higher. Most of these men had reached an impressive height before falling and giving up the ghost. Had the corpses been intact, it might have suggested that the accidents occurred almost right away. The climb begins as a hike, even a jaunt. It is hard to kill oneself at the outset. Then the pass narrows and steepens and travelers begin to realize they are damned fools for being where they are. It is then a foot slips or a piton gives way. The drawn out, dreadful feeling of freefall begins, and soon thereafter ends in a quick flash of anguish with no rememberer to remember it.

Hardly a "pass" at all is this colossus. More like the giant, flowing robe of some pagan god of suicide. Nonetheless, to the best of Junk's knowledge, the top of the Qila Pass was the lowest elevation and least steep approach into the domain of Fumu. Just to be sure, Junk sent two parties out at sunrise to check for alternative entry points into Qila. One party went east along the ridge toward the mountain the locals called Abel. They found nothing but a relatively featureless wall of loose rock. There was no variation in its steepness, its shoddy structure, or its height. The height of the ridge also increased as it moved toward the summit of Abel. The other party, which had moved west toward the mountain called Asha, found more of the same. The parties returned by dinner and shared the bad news with Junk. Regardless of the fear roiling the gut of every expedition member, they needed to brave the Qila Pass. They would begin climbing the next morning.

Despite their prayers, morning came. With the exception of the handful of porters who would remain at Base Camp, Junk's team left the foot of the Qila Pass with the intent of mounting it, descending the other side, and setting up Advanced Base Camp One (there would also be an Advanced Base Camp Two when they reached the north side of Fumu). The hike started out peacefully as expected. The bottom of the pass was a gently sloping basin holding little snow. Walking over the uneven amethyst was at times slippery but by no means difficult. They walked in single file with most of the Sherpa and porters in the front, led by Pasang Dolma, and the Americans in the back. Cole led the Americans with Morrow and Fenimore close behind. River Leaf was behind Fenimore. She practically disappeared into her clothing and equipment which were designed for a man's frame. The collar came up to her ears. Her mitts could not be seen within the sleeves of her coat. Only her boots fit properly. Junk took up the rear. He chose to be there because of McGee.

He did not want the man out of his sight. Before the pass became steep, McGee was already stopping regularly, wiping his brow, and breathing heavily. Nonetheless, he kept up fairly well only falling behind a few hundred feet. Base Camp had sat at about thirteen thousand feet above sea level. The top of the pass was at sixteen thousand five hundred feet. The team made it to fifteen thousand feet within a few hours.

When the first person slipped and fell (it had been Taylor), Junk sent word up the line that the increasing gradient now called for the Elevator. The Sherpa would continue to climb, bringing several lengths of rope with them. The others would wait for the Sherpa to drop one end of the rope down and then they would tie it to a short rope on the top of the Elevator. The short rope was permanently tied to the Elevator through eyeholes in its top two corners, like a giant carrying handle. Using this rudimentary contraption, porters, cooks, and equipment would be brought up, followed finally by the Americans. This process would be repeated eight times on eight consecutive pitches to make it to the top of the pass.

Pasang Dolma and his Sherpa team climbed the ever steepening "Fumuri La" with admirable aplomb. They did not even try to hammer pitons into the amethyst. It would have been pointless. They simply roped off in groups of four and climbed. Whatever payment they were receiving from the Sahibs, it was not enough.

The Sherpa reached the top of the first of eight pitches without a casualty. Morrow recalled the wild applause from below as the last Sherpa made it up. It set off an avalanche about one hundred yards to the west of them that came barreling down the mountain, entirely wiping out the Base Camp below. "We could just make out porters racing from the tents and escaping with their lives" Morrow wrote. Surplus tents, food, fuel, and climbing equipment were now buried and would have to be recovered at a later date. Junk held back a howl of anger for fear of setting off another avalanche. He quietly ordered several of the porters who had climbed up with them to climb back down and invite those below to come and join them. Waiting for the camp-less porters to catch up slowed progress dramatically and risked putting them on the last pitch after sunset. Setting up advanced Base Camp on the bottom of the other side would no longer be an option. They would have to set up camp at the top of Qila. Junk made a rule as they waited for the porters to catch up: There would be no more clapping on the journey for any reason.

When the porters had caught up, the long rope was dropped down by the Sherpa and tied to the short rope attached to the top corners of the Elevator. As if the poor man were an experimental rat, one unfortunate porter from Calcutta was told by a lead porter to get on the elevator first. The man reluctantly stood on the small board that acted as a platform and tied himself to the larger board at his back. Several pieces of cooking equipment and containers of pemmican were loaded on as well. Other people then gently brought the larger board to rest against the uneven surface of the pass. This put the passenger at a roughly forty-five degree angle, lying with his back on the board and the board on the mountain. They were ready to go. Junk signaled to the Sherpa above to begin pulling on the rope. The Elevator began to rise in an awkward, wild fashion, jerking violently in every direction as it went up. The man on the elevator seemed petrified. Despite his fear, within a minute, he and the equipment were with the Sherpa on the ledge above. The people below refrained from applause, but instead chose to pat one another on the back. This set off another avalanche, this time to the east. Quite redundantly, it too hit the former location of Base Camp. Digging out supplies would now take twice as long. Junk made a new rule: Until they ascended the Qila Pass, there were to be no expressions of joy whatsoever.

Moving people and equipment up the pass went much quicker now. Two by two and pitch by pitch, up they went. And as the Americans rested at the top of each pitch, the Sherpa would ascend the next pitch without any security but each other. The weather grew consistently colder despite the southern exposure. The air also grew a little thinner. Pasang Dolma bravely took the lead each time followed closely by the four high altitude Sherpa, and they in turn were followed by the remaining twenty-five Sherpa.

The only gumming up of the works came from McGee, who was terrified of heights. He asked to be strapped into the elevator *facing the board* so he would not have to look out on the shrinking Base Camp and expanding vista. Junk would put a gentle hand on his old friend's shoulder before each pitch, and then signal the Sherpa to start hauling up the outsized Boston tough.

When they arrived at the final pitch before the top, the Sherpa were exhausted. They had gotten everyone within close range of the top of the pass well before sunset, but their bodies were paying the price. Many of the Sherpa complained of headaches, muscle spasms, and blurry vision. These were no doubt the effects of altitude sickness. Those symptoms would recede once they climbed down to the valley between Qila and Fumu, but for now it was compromising their ability to get up the last pitch. The slow pace at which they had climbed before now decreased even further to that of a migrating sponge. The slow pace was now a risk as much as an asset, keeping the Sherpa on the ever-steepening face much longer. Legs began to shake uncontrollably. Grunts were heard. One Sherpa slipped immediately. He fell only about six feet, but it was enough to make everyone gasp, setting off yet another distant avalanche.

The last pitch was quite nasty. It rose at approximately seventy degrees along a sliver on the far eastern side, while the rest of the surface surpassed ninety degrees and became an overhang. The Sherpa were required to limit their search for handholds to a narrow chute to the right of the overhang. They moved almost undetectably in single file. Above the overhang, the steepness slowly dissipated. Everything leveled off and became the wide, flat col at the top of the pass. They were almost there.

Morrow wrote, "As if by some miracle, all thirty Sherpa reached the top of the pass." No miracle was necessary. These men got to the top by way of their strength and skill. Pasang Dolma had been climbing for more than half of his life and, by his estimation, had been the leader on the majority of those expeditions. If anyone could climb on vertical ice-smooth stone with no handholds, it was him and the men he chose to join him on this adventure.

When the Sherpa reached the top, it was reason for loud cheers of respect from below, but no one could celebrate. They Americans simply tied the dropped end of the rope to the short rope on the Elevator once again and began to board. Within an hour's time, everyone but River Leaf and Gil Taylor were at the top. The two were required to load the last of the equipment onto the Elevator before climbing aboard themselves. With everything and everyone else now at the col, River Leaf and Taylor climbed aboard the Elevator and tied themselves to the big board. Taylor gave the sign to the Sherpa above to begin pulling. Leaving the ledge that formed the bottom of the eighth pitch, the two began to rise quickly. The gradient of the pass was now so precipitous that the Elevator did not drag as much along its surface. It dragged just enough to keep them from hanging in mid-air.

Five Sherpa stood at the top pulling the two passengers up. They were all grunting now, winded and suffering from the altitude. Due to their almost obsessive obedience, they would not take shifts with the other Sherpa unless Junk told them to do so. However, Junk was not nearby. He had gotten his first uninterrupted, sweeping view of Fumu on the far side of the col and had been lured in by her dreadful Majesty. He stood absolutely still, facing away from the events on the Qila Pass, now likely a memory for him. Pulling deeply from a flask of bourbon, he observed every buttress, icefall, and ridge. We can only imagine that the sheer size of what he was seeing was enough to make him feel like falling backward. If he did not crane his neck to look straight up or down, then there was nothing in his view that was *not* mountain. It takes up one's entire field of vision, off to the peripheries where Reality dissolves into blur. The atmosphere lingering between him and the mountain must have given it a misty, otherworldly quality. The glaciers and scree at its wide base. The snowfields interrupted only by Rauff's Maw. The massive cliff up to the Eastern Ridge petering out as it moved toward the summit. The treacherous Western and Eastern Ridges, climbing gradually but erratically to the top, their cornices sullied by ash. And the cloud at the top, grumbling, complaining, exploding, endlessly sheered at its outer layers by high winds but still growing from within.

Junk lit a cigar to go with his bourbon. He was looking at the route his nemesis would likely take. After climbing down from the col on which he stood, Junk's plan was to hike to the other side of the mountain, the northern side, and climb up to the rim of the Icy Bellows by way of the Rakhiot Glacier, and follow that rim as it became the Eastern Ridge. So the view in front of Junk right now could only provide him with a general sense of the mountain he was taking on. The details were still obscured.

Behind him, Junk must have heard the yelling of the Sherpa followed by avalanches, like some sinister form of call-response in a house of worship. When Junk got back to them and demanded to know what was happening, he was notified that River Leaf and Taylor were stuck, dangling over the edge of the ninety-degree overhang. The Sherpa had tried to pull them up the gentler slope on the eastern end of the pass, but two things had gone wrong at once. First, the sun had begun to lower in the western sky. The glare hitting the amethyst had all but blinded the Sherpa so they could not see the rope on which they were pulling. They did not see as it slowly tended to their right as they pulled. The second problem involved the weather. A powerful, icy wind had picked up as the afternoon progressed. Although the people pulling at the top could not see it, the Elevator was now spinning wildly. Whenever the large board was not parallel with the surface of the mountain, which was most of the time, it could not rise over the lip of the cliff without flipping and potentially removing its passengers. The Sherpa could not lower it and start again. If they lowered it, there was an even chance the board would come to rest incorrectly, in that they would end up dragging the humans underneath the elevator along the surface of the mountain. They were at an impasse.

"It was clear from his heightened state of mania that Junk was loaded down with anger and guilt," wrote Cranston Fenimore. "He had been lured away by the sight of Fumu and had not been around to oversee the Qila Pass ascent to the very end. He was at a loss for what to do next. We could only imagine the fear River Leaf and Taylor were experiencing over that ledge."

Taylor panicked as the boards they were strapped to slowly revolved. He began to say the Lord's name over and over interspersed with creative, homemade compound curses involving animals, excreta, and carnal acts. Each curse was followed by a distant snapping sound as another avalanche raged down the mountain. It was as if the entire ridge from Abel to Asha were giving way.

They were hanging roughly fifteen feet above the ground, but the "ground" in this case was a steep slope. If they dropped and they landed on top of the wood, they would slide down the pass to their deaths. If they dropped and the wood landed *on top of them*, they would essentially become sled runners for the wood, and death would come even quicker. The wind began to pick up and they spun faster.

On the elevator with Taylor and River Leaf were about five ice axes and two ropes. According to later accounts, River Leaf made quick work using a length rope to tie two ice axes together (Taylor meanwhile continued to craft colourful hyphenated words). With this new pole, River Leaf was able to touch the cliff near them and stop the elevator from revolving. At some point while they stood there in mid-air, the people at the top of the rope tried their luck at pulling them up. When they reached the overhanging lip of the cliff, part of the elevator got caught underneath the lip. They started flipping upward at an impossible angle. River Leaf and Taylor both started yelling for the men at the top to stop and lower them again. And again, avalanches sounded off. When the elevator dropped far enough to touch the amethyst surface, they were starting to come to rest face-down. Again River Leaf and Taylor yelled for them to stop. So they rose to midway up the cliff and came to yet another halt. River Leaf stuck the ice axe pole out to keep them from spinning yet again. They were back where they started. The sun was beginning to set and the weather was turning much colder. River Leaf continued to look for an escape in the fading light. That was when they heard an awful snapping sound. This time, it was not an avalanche.

If the reader would permit the author a momentary digression dripping with impossible omnipotence, I would like to briefly recount the tale of a certain tree in the Terai region of the Himalaya, not far at all from Darjeeling.[3] The author has never been in the presence of this tree nor has he traveled to the Terai, but the tree's story does not take multiple sources

---

[3] Editor's note: The section beginning with this sentence was not included in the first edition of the book, and was salvaged from Tersely's original notes for this new edition. The original editors convinced him to remove the section as there was no possible way Tersely could have known intimate details about the tree that is the subject of the writing. Keeping the section, they believed, would only fuel the arguments of Fumu detractors who claimed Tersely was mentally unstable. Dr. Bloom and the editors of this edition felt that the exercise was not evidence of madness, but simply an effort –however misguided – to spread his wings and wax poetic.

to deduce. What's more, I doubt the tree's offspring will ever come after me claiming libelous misdeeds!

Many, many years ago, under dappled forest sunlight and heavy humidity, accompanied only by the din of woodpeckers, an oak sapling began to grow. It was small and beautiful. It had but two leaves at that point, and those leaves were large enough in relationship to the tree to bend the whole of it. This tree was fortunate. Despite its diminutive bearing, it survived. Monsoon rains, rodents, and aggressive floral neighbors just happened to miss this fragile thing. It gathered nutrients from sun and soil and grew uninterrupted.

Indeed the tree grew, and grew at an impressive pace. However, if one was able to see inside its textured bark and concentric rings, one would see this tree had a flaw. It was a slight weakness in spacing of cells along a line running from sapwood to heartwood. With each passing year, cambium would manufacture a new band, and each year, the flaw would be born anew in fresh wood and become solidified in dying wood near the core. The tree had inherited the flaw from its parent tree. The broken information dropped to the forest floor in the form of an acorn and then was absconded by a hungry squirrel that carried and buried it more than a mile from the parent tree. Perhaps one hundred years earlier, the parent tree had inherited the weakness from its parent tree. Now the sapling was growing into adolescence with the imperfect branding of its ascendancy. It was not a flaw so grave it would bring the tree down early in life, but if a northerly wind happened to hit it too hard or another tree fell against it, the oak may have seen an early death. Fortunately, it did not.

Seasons passed. The oak grew into a giant, with a trunk three feet in diameter, a drip-line covering thirty feet of forest floor, and a height of almost sixty feet. Several smaller plants and trees died from the oppressive shadow it cast. A metropolis of birds made their home in its branches, giving the tree its own loud, jubilant voice when morning arrived. Rains would seasonally tear at its limbs, pruning it back ever-so-slightly, but never enough to slow its progress toward magnificence. The flaw always lay within - an internal scar spanning decades – but the oak grew stronger around it and managed to stand as if immortal.

It was then that some men arrived in the forest. They carried axes, machetes, and saws. One of the men sat down against the tree and smoked a cigarette. Another was picking his teeth with a knife. Three others looked around for some time, speaking and pointing. Their voices would occasionally rise in disagreement. Sweat dripped from them as they spoke and so their talk was accompanied by dabs of rags to their foreheads. At last their talk died down, their fingers all pointing at the oak. The oak did nothing. Its topmost branches moved imperceptibly in the gentle breezes above the forest.

The men approached and put teeth to bark. The saws moved back and forth rhythmically. With a groan that issued throughout the forest – sound waves racing past the parent - the oak tree fell, taking several smaller trees with it. Other men arrived with chains and ropes, preparing to take the tree back to their city, where they would turn their bounty into snuff boxes, mirror frames, pages of Korans, cricket bats, church pews, letters to generals in the field, ship transoms, and myriad other objects that litter the senses of Man. In this way, the flaw made itself known to the world of Man.[4]

The elevator's wood was snapping near one of the holes where the short rope passed through. Taylor continued his obscene incantations while River Leaf looked for solutions to their predicament. She grabbed the cliff again using the pole of pickaxes, once more stopping their dizzying rotation. As the sun reached the western horizon, the amethyst around them lit up brilliantly. The sunlight reflecting off the amethyst in

[4] The "problematic" section, omitted from the original edition of the book, ends here.

turn lit up other amethyst previously shaded. It was at that moment River Leaf noticed one part of the rock surface, immediately under the lip of the cliff that stubbornly did not light up.

Above the cliff, Junk had ordered the Sherpa to tie off the rope to a large boulder until they could come up with a solution to the situation. The idea of throwing down another rope was rejected outright because River Leaf did not have the expertise for such technical climbing and Taylor could not be expected to walk her through surmounting a cliff face of greater than ninety degrees. Nor could they be pulled over the lip on a separate rope because if done incorrectly, they would be tenderized against the rocks. After about a half-hour, they came to the conclusion the only way to get Taylor and River Leaf out of peril was to keep trying to pull the elevator over the lip. Sooner or later they would pull when the elevator was at just the right angle to the lip and would rise up smoothly.

Junk yelled down to the two people beyond the cliff, doubting they could hear him over the wind. "I don't know if you can hear me down there, but we're gonna pull up again, and we'll keep trying to pull up until it works. If you think you're gonna flip, just yell and we'll stop. Then we'll try again until it works!"

At Junk's command, the Sherpa pulled. Down below, the wood snapped, relieving the Elevator of one of its two connections to the rope. The Sherpa likely felt the sudden jerk, but the weight they were pulling thankfully did not lessen. The knot of the short rope stuck to the long rope, dropping River Leaf and Taylor a few feet, but still holding them in the air. The two stranded souls were now hanging diagonally, Taylor slightly lower than River Leaf. Her weight was upon him, likely making him twice as miserable as he was before. It was only moments before the extra strain on the one remaining eyehole began to snap the wood. River Leaf was motivated enough by this turn of events to stand on Taylor and take a leap of faith toward the dark spot in the amethyst, beneath the lip.

The Sherpa heard a loud crack followed by a nauseating slack in the rope and they were thrown back. The knotted long rope's end came flying up over the lip devoid of anything. Junk ran to the east to gain visuals of the Pass all the way down. To his amazement, he saw Taylor, still tied to the Elevator, glissading at full speed down the entire length of the pass. The Elevator did not crack anymore. It held strong. Taylor bumped and jerked an infinite number of directions, but he remained strapped aboard the wood and descended at a terrifying pace. There was no sign of River Leaf.

Like a gift from the inspired god who built the Qila Pass, Taylor came to a peaceful stop in the sprawling basin at the bottom, right where Base Camp had been. There was a pause and then through his binoculars, Junk saw Taylor raise both fists to the Heavens in triumph. From over one thousand feet up, Junk heard Taylor give out a cry of victory. It was long and primal and filled the air like an exaltation of larks. The ridge responded by dropping three simultaneous avalanches, all of them managing to find their way to Taylor.

The team mourned the loss of their mate. However, the mourning was muted somewhat by the confusion about River Leaf. No one could discern what had happened to her. Calls down the Pass went unanswered. Junk told the Sherpa to hold the rope again as he grappled it and hand-over-hand made his way down to the cliff. He secured his feet, digging crampons into ice and leaned over. He saw no signs of any living thing. River Leaf had simply vanished.

After climbing back up, Junk told the somber group Taylor was dead and River Leaf was missing. A prayer should be said by anyone who was religious and then they would set up camp on the col, overlooking Fumu. Many were in tears. Others, like Cole and Zeigler, stared out into nothingness, jaws slack. Zeigler said some words in honor of Taylor.

When the rituals were done the team looked for a flat area protected from the wind where they could set up camp, even though every one of them knew sleep was not going to come that night. Before the first tent pole was removed from a backpack, Pasang Dolma approached Junk and reminded him of the men who were suffering from altitude sickness, and the only cure for altitude sickness is to descend. He made a plea to Junk: Climb down the other side of the ridge immediately and set up Advanced Base Camp at the foot of Fumu. They would have to descend the ridge in the dark but he pointed out that the terrain was gradual and easy. Such an effort might save the sick Sherpas' lives.[5] Junk considered this and decided Pasang Dolma was right. They would climb down in the night and then rest until noon the next day at Base Camp. This would also allow the team to get as far from the traumatic experience as possible.

And so in the frigid night, lit up only by a smattering of torches and the light of Fumu's eruptions, the exhausted team climbed down the other side of the ridge toward the base of Fumu. Healthy Sherpa aided ill Sherpa to the bottom. They had not yet started climbing Fumu itself and already a man was dead, others were suffering from altitude sickness, and an Indian was missing. Morrow wrote: "As we climbed down, Junk wore an expression I had not seen on him before: Defeat. In all of the years I had known him, I had become used to an upbeat, robust, hearty character. But on the climb down to the base of Fumu he looked beaten before the real climb had even begun and it deeply concerned me. It was too damned soon for this."

Quite possibly Junk was not feeling defeat but rather guilt over the loss of River Leaf. He had convinced this poor woman to join him on a deadly voyage, even though by every stretch of the imagination she should have been safely in Boston right now or even better in the Dakotas with her

---

[5] Altitude sickness does not just affect those who are new to climbing. It strikes indiscriminately, plaguing experts and novices alike.

family. Regardless of whether the feeling weighing down Junk was defeat or guilt, he was clearly distraught. He asked Cole to take the lead on the way down and allowed himself to lag. By the time they were reaching the bottom in the darkness, he was all the way in the back of the team with McGee.

Upon reaching the bottom, a yell came from the front of the line. At first it sounded like a cry of terror but then nuances in its wavering pitch betrayed a kind of joy. Junk ran to the spot where all torches were pointing. He probably could not see at what they were aimed, because a crowd had surrounded the object of interest. Junk pushed through and gave out a gasp as if he was looking at an apparition. Lit from all angles was River Leaf. According to Morrow, it was the first time the team had seen her smile. "The effect was potent. The men's torches contributed only slightly to the brightness in front of us. The smile made her radiate energy as if by a thousand votive candles." Junk could not contain himself. He reportedly hugged her so hard her feet were off the ground. McGee also gave her a bear hug, probably elated to have the other non-climber back.

The obvious question followed: How? How did she survive the fall and how did she beat them to the base of Fumu? River Leaf did not answer with words. Instead she pointed up to the dark world behind them, the gradual slope they had just descended. The torches turned and aimed at the spot where she had pointed. About fifty feet up the slope and slightly to the west, between two large boulders stood the entrance to a massive cave.

Chapter Ten: Naked, Silly, and Godless

It was sunrise at the base of the Qila Pass, and no one was sleeping. The entire Hoyt expedition was worried that if they did not head up the Pass today, then they would have to head home by sunset. It had been nine days since they parachuted down and still there was no sign of the Sherpa. They were living off of rations given to them by the Japanese plus whatever they could salvage from Junk's destroyed Base Camp, but everything was running low. If their Sherpa did not arrive today, August 29th, then the expedition had to leave for Darjeeling immediately or risk running out of supplies and not making it out of the wilderness alive.

Yuudai the Japanese soldier smoked cigarettes and organized his backpack. Drake the inventor was experimenting with an oxygen mask attached to two tanks capable of detecting low oxygen in one tank and automatically switching to the other. The experiment was failing and Drake kept passing out. Chatham the dashing thrill-seeker spent hours on nothing but his morning ablutions. Wilde the prim and proper gentleman folded his clothing with a style so meticulous it bordered on insanity. Thornton the young linguist and athlete read a book about conversational Sherpa in preparation for the arrival of their help. Ferguson the altitude sickness specialist and disciple of Kellogg ate figs, yams, and yogurt very slowly, chewing fifty times per bite with almost a full second between bites.

Ferguson wrote:

I completed my breakfast an hour after sitting down to it. Then I entered Hoyt's tent. He was sitting there, head down, studying the flag he intended to plant at the top of Fumu. It was made of white cloth

with non-descript black lettering sewn in reading 'W.J.H.' I asked
him how long we should give the Sherpa team before we give up and
head home. An hour? The entire morning? Hoyt seemed to not hear
me. He said 'Do you know, young man, that when you get older,
decades pass as fast as years did in your youth?' That cheerful
sentiment was the most he had ever said to me, or anyone else on the
expedition for that matter. He finally turned to look at me and said,
"We will give them until noon."

The thought of an about face must have been deeply upsetting to Hoyt. It would mean he was done with climbing forever, he had lost the competition to Junk, and he had lost his brother, wife, and maybe his children for no reason whatsoever. When Ferguson entered the tent, he had likely come across a man lost in self-evaluation; a man taking an inventory one only takes at the most significant of life's crossroads.

According to Ferguson, Hoyt ambled out of his tent a few minutes later and walked to a location he had returned to repeatedly over the last nine days: the body of Zachary Taylor. Hoyt knew this man. He had climbed with him on Everest. What was he doing frozen and strapped to a board at the bottom of the Qila Pass? The only answer was that he had joined Junk's team (What other team could it be?) to get revenge on his former expedition leader, met a terrible demise, and the board was some sort of half-completed coffin. Junk must have had to leave in a hurry if he was unwilling to complete the coffin. Knowing Hoyt, he probably suspected laziness on the part of Junk. Or an avalanche. The latter explanation would make sense given the condition of Aaron Junk's Base Camp. It had been hit by some breed of colossus that had flattened it entirely and then disappeared in the warm weather of the past week. However the events may have transpired, Taylor was now laying there wearing a look of complete surprise.

The day blossomed warm and sunny, as had each day since their arrival. The team had gotten into a routine. There were early breakfasts consisting of eggs, sausage, and coffee (Alas, the sausage was gone after the fifth day). After breakfast they would split into parties to explore the area, much like Junk's team had done earlier. They found no alternative route into Qila. They would then have dinner at noon, which usually involved fish stuck in the snow to keep frozen and then grilled in chunks over the Rob Roy by Yuudai. Afternoon found them keeping in shape and warding off altitude sickness by hiking up the pass as far as they could make it without risking serious injury. At sunset, they would climb down and eat supper like paupers, bread and oleo, in order to save their rations as much as possible. By the ninth day, supper was bread with no oleo. After supper, Hoyt retired while the others sat around a campfire and drank. "They share tales of past adventures and women. No one can keep up with that loud-mouth Chatham. I have the urge to poison him or fatally punch him or both. I need to keep instinct at bay. He is apparently a top-notch climber and the expedition needs such men."

The porters and Sherpa arrived just as the team was beginning to pack for home. They were slogging in single file across stone and ice from the southeast, with Chhiri Tendi in front. There were easily over one hundred and fifty of them. Major General Ubugai must have hired on more men to ensure the successful climb of his son. The army of support brought with them beasts of burden and huge packs on their backs, all weighed down with food, clothing, and climbing equipment. A cold-climate mirage. Hoyt's team let up a cheer and Chhiri Tendi's hordes cheered in response. Avalanches raced each other en masse to the bottom of the ridge, but distant enough to avoid harm. The previous week's events must have drained the local heights of precariously placed snow. Hoyt wrote later that day:

I was not happy at all. They were late and had caused us unnecessary anxiety. I stormed over to Chhiri Tendi with the intent of venting my spleen. All I could say was 'Where the devil have you been' before he had his huge arms around me, hugging me as if we were long-lost brothers. He kissed me on both cheeks and called me a 'handsome bastard.' Then he turned to his men and spoke to them in what may have been Nepali. As he spoke, he pointed to me every few seconds. This was accompanied by occasional laughter from the crowd which I found quite insulting; but when he finished his speech the men let up a giant cheer (the cheering ended abruptly when a distant avalanche was heard and seen near Asha) and each man in turn came to pat me on the shoulder or hug me and give me a warm verbal greeting in a foreign tongue through horrible teeth. After about one hundred and fifty kind salutations, I could no longer be upset.

Chhiri Tendi and Hoyt spoke at length about the plans. There was likely no way to get all of the porters and cooks over the Qila Pass, so they would unfortunately have to make their current location base camp. Only the American members of the team, the Japanese soldier, the high altitude Sherpa, and one cook would proceed. This made for an overall team of about thirty-five. All thirty-five would proceed to Advanced Base Camp and the four camps on Fumu, then Chhiri Tendi, Yuudai, and Hoyt would make the push for the summit. Chhiri Tendi was very excited. He knew the route from his attempt with Hoover. Chhiri Tendi said, "Had he not been decapitated, Hoover would be honored to know we are working together, and that we are recreating his steps in our struggle for the top."

Hoyt also explained to Chhiri Tendi that Junk's team was over the Pass already and probably making a go for the northern route up the mountain. Their hope was that Junk and team would already be half-spent just getting to the northern base of Fumu and would not have the energy nor the supplies for a summit attempt. According to Hoyt, Chhiri Tendi added "That [expletive] is too capricious and too inexperienced to carry out such an endurance test. He is likely to fail." Hoyt asked Chhiri Tendi to please minimize the blue talk. Chhiri Tendi apologized and said he would try. Moments later he was swearing again.

Everyone awoke at sunrise the following morning ready to take on the Pass. Gear was packed. Cigarettes and pipes were smoked. Prayers were spoken. A delicious breakfast was eaten. Packs were placed on backs and goodbyes were said to a large percentage of cooks and porters who were to stay at Base Camp. It was time to take on the Pass, glowing purple and yellow in the sunrise like a giant bruise. Hoyt wrote in his journal: "They are all jovial, but I know Death awaits at least a handful of us today."

They had begun to walk across the basin when the unexpected occurred. A line of other people approached from the southwest. Everyone's journals gave different estimates, but the average estimate was thirty men. As they grew nearer, it seemed the men were wearing nothing but loincloths and backpacks. Each was pushing a large, wooden box on wheels, the boxes having one corner carved out and open, but covered with white cloth. When they reached Hoyt's team, the wheeled objects appeared to be over-sized prams. Thornton documented the interaction that followed in minute detail (In addition to being a linguist, he also dabbled in anthropology and sociology and he must have been compelled to make a record of these human anomalies):

The men were not of one race. Some were brown, others red,
others white. Hoyt turned to me for my linguistic expertise but I
simply shrugged. Like Hoyt, I was utterly at a loss. Hoyt lifted up

his hand to greet them. "Hello. Do you speak English?" The man in front, a short, white, blond fellow with a terrible sunburn lifted up his hand just as Hoyt had. The morning was still cold and the man shivered. Then through chattering teeth he said, "Goo." Needless to say, this confused us, but then he said quite eloquently in a German accent, "Yes. I speak English. We all can speak it." This was quite a relief.

Hoyt introduced himself and explained that we intended to climb Mount Fumu. "Why would you do such a thing?" The question came not from the German, but from inside the box. Hoyt and the rest of us were taken aback. After looking at the rest of us - possibly searching for some glimmer of understanding in our eyes and finding none – Hoyt moved to the pram and lifted up the cloth. We gathered around. Inside was a full-grown man swaddled in blankets. "Goo" he said in a strong and confident voice. "It is a pleasure to make your acquaintance."

Hoyt seemed angered by the bizarre state of things. "What is the meaning of this? Stand up and address me like a man!" The supine fellow in the pram wriggled like Houdini in chains, unable to break free from the blankets. He looked to the German who quickly offered assistance. Within moments the man was standing before us, naked. He was tall and skinny with dark skin. Running down past his shoulders were oily, matted strips of graying black hair, thinning on the top. He looked quickly to the German. "Capital swaddle," he said. The German smiled, bowed slightly, and went back to shivering. The naked man spoke. "Let me tell you right away who I am because the last time I met someone from the West they seemed eager to know that piece of information before talking to me. My unofficial name is Mano and this group has no name and we all live in the ring of monasteries you undoubtedly passed on your way here and we worship Fumu and we act like good children to please him and so on and so forth. Now it sounds like you are going to the mountain, as are we. Would you like to accompany us?" He seemed to have an accent. It may have been Portuguese.

Hoyt replied quite tersely, "First, we did not see your monasteries because we were dropped from the sky by airplane. Second, I refuse to speak to you further until you are clothed." The man, who was skinny and quite tall for a local, let out a frustrated breath and then went to the backpack of the German. He pulled out an enormous white bunting and pulled it on. He looked ridiculous with his arms out to his sides and pointy hood on the top. "Is this more acceptable to you than my nakedness?"

Hoyt did not reply. Mano explained that his brethren came from all around the world. Some had been part of expeditions like Hoyt's and had had a change of heart. Others had been locals who simply stumbled across the monasteries and seen a chance at starting life again. Now they spent their days living in the monasteries, playing well with each other and going to bed at sunset. They would continue to do so until they had pleased Him (pointing to Fumu). Hoyt asked how they would know when they had pleased him. Mano responded quite seriously, "When she stops bringing forth magma and starts bringing forth milk." Mano paused dramatically and then said "And I mean that quite literally."

A very odd thought this. A mountain producing geysers of milk. This seemed to be taking animism to a ludicrous extreme. Beyond your basic Shinto. When we anthropomorphize something in our culture, we do not expect that thing to actually mimic a living thing. If we think our automobile looks like a man, we do not expect it to tell a joke. And likewise, most people who think a flower has a soul do not think it is going to start tap dancing. Yet this fellow and his colleagues think that somehow this massive rock is going to lactate."

Mano continued. "Our belief in this unlikely event is an expression of our hopefulness. In our temple we believe all things are possible. Surely men can get along with one another. Surely the sick can be healed. Surely there can be a place where children are safe from hunger."

"We've found the 'Surely Temple!" interrupted Chhiri Tendi our Sherpa sardar. No one laughed at this except Chhiri Tendi, who responded as if it was the funniest thing since the circus midget hopped onto J.P. Morgan's lap.

After being clearly annoyed by these interlopers, Hoyt was done with the conversation. Fidgeting, he looked to the Pass as if in haste. Then he simply walked away from the dialogue with Mano. He found his backpack and put it on. Looking back at Mano, he said, "If you'll excuse us, we have some climbing to do."

"Why are you climbing the Fumuri La?" asked Mano, using the local term for the Qila Pass. "I thought you were climbing Fumu."

Hoyt's face was red. I could see the infamous temper coming to a boil. The feeling of logic breaking down did not sit well with William. He barked, "What are you talking about? We are climbing Fumu but we have to get to Fumu first. Enough of these antics. The Qila Pass awaits!" I put my pack on my back as Hoyt had done and followed him. Everyone else on the expedition followed suit.

Having not moved from where the conversation had taken place, Mano yelled to our backs, "So tell me, sirs: When you come home at the end of the day, do you climb through a second-story window?"

Hoyt could have ignored this last statement and kept walking. Had he done so, who knows how many lives would have been lost? Who knows if we would have made it to Fumu at all? Fortunately, for whatever reason – perhaps simply God's gracious intervention – Hoyt did not ignore the question. He turned and looked back at Mano. "Do you mind clarifying what you mean, sir?"

Mano replied. "That wall of solid rock you call a 'pass' is no such thing. It is glistening Death. Do not go through the high window. Go through the front door." And with that he pointed to a spot just to the west of the basin and at just about the height where a man can no longer climb freely and requires equipment. There was an outcropping of three long, narrow boulders. The boulders had likely arrived there during some ancient cataclysm, sharing and losing the same perch somewhere hundreds of feet above. Two had fallen in such a way they made a line, like train cars moving up the fall line of the mountain. The third boulder had fallen atop the others and cracked in the process, resting diagonally off two sides of the other boulders, one to the left and the other to the right.

"What am I looking at?" Hoyt asked in an impatient tone.

"Look. Beyond the stones." Mano answered.

Just behind the top of the cracked boulder could be seen – but just barely – a darkness. It was then that I understood what I was seeing and I suspect Hoyt understood at the same time. The

boulders formed a massive arrow pointing to a cave. I prayed
Mano was about to tell us what we all hoped.

Indeed, Thornton, Hoyt, and the rest of the expedition were about to catch the luckiest of breaks. Mano informed them that the cave runs through the ridge, providing a passage right through to the base of Fumu. There were actually multiple lava tubes along the ridge, some at higher elevations than others and some further east and west along the ridge. All of them were dead, seeing as volcanic activity this far away from the summit had ceased eons ago. The caves inside connect and diverge haphazardly, creating a formidable catacomb. However, one large, main artery ran a straight line through the ridge, and that was the one they were looking at now.

By the accounts of all fellow climbers that day, Hoyt wore an expression of joy the likes of which no one had ever seen on him before. He actually laughed. Returning to where Mano was, he patted the man on the back, a display of affection new to Hoyt's repertoire.

Thornton was able to extract from Mano that the arrow was put there by his predecessors because "children need help remembering things." The man-children returned to Fumu constantly and required indicators like the massive arrow to guide them so they would not get lost in the wilderness. The path from the monasteries to the mountain was apparently covered in arrows. The massive boulder arrow at which they were looking was merely one of many.

Mano and the man-children invited Hoyt and his expedition to follow them into the caves, an invitation which Hoyt gladly accepted. Hoyt wrote, "I was sincerely thrilled to go with them. However, my excitement suffered gradual source decay due to the oddness of our temporary guides. Out of the other prams rose men of varying height, girth, and ethnicity, each shedding their blankets. They donned their own buntings and prepared for travel. I do not like these ridiculous harlequins. They are naked, silly, and godless. I can only pray that they will stumble across Jesus somewhere in their travels. When they do, I hope for their sake they are wearing trousers."

Led by Mano, the long line of people and equipment began to move toward the cave. All but one pack animal was left behind; a large yak lead by a negro in a bunting. The animal carried a load on his back too heavy for a man, possibly 120 pounds. What the load was unclear to the mountaineers, Sherpa, and porters, but the man-children clearly felt it was important enough to risk an animal going through the caves.

Progress toward the cave was slow because the man-children wore only rudimentary sandals, completely inappropriate for such terrain. As the amethyst began to steepen and become too uneven, progress slowed further and prams were abandoned. After approximately one half hour of hiking, the line reached the top of the arrow and stood at the mouth of the cave. It was roughly eight feet in diameter and ringed by nothing but granite and ice. Cool air, but not cold, blows out of it at all times. Moist and reeking of mildew, the atmosphere belching from the darkness is far from inviting. It is actually quite unnerving. The expedition and their new guides entered the cave, the Americans possibly questioning whether they might have been better off scaling the Pass overhead.

After only seven yards the cave narrows slightly to a diameter of seven feet. It also grows dimmer. The walls become amethyst after three more yards. The mineral's reflective nature multiplies natural light, keeping things bright for a while. Even after forty yards, one can see a point of light from the rear because of the bright walls and also because the cave is so straight. However, well before a furlong, without the help of lanterns or torches, travelers are completely shrouded in dark and mildew. The tunnel varies little in terms of altitude and direction, and so the walking is relatively painless. But as someone who has been through it, the author can attest to its less than comforting impact on the psyche. The claustrophobia can get the better of you if you dwell too long on the facts that you cannot stretch out your arms to full extension and men block your exits in both directions. Breath already restricted by altitude is restricted further by the cave's scarce oxygen, producing a feeling in the traveler of a belt tied around the chest and synched up several notches too far. Then there is the sound. Near the entrances and exits, one hears constant rushes of air whistling through the ears. As one moves toward the core of the ridge, one mile within the Earth, the rushing has ceased and is replaced by a pervasive, heavy Nothing. Air pressure on the ears increases and close quarters make for no echo at all. Man-made sounds seem muted. If the dark did not fulfill the sense of premature burial, then the dulled sound hammers in the final nail. The cave continues like this – straight, narrow, and evoking death - for almost two miles before spitting travelers out into the blinding daylight on the other side.

They walked single file, Sherpa, porters, expedition members, Man-Children, and one yak. Mano and Hoyt took the lead, the former before the latter. Chhiri Tendi was not far behind. The other expedition members were interspersed quite randomly. The entire line of hundreds was spread out roughly one mile from fore to aft.

Progress through the cave was by all accounts smooth. The men walked comfortably. Only the yak complained at first. Although a sure-footed beast, the yak did not take to the dark nor did it appreciate the enclosed space. It snorted and reared back its head. The man-child guiding the yak needed to fight with the animal repeatedly. With that exception, the journey through the cave started peacefully.

Hoyt wrote: "As we grew more accustomed to the darkness and the monotony, my mind began to wander. I thought about these large infants who guided us. I understood they came from all corners of the Earth and that they worshipped the mountain, but other questions remained in my mind. For example, how did they survive? Did they farm and hunt? They certainly did not seem the type to live off of the land; they took turns pushing each other in baby carriages for goodness sake! No, they must subsist on something else. Someone takes care of them."

It had already been a day of firsts for Hoyt. He had laughed. He had patted someone on the back. He had even stated an ontological thought in front of Ferguson in the tent that morning. Now, possibly out of boredom, Hoyt did the unthinkable and struck up a conversation. He asked Mano about his people and their culture. Hoyt later tried to recreate a transcription of the cave conversation from memory in his journal.

ME: "So, you're children who are men."

MANO: "Well, we are men of course. We choose to act like children. Licorice?"

ME: "No thank you." [He seemed to offer people sweets quite a bit. I am not sure where he stowed them.] "Do you know how to hunt?"

MANO: "No."

ME: "Does anyone in your little group know how to hunt?"

MANO: "We are not so little and no."

ME: "Do any of you know how to tend a garden?"

MANO: "What is a garden? I'm just kidding. But no, none of us knows how to tend a garden. Not to mention that the earth around the monasteries cannot be farmed. The soil is rocky and devoid of nutrients. My bunting is too small and riding up my bottom."

ME: "How frustrating your answers are! Then tell me, how is it you aren't dead from malnutrition?"

MANO: "Allowance."

ME: "Come again?"

MANO: "Allowance."

I paused for a quite a while, trying to imagine what on earth this oddity was going on about. We heard someone down the line whining like a baby, complaining in Spanish about having to make water. Mano yelled back in fluent Spanish that the person should "hold it."

ME: "Explain yourself. What allowance?"
MANO: "Look around you."
ME: "I see nothing."
MANO: "Lift your lantern to the walls."

I held my lantern to the stone surrounding us. It was no longer amethyst. The cold, sweating surface still had a shine to it, but it was much duller now with a yellow-brownish cast. I stopped, removed my knife from my belt and scraped. The scar in the wall glistened marvelously. Gold. "Allowance" Mano repeated.

It seemed the man-children returned to Fumu regularly not only to worship, but to harvest the gold of her fortress. The lava tubes extending out from her burrow through gold, and according to the man-children, Fumu itself has hidden strata of the precious metal. Granted, silver is the coin of the realm among Nepal's local inhabitants; but gold by the *pram-full* could still keep a man in boundless comfort.

Perhaps it was because Hoyt came from money but he did not become crazed by the realization he was walking through an uncharted gold mine. His notes continue as if he had just learned a dull mathematics fact at school. No other expedition members mention the gold in their journals either. Hoyt must have kept it to himself to avoid a widespread outbreak of Greed.

Mano explained that neighboring Nepalese people brought them whatever they needed thanks to Fumu's allowance. Food, services, toys, games, books. Everything they required. There was no reason to farm or hunt. On this trip, Mano's people would collect gold from the caves upon their return trip to the monasteries, after they had paid their respects to the mountain. They would stuff their buntings with gold, deposit the gold in their prams, and wheel it home. "We will sleep first at the base of the mountain before mining" he apparently said. "We will need to rest before we dig and scrape with our toys. Rock candy?"

Hoyt turned down the offer, but the topic of being tired must have triggered another question in Hoyt's head, because according to his journal, he also asked Mano about the average age of the man-children. None of them seemed young. "Most of them slouched, had sagging bosoms, and wore thinning grey manes" Hoyt wrote. Mano's explanation was minimal and far from satisfying. "We do not have children because sex is naughty. We have also stopped recruiting because the sibling rivalry is getting to be ridiculous. Fumu can only have so many children. He is not a Catholic after all."

Time passed slowly. Patience was tested. Tempers shortened. Stomachs growled for dinner. The yak bellowed. "Each expedition member looked at the feet of the man in front of them and waited for a cry from the front of the march announcing daylight" Thornton wrote. "No announcement would come. A man-child would occasionally cry out, confessing to fear of the dark, and a Sherpa would tell them to calm down." The urge to get out was growing strong among everyone.

Like Hoyt and Mano, many of the men talked to pass the time. After getting over his reservations about Yuudai's nationality, Drake discussed an idea for an invention he had had while sitting in his broken down automobile on the side of the road many years earlier. Thinking her husband was late because he had been out raising his wrist with other scientists, Drake's wife had greeted him at the door with a skillet to the face. At that moment, he had realized how terribly he could have used a telephone on the way home. He told Yuudai of his idea for a "wireless" telephone, an impossible contraption that worked like a long-distance two-way radio. It required no overhead telephone lines and could be used almost anywhere provided there was a "tower" transmitting a signal nearby. Drake planned to patent the idea when he returned to the States. Yuudai did not respond to this silliness.

Just when conversations had run out of replenishing topics, Mano informed the team they were approaching the end. They had reached a narrow point preceding the cave mouth. The narrow point before exiting out to the Qila Sanctuary and Fumu is five feet in diameter and continues like that for no more than three feet, wide enough and short enough to allow for the men and their equipment to pass through without much effort. About fifty feet beyond this narrow point lay the cave mouth.

Mano noticed something was wrong immediately after passing through the narrow portion. They had neared the mouth no later than one in the afternoon, but upon growing near, they saw only darkness at the end. Mano approached the place where the mouth should have been and found it had been blocked. The barrier was created by flat rocks sitting atop one another reaching all of the way to the ceiling. "Hoyt had been happy as a schoolboy all day" Chhiri Tendi told me in our discussions many years later. "But when we reached that obstruction, goodness gracious. His face contorted into a scowl and his movements came in short, enraged bursts. He was audibly grumbling. It was like he'd suffered from a life-long curse of the limbs and muscles, experienced a momentary reprieve, only to have it return in a tragic instant." He began yelling at Mano, calling him every terrible name he could think of. No one was happy at the moment, but Hoyt's abuse seemed unnecessarily vicious. Being a "good child," Mano did not fight back. He accepted his scolding. However, when the tempest of Hoyt's rage had subsided, Mano did point out that the obstruction was not natural. A viewing by lantern light suggested the stones were too flat and stacked too carefully to be the result of a cave-in.

The men pushed against the blockade but it would not budge. A quick decision had to be made between two options. The first was to turn around and briskly make their way back to Base Camp. The other was to begin the potentially back-breaking task of razing the wall. They could not be sure how much effort would be required until they started having a go at it. There did not seem to be any cementing of stones, which was good. But the stones were heavy and wedged in tightly. They could disassemble them, but it could take a while, and who knew how thick the wall was? No light shone through.

Decisions must have been difficult to make in the sparse air shared by hundreds of tired men. Chhiri Tendi, Mano, and Hoyt tried to talk through the options and come up with a utilitarian solution that would bring the greatest benefit, or at least minimal suffering. Chhiri Tendi recounts:

"The decision was made even more difficult because, despite hypoxia, Hoyt was managing to find enough sustenance from the air to be visibly enraged. But the rage was not aimed at Mano anymore. Hoyt seemed to finally understand that anyone wearing a bunting was inherently innocent. If you willfully choose to follow someone wearing a bunting, whatever happens after that is your own damned fault. No. His rage had turned to someone not there. He seemed to know in his gut that Junk was the mastermind behind this wall."

Entries into journals from the Junk expedition suggest Hoyt was correct in his theory. After River Leaf has escaped certain death on the Qila Pass and made her way to the base of Fumu via the caves, Junk had indeed told the porters to construct a wall blocking any further passage.

As Hoyt, Mano, and Chhiri Tendi tried to reach a decision, another problem arose. "Hoyt, come back here. You're not going to like this." It was Chatham's voice. It sounded as if it was coming from behind a wall, which made little sense given they all shared the same cave. Putting his pack down, Hoyt slid past the other travelers with lantern in hand, back to the location of Chatham's voice. Before he could arrive at Chatham he came across the yak. In great frustration he demanded the porter in charge of the yak move the great beast so he could determine what the problem was. Chatham said from nearby "That's the problem, William. The yak is stuck."

The yak had been guided with little effort up to that point, but then they had reached the narrow portion of the cave and the old girl had become wedged between the walls. Chatham explained that the yak had been moving fast enough to get its withers into the space, but then it became wedged in between the sides. The load on its back had also become stuck against the top of the cave. They had tried backing it up and pushing it forward to no avail. Hoyt wrote, "The animal complained, grunting and moving its head about wildly. If anyone tried to reach for her head, the horns tried to find purchase in flesh. Its eyes, wide with fear and anger, were fixed on me. Its mouth was open, tongue distended, drool flying to all points on the compass." The porter assigned to the yak pulled on the rope in vain. This only managed to make the animal more hostile.

The stuck animal posed serious problems. The slight oxygen supply for those ahead of the yak was now even slighter. Who knew if sufficient air was slowly entering from hidden vents and from between the yak's legs? Would they be smothered? Was the carbon monoxide from the lanterns and torches going to be a problem? For all they knew, oxygen was being replaced with sulfurous air coming from the Earth below. Breathing was now clearly getting more difficult but no one could gauge the rate of decrease in supply. Also, retreat from the cave had now become less probable. Until the animal could be moved, they would have to focus on the man-made wall for escape. People at the front of the line were trying to get the top stone out of the wall but were having some difficulty working fingers and the tips of ice axes into the crevices and then pulling the stones into the cave. They seem to have been placed in such a way that sending them outward *from* the cave would be easier than pulling them in, but the men could not manage the proper angle to do this. There was no doubt getting the wall down would take precious time.

After a spell, the animal calmed down, possibly due to the lack of air. It sporadically huffed and stared at Hoyt. Hoyt stared back, trying to think of what to do. Hoyt wrote: "The yak looked at me as if to say 'Now you die, old fool, and I will be the one to deliver you to the Underworld. This is the demise your hubris has wrought – not at the summit of the world but in a subterranean staring contest with a yak.'" Hoyt looked beneath to see if there was space enough between the four legs for the twenty or so men trapped at the front of the line to make an egress. There was not. Even if a person could slip under the yak's brisket, any sudden actions by the yak could lead to serious bodily damage. As long as the wall and the animal stayed where they were, there was no exit.

Several plans arose at once. None of them involved the wall because even if it was only one stone thick from bottom to top, the limited diameter of the cave and the crowded conditions did not permit a proper assault. They did not have anything to use as a battering ram and even if they did, they did not have the space for a running start. Because of this, all plans revolved around the yak. Hoyt's plan was to wait for the animal to relax further. There appeared to be perhaps a few more millimeters of width nearer to the bottom of the cave than in the middle or top. If the yak relaxed then it might drop and in the process come loose. Or at least looser. Chhiri Tendi suggested they settle in for the night and not feed the animal. He posited that there was enough air for everyone to breathe and enough water to drink. If they waited it out, Chhiri Tendi believed, then the yak would decrease in girth just enough in twenty-four hours to come loose. Both Hoyt and Chhiri Tendi's plans demanded patience. Not so Chatham's. "Kill the beast" Chatham yelled from the other side of the blockage. "Cut its throat and then take it apart." The tallest mountain in the world was only moments away, and Chatham could not hold back any longer. Safari in the Congo, submersibles under the North Pole, snake-charming in Iraq all paled in comparison to this, the greatest prize. "I am not going to waste another minute staring at this animal's ass. Let's kill it and eat well tonight."

The first to speak up against this idea were the porters, men who usually did not speak. Some came from regions where the yak was sacred, but even those who did not come from such regions knew the worth of a live yak. Its dung provided fuel otherwise hard to find at high altitudes. Its fur could be cut seasonally for clothing. The milk was good too. In their estimation, killing this yak would be hasty and wasteful. Everyone including the animal could come out of this cave alive.

Mano's protest against slaying the beast was predictable. In the eyes of a child, all violence is bad and should be avoided. He would rather die himself than watch the yak be slaughtered. "He began to weep openly," wrote Hoyt. "He jerked hard on the sleeve of my wool sweater, begging not to let it happen. He said his people would gladly share the gold in the tunnels with us for eternity if I would spare the yak's life. I told him to unhand me. The decision would be based on reason, not emotion."

Hoyt could have very easily agreed with Chatham. He must have certainly shared Chatham's urge to get to the mountain. Losing Wizzy, a deadly journey around the globe, the murder of his brother, all for the mountain that was *right there*. All he had to do was snuff out the life of an animal. The yak was pinned; cutting its throat would be effortless. One swift wave of the hand as if in salutation and the problem would be past.

But then again, Hoyt did not like Chatham very much. "No," he responded. They would wait for the beast to tire and drop, and then they would pull her out of the tight space.

The mandate did not quiet Chatham. If no one wanted him to kill the yak, then he would at least "give the animal some motivation." With that he snatched a lantern from the hand of a nearby porter and held it to the yak's hindquarters. According to Chatham's anguished recollections that evening, the result was immediate. The yak convulsed and bellowed, all limbs going into action. The hind legs bucked, finding first Chatham's lantern and then his face, introducing the two in the process. His hair was an oily fire and his face bloodied before he even hit the ground. The enraged yak fared much better than Chatham, coming loose and stampeding forward. The fellow holding the rope around her neck knew he was no match and let go immediately. The animal trampled and knocked aside men in her path as if they were no more than pappus from a dandelion. When she reached the wall she did not slow. Horns and then skull found stone and the wall gave way without resistance. Gold, granite, and amethyst exploded out in all directions. The enraged ungulate ran away into the snow and sunshine, kicking up rubble and dropping its burden in the process.

Men on the ground and against the walls of the cave breathed deeply of the fresh air and squinted into the blinding daylight. They could see nothing as their troglodytic eyes had not yet adjusted. Moans could be heard from those who had been trampled. Chatham was unconscious; his newly bald head still smoking. Hoyt had suffered only a mild abrasion when the back of his head hit the wall of the cave. Mano and Chhiri Tendi were spared entirely. The able-bodied helped gather the injured, putting arms around shoulders and picking up those few who could not walk. And then, in a stream of exhausted humanity, the expedition exited the cave and looked upon the view before them.

Imagine you yourself had just stumbled from the cave, head down, exhausted. Train your eyes very slowly skyward, starting from the ground at your feet. You would have first seen little of interest. Loose grey rubble pounded by receding glaciers lie under your hiking boots. Some of the stones around you are as big as boulders, but mostly you are surrounded by pebbles you could hold in your hand. Look up a little more. Patches of snow and ice lay about. There is almost no flora save the occasional scrappy blade of brown grass peeking up between the rocks. Raise your eyes further. There are no inclines or declines to speak of; the earth is perfectly flat for one mile ahead of you up to a scree where foreground meets background. The flatness extends all of the way to the horizons on your left and right. All of this landscape is covered in black soot come to rest after its descent from above.

Now look straight ahead. But brace yourself first. For beyond the one mile stretch of nothing lays Fumu, tall and wide and terrible. The moment your rising eyes see it, all else you have just witnessed - the rocks, the soot, the scrappy grass - is gone from memory. You grow dizzy taking all of it in. The world before you is a vast palimpsest etched in ash over snow and rock and they all say the same words: "Stay away." There is more mountain in your field of vision than blue sky. Fumu's white buttresses flay out beyond your peripheral vision. The Eastern and Western Ridges (the eastern one *you* will have to ascend) follow the mountain's flanks like sharp, cumbersome shoulder armor. They meet at the shrouded summit, which is the highest thing you have ever seen. Its dark cloud billows outward and is sheared flat at the top by the jet stream. Could it possibly be within the Earth's atmosphere? There but for the Grace of God go you.

"The cook wet himself immediately upon seeing her," Thornton wrote. "I had to sympathize. Had we simply been paying a visit to Fumu's base, it would have been a different matter. But knowing we had to wake tomorrow and begin going up – up this cold giant that was completely indifferent to our hopes, fears, and will to live – well, that was enough to seize any man's urethra." Thornton's words are certainly no overstatement. The effect of seeing Fumu from the base is unsettling when paired with the knowledge you are about to scale it. The team had to take some time think about this before proceeding. They tried to eat lunch and meditate on their fate while Ferguson did his best to administer first aid to the trampled and the burned. Ankles were twisted and ribs bruised although most of those who had been in front of the yak simply had the wind taken out of them. Chatham was no delight to behold with his swollen face, exposed scalp, and lack of eyebrows. However, the beating and scorching did not stop him from prattling on about past adventures. "This is nothing compared to the damage I sustained in Yellowknife on my way to the Arctic Circle. I was caught standing between a mother grizzly bear and her two cubs. The bear already carried my colleague's right leg in her mouth when she set upon me. The claw marks are still quite visible on my torso." No one ever happened to see the claw marks, but then again, no one was looking.

Once bellies were filled and burns soothed, Hoyt gave the word to proceed. They crossed the moonscape of the moraine within one hour and came to the base of the mountain. There stood Junk's Advanced Base Camp; a series of tan silk Mummery tents and prayer flags huddled together in a circle, attended to by a large team of porters. Two of the porters stood side by side and motionless watching the approach of Hoyt's team. Hoyt wrote:

"One was holding a lowball of scotch, the other a deck of cards. Their angle of loll suggested acute inebriation. I had no question in my mind as to whose camp this was. The anger built in me as we neared the outpost. I began to hike faster as we approached the few Nepalese

minding the camp. When I reached them, I did not waste a moment with formalities, nor did I ask if this was the camp of Junk. Who else's could it be? No, I jumped right in to asking the two questions I cared about. First: 'Did he go up or around?' Thornton translated. The coolies pointed to the northeast. Just as I thought. Junk was gambling again, taking the time to go all the way around the base in order to take the "easier" route. Then I asked my second question: 'Which tent is Junk's?' Thornton translated again. The men pointed to the tent furthest away from us. I wasted no time. Junk had been dogging me for years now and I had only returned the favor in little ways like slighting him on the Presidential hike money and punching him in the face. I was ready to provide another small repayment (that is, until it was time for the enormous repayment of reaching the summit first). The wall in the cave could have killed several people. Junk had stepped over the limit. I calmly walked over to his tent, untied the lantern that had been attached to my pack, and spilled the remaining contents all over the place. Not much was needed, given the highly flammable material these tents are made of. The coolies began to run toward me followed by my own men – Chhiri Tendi, Thornton, Drake, Wilde, Ferguson, and the jap. They were too late to stop me. I had already struck the match I had held in my hand all the way across the moraine. I dropped it and the effect was instantaneous. Junk's canvas tent went up in a fireball. I am a man usually drawn to cold, but at this moment, the heat on my face and the joy in my heart were turkey and stuffing on Thanksgiving."

According to other people's writings, no one said a word to Hoyt about the tent burning. They were deathly afraid of his temper and besides, there was nothing that could be said about it anyway. Junk's porters scooped up snow in cooking pots and threw it on the fire. Smoke and steam billowed up and out over the moraine, a small simulacrum of the gargantuan grey cloud roiling 30,000 feet up. The team watched the tent burn and then walked back to their equipment.

They ate dinner in the cold, clear night. Because they would not down climb the scree, this would be their last meal at the base. Come four in the morning, they would awake and begin going up.

Mano and his "men" had been gone for several hours late in the day delivering their gift – whatever it bloody well was on the yak's back – to Fumu. Now Hoyt's team fed Mano and the other man-children, filling them deeply with eggs and rashers of bacon so the return trip under the Qila Pass would not be too draining. Hoyt still did not like these "bent primitives and their pagan deity," but they were God's creatures and could not be sent off tired and starving. Before striking out across the moraine in the dark, Mano put his arm around Hoyt and took him aside. He then asked Hoyt to reconsider the plan to climb Fumu. He did not need to do this, he said. There were other ways to conquer the world, like for instance planting your seed. Mano cited Hoyt's favorite book. Deuteronomy: "Be blessed in the fruit of your fields, and in the fruit of your cattle, and in the fruit of your body." Nowhere, Mano pointed out, does it say "be fruitful in your conquests." Stay at home, Mano said, and have more children. The man-children, he explained, should not reproduce, but all others should do their best. He continued; "Walk away from my father mother, Fumu, and be at peace." With that, the man-children turned their backs to the Hoyt expedition. Many were whining about their exhaustion. Mano shushed them. They walked off into the darkness across the vast expanse of stones, their torches disappearing under the Qila Pass.

Hoyt turned now to Fumu, looking up at the sporadic orange explosions coming from within the clouds at the summit. Each time they flashed, the mountain underneath would light up. In those flashes, Hoyt could see the route they were to take starting the next morning: up to the right at first over the scree and Southeast Face, then a sharp turn to the left along the bottom of the Eastern Ridge, crossing Rauff's Maw, and then a final push up into the history books.

The mountain continued to spit fire and ash in the darkness. Hoyt writes:

"I looked at my team members and said 'Gentlemen, Hell is above us!' No one responded as if they heard me, perhaps because they were too busy cleaning up dinner and preparing themselves for sleep. I decided to repeat myself because it seemed like a poetic sentiment worth sharing. This time I said it louder. 'Gentlemen, Hell is above us!' Many turned to me upon the second pronouncement but looked confused. Perhaps they did hear me this first time and could not figure out why I had repeated myself? In the end, my words had far less impact than I had hoped."

Chapter Eleven: The Rakhiot Glacier

In the pre-dawn hours of September the first, Junk's team consumed a hearty breakfast of beans, sardines, and coffee. So exceptionally frigid and dry was the morning many of them donned layers originally intended only for the summit. Gabardine coats were worn over wool jumpers and trousers, flannel shirts, and silk underwear. Hareskin mitts and puttees over boots protected extremities. Junk wore four pairs of socks! Sun goggles, wool hats, and scarves protected heads from cold and sun. Pitons, carabiners, ice pegs, ice axes, and ropes were placed on belts and slung over shoulders. The Sherpa also carried tents, food, sleeping bags, and other supplies. The cumulative effect of breakfast, clothing, and equipment surely made everyone feel like battleship anchors. And it was in this heavy state that Junk's team began to climb Fumu.

Junk's route up the mountain started out much like it had on Everest with the scaling of an icefall. The Rakhiot Glacier pushes its way down the northern side of the mountain, providing the only interruption in the scree ringing the bottom of Fumu. It is like the steep, stretched staircase of a Mayan temple, and it leads up to the lip of the Icy Bellows from the rocky moraine below. These "stairs" move and break away without warning. Loud snapping can be heard at random intervals followed by seracs the size of city buildings falling into the hidden depths of the glacier. The force generated by these large objects hitting one another leads to the physical process of *sublimation*; ice is converted directly from a solid to a gas, skipping the liquid stage entirely. As a result, steam rises all around. Atop the glacier at Camp One that night, Morrow would write: "The icefall offers a visual paradox, what the Europeans call an "impossible object." You hike atop the glacier, but you are also not 'atop' it because there are seracs above you and below you. There is no reliable horizontal plane, no reliable horizon, no floor." The goal was to make it up this impossible object on the first day and establish Camp One near the lip of the Icy Bellows. They would then climb down and back up twice more in order to acclimate. On the fourth day, September the fourth, they would strike out from Camp One and make their way along the eastern lip of the Icy Bellows. Halfway to the Eastern Ridge, they would establish Camp Two, further taming the unruly mountain.

The transition from hiking relatively flat ground to ascending the mountain proved jarring to everyone's respiratory system. To compensate, they hiked at a very slow pace. Any slower, and the glacier upon which they hiked would outpace them in the opposite direction and thus return them to Base Camp. For even the most seasoned climbers of the lot, taking constant breaks and massaging cramped muscles were mandatory.

As they began the ascent, wending their way through the great maze of the icefall, McGee was complaining. He was not complaining about exhaustion any more than the others (the hike from Darjeeling and then around the base of the mountain from south to north had gotten him into relatively good shape), nor was he complaining about heights quite yet. He was complaining about glare. One thing many new climbers do not expect is the intensity of the sun at such high altitudes. Paired with the reflective snow and ice, the result is blinding. When Junk's team was in the shade, the world was a gorgeous luminous blue. When they moved out into the frigid sunshine, vision was lost. Even with the aid of goggles, squinting was a must.

The landscape was marred by rather unpleasant touches that alerted the team to the threats that faced them at every moment. After only three minutes on the icefall, they came across a severed arm. It was devoid of clothing and colour. The poor sot could have been any one of the countless individuals who had lost their lives on the northern route. The accident that severed the arm from its owner may have happened hundreds or even thousands of feet higher up the mountain; the glacier's slow downward motion delivering the arm to its current location over the course of decades. After the arm, Junk's team came across a length of rope tied to a piton and dangling off the side of a crevasse. "Fortunately, no one was tied to it" Cole wrote.

> *"I do not believe our team could have handled any more macabre visions. The rope's free end simply blew in the gentle updrafts of the crevasse. Less than one hour after the rope, we came across a sight far less explicable. Two legs and feet stuck straight up out of the ice. German boots and grey woolen pants still adorned the limbs. There was no blemish in the ice around them. Junk posited that perhaps a crevasse had crashed shut on the fellow and then fused after years of wind and temperature fluctuations. No one else in the party bothered to venture a guess. They simply looked on with concern. It was hard to reconcile all of this unpleasantness with the blinding sunshine and blue skies arcing above us."*

Using his uncanny mental talents to memorize the map and Hoover's route along the icefall, Morrow led the way. His challenge was not a simple one given that an icefall is not a static thing. Some crevasses had formed anew since Hoover's time and several fallen seracs had blocked the way. The team had to adjust their route somewhat and they proved quite adept at it. Pasang Dolma was alongside Morrow and he seemed to have a good sense of safe routes to take. Not far behind Morrow and Pasang Dolma were Zeigler and River Leaf, followed by Fenimore, followed by

Junk and McGee. The remainder of the Sherpa brought up the rear. The team had made the unusual decision to not tie off to one another on the icefall. If a snow bridge or a serac gave way, Junk did not want the bad luck of one person pulling the remainder down. The unsafe nature of an icefall is usually the exact reason why a team would tie off. If one person falls, the others can arrest themselves and stop the person from dropping. But Junk the gambler felt his team was comprised of good judges of terrain and would know what routes to avoid. In addition, ropes hinder faster climbers and put pressure on slower ones. No, Junk wanted to wait until they were on steep, technical portions of the mountain before breaking out the ropes. They would play the odds on the icefall in order to make for a faster, more comfortable ascent.

Occasionally the route would come to an unexpected dead end. Once, the team had to take out pitons and ropes and climb a near vertical face some forty feet tall. It was their first experience with technical climbing on Fumu (aside from the Qila Pass where the Sherpa had done all of the hard work). Those with more experience climbed beneath those with less and motivated them with compliments, advice, and distractions. After an hour, the entire team was up and unscathed. However, they were all exhausted. Junk and Cole, the two most experienced climbers on the expedition, suffered the least, but even they felt the future held nothing but discomfort. "Morrow lay at the top of the cliff panting," Cole wrote. "I thought McGee was going to have a cardiac arrest. River Leaf sat cross-legged with her head down, breathing deeply. Being young and experienced, Fenimore seemed to be like Junk and I; winded but ready to continue." Cole went on to describe Pasang Dolma and the other Sherpa as "downright chipper." Their bout with altitude sickness on the Qila Pass earlier in the week was now clearly behind them. Because of their recovered fortitude, the responsibility fell mostly to them to help the Americans push on.

They reached the location of Camp One, near the top of the icefall at 19,000 feet, shortly after two in the afternoon. The lip of the Icy Bellows was only about one hundred vertical feet further ahead. Several hot pools of water bubbled on the lip, sending steam into the air to be caught by the battling wind patterns. They chose to make camp below the lip and not on it because of said troubled, raging wind. Its way of blowing one direction at full force and then coming about without warning – taking with it equipment and human lives - made it notorious. The dreaded wind would be their constant, malevolent companion soon enough. No need to hasten that relationship.

After pitching the tents, the team took a brief respite. Dehydration from high altitude plagued all of them. Headaches and nausea were experienced by some of the climbers but its victims were arbitrary. Junk was doubled over from a headache while River Leaf seemed untouched. Junk struggled to speak, but when he did, he commanded everyone to put on their packs as quickly as possible and begin the healing climb down to Base Camp.

As you climb at high altitudes, your intelligence drops. This is a scientific fact. You assume more and more of the qualities of childhood. Your capacity to utter certain basic phonemes, make informed decisions, and store memories are all shot to hell. The lisped "s" – the shibboleth of youth – returns in full force, along with the unfulfilled "r" and the "l" masked as "w". What's more, the poor choices of more carefree days come back to pay a visit. The process begins above 10,000 feet and gets steadily worse. That would all be well and good, but at higher altitudes, the need to be on your toes gets greater. The risks increase. You are farther from help with each step. Your ranks thin so fewer and fewer other people are present who could possibly aid you in an emergency. To be sure, impaired judgment, compromised physical agility, and weakened communicative skills do not jibe with the necessities for survival at great heights.

Nothing exemplifies this problem more than the drama that inevitably arises around the acclimatization process. The physical and emotional investments involved in climbing a Himalayan mountain are enormous. The thought of climbing down *during ascent* is almost unfathomable. You struggle up to a lofty perch, strain your body to its breaking point, and then have to give up your claim! How can one expect a child to understand and make such a long-term investment?

That is one of the distinctions between the experienced climber and the new one. The experienced climber can envision a person dying from altitude sickness - the pain, the bloody coughing, the final, failed gasps for breath. They can envision their own nausea and headaches from past journeys. These memories are enough to override any foolish passing thoughts about barreling forward up the slope. The new climber on the other hand remembers only yesterday's climb and the success of reaching a higher camp. They succumb without battle to their juvenile urge for immediate gratification. In light of this, one can only imagine the despair felt by River Leaf, McGee, and Morrow – the three who had never climbed at extremely high altitudes - when Junk led the way back down to Base Camp. The entire day's work on the glacier was being erased and would need to be repeated.

The one comfort of temporary retreat is that thicker air awaits you at end of day. The headaches and dehydration that the team felt at Camp One, which stood at 19,000 feet, were now gone at Base Camp, which stood at 14,000 feet. Sleep was possible. Some intelligence and physical acuity returned. What's more, porters and cooks awaited them with a hearty supper of canned ham, dried prunes, mulled wine, and hot coffee. They were in a fleeting Shangri-La and everyone made the best of it. They knew that these pleasures would be disappearing soon enough.

Unlike Morrow and Cole, Junk was hardly writing anything in his notes. The subjects were limited to dates, weather, routes up the mountain, camp positions, and general team health. "September 1. Excellent weather today. Cold but cloudless. Pitched Camp One shortly after lunch near the top of the icefall. Everyone tired but otherwise game." There was nothing more in these entries. He gave no sign of writing to anyone in particular, nor did he provide any of the flourishes that often accompanied his speech. Other than the connections he kept at home for work and general social climbing, Junk probably had no one expecting writings upon his return to the states. We can only theorize that Junk was keeping barebones documentation just in case he was going to die on this journey. The journal would provide those who discovered his corpse with some idea of who he was and what he had been up to. After all, he had lied to everyone back home about where he was going. Most people thought he was relaxing in New Hampshire.

Junk could have spent the night at Base Camp writing like Morrow and Cole, but instead spent it on drink. No one could keep up with him. Everyone else stuck with supper and tobacco. Alcohol and altitude are a lethal pairing and Junk was inebriated moments after opening the flask. McGee shared a few sips to calm his own nerves but was in no state to revel or drown sorrows.

Cole, River Leaf, Zeigler, and Fenimore had retired immediately after supper. Junk, McGee, and Morrow met in Junk's tent to partake in a game of cards. It must have been a pathetic affair given their exhaustion, but they were desperate for the comforts of home. They played five-card stud, no variations. This would hopefully minimize foolish mistakes.

Morrow wrote: "Junk had always been a bluffer, scaring people out of their ante regardless of what he held in his hand. That night was different. Even intoxicated and out of energy, Junk played a conservative game."

The larger stakes he was playing with Hoyt may have overwhelmed the game in the tent. But what came next provided an even stronger explanation for his behavior.

"I'm broke" Junk mumbled to the others. Everything was spent on securing passage to Fumu and paying for the Sherpa and porters. There was nothing left to pay for the land journey back to Cooper's ship and nothing waiting for him personally when he returned to the States. What happened after the ascent was of no importance to him. Beating Hoyt was the single item on his calendar. What's more, he had no more sources of future revenue as he had liquidated all business concerns to fuel this expedition. He had no family to which he could turn. No woman he was seeing. He had also vowed never to take a red cent from the daft old woman he had married (he had married her for revenge, not for money). He was indeed broke.

The news must have surprised the others in the tent. They would have to pay for Junk to get him back to America. And what of McGee, whose financial standing was inextricably linked to Junk's? McGee must have been livid. Junk was essentially telling him he too was broke. McGee had always left issues of money to Junk. Providing muscle and companionship had been his focus. Now McGee was freezing, slowly falling apart on the side of the tallest mountain in the world, making impossible sacrifices for his closest friend, only to find out his closest friend had knowingly bankrupted him for selfish reasons. Forget the one million dollar bet; McGee likely did not care about that. They had not even set up the joint account...the corpulent Irishman could dismiss it as a symbolic gesture. But everything else? His living? According to Morrow's notes, McGee's only response – exhausted and devoid of affect - was that he was tired and he was going to his tent to get some sleep.

Being on the north side of the mountain, sunshine did not touch them until late in the morning. It would be plentiful from ten until noon, then it would get lost behind the cloud at Fumu's summit, and finally it would blaze down on them from one until four as it traveled just above the Western Ridge. But for now, the cold of dawn permeated everything. Ice clung to beards. Their scarce breaths burned and then escaped through bloody, chapped lips as steam. Only one day in, and the team was concerned that Cole was already experiencing frostbite around his right cheek. The telltale blackening was evident, and Cole spoke of pain followed by total numbness. Not much to be done in such a situation other than to ensure Cole covered up the area completely. He pulled his scarves tighter and continued with the others up the Rakhiot Glacier.

They moved quicker this second day. The uncertainties of the route were gone and so they climbed with more confident steps. Ropes for technical climbing waited for them, having been left in place from the previous day. No precipitation had occurred the night before, leaving crucial handholds and footholds visible. The experience was still exhausting but perhaps slightly less than it had been twenty-four hours earlier. No one was cocky about their mounting progress; an occasional eruption heard from the summit was all it took to sap their pride.

Junk was climbing near the front, now confident McGee could take care of himself near the rear. He walked alongside Pasang Dolma and Morrow, easily following the tracks they had forged the day before. The previous night of gambling had ended well for Junk despite the difficult confessions. He had won three hundred dollars after a streak of good luck that had included a full house, a straight flush, and four-of-a-kind. Now this morning he decided to raise everyone's spirits by announcing another game, this one to be played while climbing. It would take very little thought or effort from the team. They would play as they hiked and the winner would collect their money that night at Base Camp. Junk's hope was that the game would provide a distraction for everyone as they slogged over old territory. Morrow, Fenimore, Cole, and McGee said they were in on the game. River Leaf declined, as she had seen far too many Dakota men torn asunder by "moccasins" and other games of chance.

Junk called it "Icefall Craps." Each player took a turn being "the roller." The roller would play traditional craps; he would just replace dice with humans. The roller would start at the front of the line of climbers by announcing a bet of a certain amount of money. Then he would walk down to the two nearest climbers, "the dice," one at a time. The first and second climber would each say a number between one and six to the roller quietly. It was essential that the "dice" could not hear one another. The roller would then walk down to another set of climbers who would each quietly utter a number between one and six, the sum of the two being the roller's next roll. The roller would keep doing this, moving down (and if need be, God forbid, back up) the line of climbers, until he either hit upon two people whose numbers summed to seven, in which case he lost the bet and owed everyone else a percentage of the money, or he hit his come out number again, in which case he won the bet and everyone else had to pay him a percentage of the money.[6]

Given the exhausting job of walking up and down the line, Junk offered to start out as the roller. Pasang Dolma had respectfully declined to play, so Morrow and Fenimore would be Junk's first pair of dice. Junk announced a bet of twenty dollars, just to start off easily. He hiked next to Morrow and asked Morrow to whisper a number to him. "Three." Now Junk slowed down and waited for Fenimore to catch up. Fenimore quietly said "two." Junk now walked down the line, hoping future "rolls" would sum to five before he hit upon a pair that summed to seven.

---

[6] The only time a roll of seven was a good thing was in the case of the come out roll. That would make you an instant winner.

Junk stopped and rested against a large serac. He waited for Cole. Cole approached after about five minutes with a Sherpa next to him, carrying his equipment. Cole said a number between labored breaths. River Leaf, carrying her own equipment, arrived at the spot where Junk was waiting. She had said previously that she did not gamble nor did she have any money to wager; she would provide numbers but did not want to put money on the line or be a roller. When she arrived at Junk, she muttered a number as well. Whatever Cole and River Leaf had each said – no record exists at that level of detail – the numbers summed to neither five nor seven. Worthless. Junk had not won or lost.

Junk climbed down to McGee who was huffing over an ice bridge. Several high altitude Sherpa were behind McGee. They were clearly dedicated to their job, preventing any customer from getting lost behind them. Even though they were moving at half of their normal rate of ascent, they stayed behind the man and kept a close eye on him. After McGee gave him a number, Junk was stuck. He needed one more number for a pair, but was out of Americans. Turning to the closest Sherpa, a man with a cobra inexplicably tattooed on his hand, he said "A number please!" He counted to six while touching fingers to give the Sherpa an idea of what he wanted, using slow, sing song-y prosody to indicate they were all reasonable choices.

"I speak English, and four" was the response. The Sherpa seemed almost angry as he spoke to Junk. Junk was surprised by the negative response. Several other Sherpa around this particular Sherpa also seemed to be of unpleasant disposition. "Wait, you're the asshole I saw spit on Mano's monastery."

The Sherpa was now clearly angry. "My name is Kyidug, not asshole."

It is true the relationship between porters and sahibs on climbing expeditions has always been quietly strained. The exploitation is obvious to all involved. The sahibs do not pay as much as they should and the porters know it. But it is quite unusual for porters to put their distaste on display unless there is a clear case of abuse. "Thanks for the number, asshole" Junk said to Kyidug. "You made my come out roll." Junk had won. Kyidug only paused for a moment before hiking again.

Junk had reached the end of the line. Now he needed to use his impressive climbing skills to race past everyone and return to the top of the line. He hiked at a rapid clip and collected pairs of numbers as he went. His come out roll from McGee and River Leaf (he skipped Kyidug this time) was three. Cole and a more affable Sherpa provided a number having no effect either way. When he returned to the front of the line, Fenimore and Morrow hit him with a one and a six. Craps. Losing that second round, he had broken even.

Fenimore was the next roller. He bet twenty dollars. After Junk and Morrow whispered in his ear, Fenimore let out a small, oxygen-deprived laugh. Seven. He had won right away. Junk and Morrow verified they had indeed whispered "two" and "five" respectively. A quick win and a delightful distraction for the young stripling.

Morrow chose to be the next roller. He was not concerned about leaving the front of the line because his navigational skills were in less demand today. The team knew to simply follow their tracks from the day before. Morrow's only hesitation about being the roller was driven by the fact that once he had worked his way down the line of climbers, he would have to double his regular rate of hiking in order to return to the front. Nonetheless, the distraction was what he needed.

He chose to make the distraction enormous. "One large" he announced, using the American parlance for one thousand dollars. This likely surprised and thrilled Junk. He told Morrow he would be good for his percentage of the winnings, should Morrow win, when he returned to the States and got back on his feet. Morrow accepted this. Fenimore also approved of the stakes.

Three and three. Indeed, six was a smashing come out roll which probably made Morrow highly confident that he would win one thousand American dollars.

He moved down the line. It must have been a pleasant, temporary relief to stop and wait for climbers to pass. As he worked his way through Cole, River Leaf, a Sherpa here and there, and McGee, no pair of rolls summed to six. He became frustrated. When he got to the irritable Kyidug and asked for a number (Junk had not told him to avoid conversation with the four Sherpa at the end of the line), Kyidug apparently responded by asking Morrow why he doesn't put more focus on climbing and less on gaming. When Morrow strained his way back to the front of the group, still not hitting his come out roll, he complained to Junk about the quality of the Sherpa they had secured for the expedition. "Rude." "Disrespectful." "Insolent." These were the words he used in his rage. He also recalled that the Kyidug character had been the one to spit on the monastery they had passed on their way to the Qila Sanctuary. Pasang Dolma, who was in ear shot of the Junk and Morrow, apologized profusely. He took responsibility for the hiring of the four other high-altitude Sherpa. He had had no problem finding regular porters and cooks, but high altitude Sherpa had been hard to obtain. With the war going on in Europe and foreigners unable to visit the Himalaya, most Sherpa had taken on other vocations to survive, the majority of them humping supplies through the passes between Nepal and Tibet. They could not walk away from these responsibilities. Therefore, Pasang Dolma had to take what he could get. Most of the hires were of the best quality, he said, but four of them came without any reference but their own. He was not even sure they were Sherpa. They may have been of another Nepalese race. Appeased by Pasang Dolma's apology, Morrow chose not to go on with his litany of complaints.

Morrow was still collecting numbers. He asked Junk for one. "Six." There was the problem with Icefall Craps. Junk had provided a number he must have known would make attaining the come out roll impossible: Six plus any number, of course, could not equal Morrow's come out roll of six. Junk apparently said through a laugh and iced-over beard, "I was just trying to be arbitrary in my choice. I was not trying to vex you." Despite the inevitable fact this roll could only be bad or neutral, Morrow grunted and moved to catch up with Fenimore to get a number to add to six. Fenimore led the team about thirty feet ahead.

Unfortunately for Morrow, the way became steeper in those thirty feet, so getting that second, useless number was an arduous task; Fenimore ahead of him was approaching an ice bridge, a structure which bulged up as it passed over a rather nasty, gaping bergschrund several hundred feet deep. The bulge made the whole thing look not unlike a pedestrian bridge one sees crossing over a pond in a city park, rising to a rounded peak in the center of its span. But this bridge had no flirting young lovers on it and no lily pads floating by. It was nothing but a white hill of ice hovering precariously over a slit in the earth.

According to my interview with Pasang Dolma years later, Morrow made it up to Fenimore but hiked behind him, not able to summon the energy to make it the extra three feet required to hike abreast with the man. No one could hear, but he was most certainly asking for a number from Fenimore when the bridge, possibly compromised by the expedition crossing over it the day before, collapsed. Fenimore dropped so quickly away from the world of the living that he did not have time to scream. He was simply there and then he was not.

The only evidence that some structure had been there was Morrow. He had been spared from a fall because he had been climbing *behind* Fenimore by mere feet, and also because his axe, tied to his belt, had become lodged in the ice. But he was not yet out of the woods. The terrain upon which he now depended was loose. At any moment, he could begin sliding to the edge and then take the fast journey downward to join Fenimore, and then, shortly afterwards, God. Junk and Pasang Dolma rushed forward as quickly as their physical exhaustion would let them, but were also careful not to put themselves into a perilous situation. They stopped short of the edge. Junk stood a healthy fifteen feet back, unraveled the rope from over his shoulder and tied one end around his waist. He threw the other end to Pasang Dolma and then lay flat on his belly, digging his crampons and axe into the ice. Pasang Dolma wrapped the other end of the rope around his own waist until there was little slack.

He moved slowly to the edge of the deep, echoing schrund. Removing his backpack and mitts, Pasang Dolma sidestepped down the edge of the schrund until the angle became too great for him to proceed. There he positioned himself roughly one yard above and to the side of Morrow. He rested his right hip against the ice and planted his crampons into the ice, one boot placed several feet in front of the other. The American below him was not moving, possibly in shock. The fall had landed him in such a position his back was to the ice cliff, his front facing out over the chasm. An unpleasant vista to be certain. His trousers, attached to the ice axe, were riding up his undercarriage, supporting all of his weight. He was moaning now – a low, sad keening - and he was refusing to put out his arm despite Pasang Dolma's firm commands he do so. The Sherpa did not ask for long. He took a calculated risk, bending his knees and back, moving his arms to full extension and swiping aggressively at Morrow's jacket. His left hand found purchase and began to pull. Morrow screamed and flailed his legs. By a stroke of luck, one of Morrow's crampons made a fruitful dig into the ice and he was able to rise several feet. With that, Pasang Dolma was able to grab the man with both hands and lift him up. Junk pulled on the rope while the other two men half fell and half stumbled backwards up the edge of the schrund. When they were up, all three fell into the snow and gasped for air.

Most of the team had caught up by now. They gathered around Morrow who remained on the ground for quite some time, crying. It was easily five minutes before his first word came, and when it came, it was garbled by chattering teeth and frozen lips.

"Craps."

Their route was destroyed. The bergschrund was capacious, spanning the entire width of the glacier. Without that ice bridge, they would have to trek a half mile to the west in order to get to the other side. Climbing back down was not a better option; they were only five hundred vertical feet from Camp One and forty-five hundred from Base Camp. So they would press on, around the schrund and then up.

Morrow had gone quite barmy. He babbled, producing words that did not go together at all. "Take me to the warm crevasse! It's time to be the troglodyte we all were! But no hieroglyphs or she'll bleed." He went on with these half-cackled ramblings while River Leaf and Zeigler helped him up. "The man was still shaking and looking around confused," Zeigler wrote in his journal that night. "I couldn't understand most of what he said because he was mumbling and chuckling madly. I would pick up the occasional word. 'Forget' came up a lot, as did 'warm.' But the rest sure seemed like gibberish to me." Junk walked up and slapped Morrow. He told him he was sorry for the terrible experience he just went through. Junk said he even felt a little responsible because Morrow would not have been in that spot had not Junk invited him on the expedition and suggested the craps game. But damn it, Morrow would have to pull himself together. They could not walk him around the schrund and then up to Camp One. He would have to walk himself. When River Leaf and Zeigler let go of his arms, Morrow stayed upright, albeit still shaking and going on at the mouth. The team could proceed.

The thought of resuming must have been devastating for everyone given they had just lost a colleague. None could see the body of Fenimore. Some of the Sherpa hiked over to parts of the crevasse edge that were sharp enough to offer a view straight down, but still they could not see their fallen friend. There was no light down there, and the scarce light that did make it down suggested the whole schrund curved as it descended. The bottom was likely somewhere right under them. There would be no retrieval of the body. As usually happens on the ascent of a mountain, the body would remain where it had fallen.

They hiked westward around the crevasse. The east had been a shorter route, but also uneven and blocked by seracs. The west was practically a snow field, albeit a long one. They hiked single file, at least ten yards down from the crevasse that had taken Fenimore. The team's greatest mind – the one who was uncanny with routes and maps – had given way to some kind of insanity. Whether it was temporary or permanent, no one knew. Morrow himself would have been the most qualified to figure that out. The best they could do was help him along and hope he would recover with food and rest. River Leaf guided him. He still talked under his breath, but he did say some occasionally lucid if rather odd things. One specifically had to do with a need for "the medicinal qualities of warmth." He pleaded with the River Leaf to steer him towards warmth. She reassured him a warm tent would comfort him for a short while at Camp One. He became frustrated and belligerent. "That will not suffice for my needs!" No one bothered trying to understand him. He would just have to move with the team, and perhaps remain at Base Camp when they descended at the end of the day.

They reached Camp One at noon with the intention of staying for only one single hour and then climbing down. Morrow made a bee line for his tent while the rest of the team ate a small lunch, drank tea, and smoked. The ritual of smoking, so common on climbing expeditions, was especially precious for the team that afternoon. All of them were wrestling with the second death of the climb. The odds of survival on this journey were not good, and the rate of expiration so far only served to reinforce that truth.

After their needs were sated, the team broke apart and focused on individual strategies for calming nerves. Cole nursed his frostbitten cheek and read books on physics. Although he did keep a journal, most of his writings were meditations on particle physics. Small particles revolving around larger ones, trying to make connections. It did not matter that his brain was getting softer with each increase in elevation; the mere attempt to understand the words brought someone like him comfort. McGee and Zeigler played guts poker for no money. The four surly high altitude Sherpa retired to their tents, not to be seen until it was time to go back down. The remaining Sherpa checked the camp for damages that may have occurred the night before..

Pasang Dolma and Junk soothed themselves in a manner common to those of exceptional character: They planned. They had hoped Fenimore and Cole would comprise a second team to the summit should their own attempt fail. The third team was to be comprised of Morrow and Zeigler. Pasang Dolma suggested River Leaf could make a go for the top in Fenimore's stead, may he rest in peace. Junk chafed at this suggestion, becoming almost outraged. Junk would not say as much, but the others could tell that his respect for River Leaf was becoming greater by the day. It was beginning to border on fawning. He would bring her tea and help her put on her backpack. He asked for her opinion about the weather and the route ahead. Her responses were often shrugs. But when she did answer, she was almost always right. "If I am not mistaken" Cole wrote in his journal, "our fearless leader has become smitten with the Indian squaw!" Clearly, Junk was not going to risk River Leaf any more than he had to. They would have to consolidate down to two teams for the final attack, with Pasang Dolma and Junk comprising the first team, and Cole and Zeigler comprising the second.

Pasang Dolma and Junk also reviewed several details of Hoover's climb from two years earlier. After one more day of acclimating on the Rakhiot Glacier, they would take a hard left at some hot pools of sulfurous water that bubbled only one hundred feet above their current location, and begin looping around the Icy Bellows, following its eastern lip. Hoover's notes suggested the lip was not perfectly smooth. It had several steps, some of them twenty feet high and technically challenging. Hoover had lost three men on the lip, one to a loose cornice, one to the wind, and another who had frozen to death. That being said, the eastern lip was tea and crumpets compared to the western lip, so they would endure without complaint.

The eastern lip would then give way to the Eastern Ridge, the final path to the summit. They had seen no sign of the fastidious demon Hoyt since arriving at the Qila Sanctuary. If he was there, then he had taken the southern route. When Junk and his team reached the Eastern Ridge, provided the weather was clear, that would be the time when their rival's fate would become clear. They would know whether Hoyt was ahead of them or behind them. It would be at the ridge that the south would become visible and Junk would see enemy camps adorned with prayer flags.

"Of course! The hot pools!"

The voice was Morrow's. It burst forth from inside his tent.

He rushed out, hopping on one foot at a time as he pulled on his boots in a mad rush. He grabbed River Leaf's arm, causing her to drop the pipe she was smoking, and told her to come with him. She broke free, clearly displeased with Morrow's use of physical force. The old, reasonable Morrow came through. Calmly, he said to her, "Please."

Morrow walked River Leaf and Cole – the latter having asserted himself into the small party despite Morrow's complaints - up the mountain, away from Camp One. They were ascending to the edge of the Icy Bellows. Without their usual equipment, they moved rapidly. Ahead of them, snow blew every which way, fueled by the wind torrent of the Bellows.

The three struggled against thin oxygen, but that handicap did not stop Morrow from talking without end. Cole, an indefatigable documentarian, later recorded Morrow's academic-but-unhinged discourse:

"In an ideal world, the memory of a trauma would be forgotten soon after the offending event. But of course, a trauma is defined by its being unforgettable. If the traumatic memory remains in consciousness, to be mulled over eternally, the subject will go insane. No, the best one can hope for with trauma is containment, and in the Science of the Mind, the term for containment is 'repression.'

"What is repression? Good question, River Leaf [she had not asked]. Herr Freud described everything in terms of the most advanced technology of his time, which happened to be hydraulics. He saw the psychological life of the human as a cadre of different forces asserting pressure on one another; the Superego on the Ego, the Id on the Ego, the Conscious on the Unconscious, etcetera. Repression is merely the Ego actively keeping certain fears and unacceptable desires in the Unconscious. Certainly, repression brings about side effects such as neurotic behaviors, but such side effects are certainly better than facing the horror of reality, despite what the psychoanalytic community claims."

Being an academic himself, Cole was able to follow up to a point, although his background was in the hard sciences and so some of Morrow's words seemed alien and silly to him. Morrow continued:

"The problem is, how does one intentionally repress a memory? That is the question I have been addressing for the past decade. My solution? I call it 'repression through regression!' The subject simply simulates life in the womb for several minutes and when he emerges, he is right again. The irony and the difficulty of this approach is that memory of the womb has itself been repressed by the trauma following shortly thereafter: Birth. None of us remembers birth because it was a trauma we could not stand to carry around with us. Sadly, memory of the womb went with it. So, in the process of simulating the womb, we are revisiting that most wonderful of lost memories and in so doing we displace, or more appropriately, repress, the new trauma.

"I am the subject today. I was scarred to the core by watching Fenimore die and then almost dying myself. If I do not treat the mental scar soon, it will become infected. How will I simulate the womb? Well, I will use the gift provided to me by the mountain."

Morrow stopped at the lip of the Icy Bellows as its terrible wind hit him like one thousand fists. He shielded himself as best he could, but he had to lean almost completely forward, as if lying on a bed of air, so as not to be blown back down the incline he had just ascended. River Leaf and Cole had to do the same. In front of them, through squinted eyes, they saw the Icy Bellows for the first time. It was an enormous bowl, a wasteland. It was so enormous a large town could fit in it; a town with no laws other than those enforced by the cruel, unfeeling constables Cold and Despair.

And beyond the Icy Bellows they saw – and heard - the summit. Or at least they saw the grey cloud covering the summit.

"Stop straining to look into the distance" Morrow yelled over the din. "Look at your feet!" There stood the hot springs Junk had mentioned earlier. Cole counted six of them, each a different size and shape. Steam rose from them and then scattered chaotically, caught up in the Bellows' wind currents. Scientists today believe the volcanic activity under Fumu's cone must escape through vents other than those near the summit. Some of those vents lead to aquifers before reaching the surface. The result is steaming holes full of hot water, cooled somewhat by exposure to the frigid air.

"The womb" Morrow exclaimed. He did not waste any more time. Within moments, he had stripped down to nothing despite the frigid air and risk of instant frostbite. A reasonable man might have tested the water with a toe or at least walked in slowly. Morrow dove in. Moments later his head surfaced. A smile spanned his face. "It is lovely! Come in and experience the Majesty of your origins!" River Leaf pleaded with Morrow to get out. They were cold and Junk was waiting for them. They needed to climb back down to the team and start the final descent to Base Camp. Morrow was unreachable in his joy.

"I am being renewed!" he said through tears of joy. "Each muscle is like dough. Each nerve tingles with pleasure. My needs completely fulfilled by the warmth around me. There are no past pains because there is no past. This is the beginning."

Cole spoke up. If Morrow did not get out immediately, he and River Leaf were going to abandon him. River Leaf gathered Morrow's clothing and held it in a bundle, awaiting his return to Reason and emergence from the pool.

Eyes closed, Morrow remained motionless, head bobbing above steaming bubbles, smile etched permanently onto his face. Occasionally he would submerge his head. With the sluggishness of a minute hand, he turned his head to them and opened his eyes. "You see," he said with an air of complete understanding and confidence. "Doctor Freud was right. It all boils down to hydraulics."

One moment later, with a thunderous roar, one of the other pools burst heavenwards in a geyser eighty feet high. Then another. Morrow's smile faded, eyes wide. Another geyser. He looked around for a foothold or handhold. Another geyser. River Leaf dropped the clothing and came forward as the bubbles in Morrow's pool became more chaotic. Another geyser. Morrow cried and flapped his hands helplessly. Cole had had the good sense to bring a rope even though they had brought no other climbing equipment. He threw one end to Morrow who quickly tied it around his waist so it protruded out from his belly button.

It was too late. "The sound was deafening" Cole wrote.

"The mountain ejected Morrow. He shot into the air along with millions of gallons of water. The other end of the rope pulled free from me. Had I not been wearing gloves, it would have damaged my hands beyond repair. Morrow's scream rose into the air, changing pitch due to the Doppler Effect. With that, the geyser ended as quickly as it had begun. The wind of the Bellows carried Morrow and the spray at least twenty feet leeward. He came down with a sickening thud and slid, lifeless, down the glacier along with a cataract of hot water and the sulfurous stench of the Earth's innards."

River Leaf and Cole half-walked, half-ran down the glacier to Morrow. They must have known he was dead before they reached him as the body was "motionless and impossibly bent." Upon reaching Morrow, they verified he was deceased and glumly pulled his corpse down the route upon which they had ascended, the terrain under their feet now slippery with fresh ice.

The ice was too hard and thick to permit burial so the team simply took a blanket from Morrow's pack and wrapped him in it. No one wept. They were too tired and perhaps too shocked to weep. Junk took out a pack of playing cards and placed it inside the blanket along with a copy of William James' *The Principles of Psychology* and a naked photo of Mimi Eisenhower found in Morrow's sleeping bag. Zeigler, River Leaf, and Pasang Dolma took turns praying over the body.

Three deaths and not yet permanently situated at Camp One. If this mortality rate kept up then the summit would be out of their grasp. Low on men, out of funds, and dangerously short on morale, Junk began to waver for the first time since the expedition began. Junk was also wracked with guilt. It had been his decision not to use ropes on the glacier, a decision that had doomed Fenimore. Had he been tied to other men, the young Fenimore would have been with them now. Morrow's death had then been a direct result of Fenimore's. In Junk's opinion, all responsibility for the horrid events of the day fell to him and him alone. Now he spoke to the team about the possibility of retreat.

This must have surprised everyone. Junk - the Invincible, the Conqueror of Boston, the Viscount of the Long Shot - was talking about playing it safe and avoiding defeat. River Leaf said nothing. Pasang Dolma said he was at Junk's disposal and would do whatever Junk wanted. Cole and Zeigler both suggested they at least try for the Eastern Ridge before considering retreat. McGee said nothing, but was likely torn. He had lost everything to make this happen, so having a go at the top against the odds made perfect sense. But then again, all indications suggest he was also terribly scared. The acrophobia must have plagued him every waking moment.

Cole wrote, "I mentioned to Junk that Hoyt was probably giving up too. The other side of the mountain was almost certainly experiencing bad weather due to the monsoon and that would make Hoyt's ascent even more challenging. All it took was me mentioning Hoyt's name and Junk's whole demeanor changed. 'Who said anything about retreat?' he asked, clearly offended. 'We are going up, you girls!' So in the end, it was Junk himself who made the argument to press on."

After one more descent to Base Camp, the team climbed the Rakhiot Glacier for the last time. They shed several Sherpa at Camp One, leaving only fifteen. They turned eastward at the hot pools and began to make their way up the lip of the Icy Bellows.

The four dyspeptic Sherpa mumbled their way toward Camp Two. Pasang Dolma was fearless and strong, carrying more than his share of equipment, helping in the setup of camp and the preparation of meals, and making climbing recommendations to Junk when called upon. Zeigler proved a solid replacement for Morrow when it came to knowledge of the terrain and the moves of previous expeditions up the northern route. Cole was consistent and trustworthy in his climbing expertise, although his frostbite problems seemed to be more widespread now. His toes had become a problem. Perhaps the poor sot had bad circulation. Whatever the reason, he was in pain. But being the brave, reliable gentleman he was, he never let the pain get in the way of his impeccable climbing technique. Upon reaching the Bellows, McGee now fought agoraphobia in addition to acrophobia. The dizzying open spaces, the lack of enclosure on any side, made him close his eyes as he walked.

River Leaf moved forward without a misstep, without complaint, and without a moment's hesitation. Junk hiked behind her much of the time now. Her figure must have blocked Junk's view of the summit at times.

But if her body did obstruct the view, he apparently did not mind for he never asked her to move.

Interlude: Winter, 1920

Chhiri Tendi was ten years old when he saw the colossus that was his father begin to crumble. The harvest had been a good one for the village of Thame, as it had been across the entire Khumbu region. Families gathered and celebrated in each other's homes, drinking, dancing, and making boasts. Chhiri Tendi and his parents were attending one such occasion at the home of their neighbor. It was late. Possibly after midnight. No one owned a timekeeping piece and no one particularly cared how late it was.

Chhiri Tendi's mother, Pasang Lhamu, had been a little woman, no more than four and one half feet tall. Her face was a sea of wrinkles, troughs and crests summoned by life's hard weather. The old visage seemed to pour into her toothless mouth and disappear. She said almost nothing and took in everything. The croaked words that did come forth were crafted to exact the most damage. Tonight she did not say a thing. She nodded her head politely and tapped her fingers on her knee as her lady friends conversed.

Chhiri Tendi's father was Phurbu Tawa. Completely devoid of any credentials or experience, Phurbu Tawa had become the unspoken viceroy of the village due exclusively to his charm, quick intellect, and imposing size. A porter by trade, the villagers turned to him to settle land disputes, arrange marriages for their children, and consult on crop and livestock trades. He stood almost six foot tall, a height unheard of among the Sherpa people. Wrinkled to the same extent as his wife, when the two stood next to each other, their faces were two halves of a split open dried fruit. Shoulders fanned out from Phurbu Tawa's beefy neck like the high ridges of Kanchenjunga. When his mouth opened, which it did regardless of the presence of others, his voice projected far and wide. Simply put, he met all requirements for leadership. No one knew this more than Chhiri Tendi. A rambunctious lad to be sure, his clever tongue and mischievous larks stopped when his father was present, replaced almost at once with humility and respect.

As the party wore on that night, Phurbu Tawa went from dancing and slapping unsuspecting women's rumps to telling a scandalous tale of a recent journey to Kathmandu. Those still sober enough to listen did so. Portions of the tale drew laughs from the crowd of friends while others inspired gasps. Chhiri Tendi sat at his father's side, listening intently even though he did not understand every unseemly detail. The story's contents were irrelevant. Chhiri Tendi was delighted just to watch his father tell a tale.

It was during the middle of this story that a group of strangers, unexpected and uninvited, walked into the celebration. There were nine of them in all. Their snow-covered military boots clomped hard against the wooden floors. They wore strange clothing that appeared to consist of odds and ends from several different nations' uniforms. One wore the boots of a British soldier. Another wore the medals of a Turkish soldier. Another the helmet of Greeks. Chhiri Tendi remembers thinking, even as a child that their ill-gotten attire may have been poached from corpses.' The only consistent part of their garb was a dead king cobra around each man's neck, stuffed with some kind of material that allowed the animal's husk to be used like an ascot or muffler. One man stood in front while eight others stood behind shoulder to shoulder.

The revelers ceased discussion just as the leader of the unwelcomed fellows began to speak in Nepali. "We are the Squad of Schismatic Gurkhas..." he proclaimed. He turned to look at one of the men behind him who looked back disapprovingly. "...until we come up with a better name." The leader walked forward, each step slower than the last. The man studied all of the faces in the silent room. "We have come to this village of Sherpa people because we are starting a revolution across Nepal and we want to recruit you. For too long, the British Crown has held Nepal in its pale talons. They have controlled our government. They have sent us to fight in their name across Asia and Europe. And what do we get in return? Protection? We do not need their protection. We are not children. We are the Kingdom of Nepal, and we are prepared to draw blood from the British and watch their innards spill out, steaming in the cold Khumbu air. Now I know the Sherpa are lazy, unreliable, untrustworthy drunkards unlike the Gurkha people, but we are from the same country and so we are obliged to ask for your participation. Also let me add: If you are not with us…" the nine men pulled out their crooked *kukri* swords, "…then you are against us."

A collective, audible inhalation filled the room, followed by silence. Chhiri Tendi remembers a tension in the room so great he felt the air itself would snap. The only people who did not seem terrified were Pasang Lhamu and Phurbu Tawa, his mother and father. Pasang Lhamu scowled at the strangers and whispered something under her breath, her toothless mouth moving almost imperceptibly. Phurbu Tawa rose from his seat which happened to be only feet from the man who threatened the group.

"My name is Phurbu Tawa. Do you have a name as well."

"It is none of your business unless you agree to join us."

"I see. Well let me ask you this, and please understand that although this is my question only, I am sure all of my fellow untrustworthy drunkards would like to know. I have done my share of walking across the Kingdom so I know a few things about its people and places. And from what I know, the Gurkha people are renowned for their bravery in war. For their unwillingness to ever turn away from adversity. For their vicious skills in combat. Most importantly, they are known for their dedication. For over one hundred years, your people have been the ones Nepal and England have turned to for help, and you have never let them down. Ever."

"That is not a question." retorted the stranger.

"My apologies. Here is the question. If the Gurkhas are such a wonderful people, trusted by everyone to do their job, then is it not the nine of you traitorous donkeys who are the untrustworthy ones?"

The stranger did not move. His expression did not change. He simply stared at Phurbu Tawa. "I have served England for over ten years, and in the past four I have done more for them than you can possibly imagine. I have marched across the deserts of Iraq, protecting the oil fields of Basra from the dreaded Turks, flies on my face and broken, weeping blisters on my feet. I have cut the throats of men, women, and children in the name of the Crown. The men who stand behind me fought on the beaches of Gallipoli, a place you have probably never heard of but they will never forget. They watched as their fellow Gurkhas were cut down by machine gun fire and they fought back when all hope was lost. So do not dare say we are untrustworthy."

Phurbu Tawa had a dreadful habit of cleaning out his nose with his finger. He had begun doing it again while the Gurkha spoke. The Gurkha was not deterred nor distracted by this behavior. He continued.

"Then, unlike our Gurkha brothers who were not smart enough to do so, we began to question the British army. Recommendations for our decoration from British field officers were written in pencil and therefore dismissed as 'unofficial.' We also found it is a rule that no Gurkha can ever be promoted to officer. Correspondences between British soldiers about our battalions always referred to us as "the little fellows." Little! Again like we were children. What is dedication when it is to an aggressor? I'll tell you what it is. It is foolishness. All of Nepal, not just the Gurkhas, deserves liberation from these white oppressors. Now I will try to ignore your last comment, Phurbu Tawa, the one about us being 'traitorous donkeys' and ask again, are you and your neighbors with us or are you against us? If you are with us, you will provide us with your village's young, healthy men." The man momentarily glanced at Phurbu Tawa' son, Chhiri Tendi. "If you are against us, we will do damage tonight and come back in the future to do more. We will keep coming back until you acquiesce. So, what will it be?"

Phurbu Tawa was still cleaning out his nose with his index finger, in no rush to finish and answer this man. When he had finally succeeded in cleaning out the left nostril, he admired the contents for a moment and then wiped it on the stranger's medals.

"Your gripe with the British military seems like a legitimate one. The Gurkhas are people, just like them, deserving of respect, good treatment, and the chance at promotion. Nonetheless, you are going about things all wrong. You are choosing to solve the problem in a bloody manner, a strategy by which the Sherpa do not abide. You talk about spilling British blood and then you even threaten us! You are behaving like those German scoundrels who sometimes come to climb Kanchenjunga. Why would you threaten us so? There has been no animosity between Hindu and Buddhist in our country. No aggression between Sherpa and, well, anyone. There is no need for abuse if we are brothers. But you choose to come in here with the force of a truncheon."

Then Chhiri Tendi remembers his father touching the cobra around the stranger's neck. "Sorry. We might have helped you if you had asked with kindness and if your plan was to peacefully address the issue. Alas that is not the case. You chose instead to act like Nepalese cobras."

Finally the stranger moved, turning his head around to glance at his men. He nodded to them. Looking back at Phurbu Tawa, he said "First of all, let me thank you for giving us our name. I can't believe I did not think of it before. The Nepalese Cobras. How obvious. I feel silly. Second, let me inform you that you are going to die now."

The Gurkha thrust his kukri at Phurbu Tawa's chest, but the rascally Sherpa changed his stance only slightly thereby averting the blow. The

Gurkha's arm now extended, Phurbu Tawa grabbed and twisted, quickly forcing the unwelcomed guest to roll up with his arm behind him. Phurbu Tawa then dug his fingers in between the bones on the top of the Gurkha's hand, forcing him to drop the kukri. Phurbu Tawa had not even started using his left hand. He used it to grab the falling kukri and hold it to the Gurkhas back. Finally, Phurbu Tawa let go of the Gurkha's hand and pulled the snake's head around back and pulled. Knife in back and neck constrained, the Gurkha stopped moving. A gagging sound emanated from his mouth.

"Putting a snake around your neck was not a good uniform decision" Phurbu Tawa jested quite casually. "Did you also consider wearing a codpiece full of gunpowder?" The eight other "Nepalese Cobras" edged forward. "Don't come any closer or I put this sword through him! I know Gurkhas are trained in hand to hand combat, but I too have learned how to fight, passing through a countryside teeming with dacoits each time I return from porting. The same goes for many of my friends in attendance. Tonight you chose to threaten the wrong people. Now walk and do not return or so help me, I will injure you so terribly that you will think your great tortoise god lumbered away and the Earth dropped into infinite darkness."

Phurbu Tawa let go of the cobra and the gagging sound ceased. The lead stranger massaged his neck as if that would cure the pain ringing it. He began to walk away from Phurbu Tawa and toward his fellow "soldiers," a look of shame on his face.

"Your wife. Your child." The stranger uttered in a hoarse voice.

"What did you say?"

The stranger looked back and pointed at the two people of which he spoke. "Your wife. Your child. I have remembered their faces. We will return and we will kill them in the night."

The threat caused Phurbu Tawa to explode. Yelling, he burst forward, closing the distance between himself and the stranger in less than candlelight takes to be blown out. The stranger turned toward the yell just in time for the crooked sword to enter his belly. He did not scream as much as expel all of the air in his lungs in a voiced manner. The expelling of air was followed by blood trickling down his chin, slowly at first, then in a swollen river. Chhiri Tendi remembers that although large amounts of blood came from the man's mouth, almost none exited the hole in his stomach which still sheathed the kukri. The stranger dropped to the floor, made some unpleasant gurgling noises, kicked his leg several times, and then ceased to move.

A few cries came from the women in the room, but after that a dreadful silence fell again. Phurbu Tawa looked down at the body, mouth agape, eyebrows raised high. This was not a look the others had seen on his face before. He did not wear it well.

The other eight Gurkhas looked around the room at the now standing crowd. The one on the far left walked forward and pointed his kukri at Phurbu Tawa. "This is not over. We can wait decades for revenge!" he hissed. The remaining Cobras turned on their heels and marched out into the frigid night. Snow blew in as they exited. The last man in the line got his cobra caught in the door on the way out. Robbing the cobras of their dramatic egress, the man opened the door again to pull the snake free.

The Sherpa all looked down at the dead man and the growing pool of blood. This type of violence was unusual for them. They were accustomed to the occasional row between inebriated neighbors fighting over women, but those fights usually ended with hugs and slaps on the back. Tonight was different. The owners of the home rushed forward after a few moments to clean up the body and prepare it for funeral. The rest of the partygoers mumbled to one another and began to leave. Phurbu Tawa was without words. How could this have happened? His life had been about peace.

Phurbu Tawa was a changed man after the episode. He drank to excess. He did not work as often, forcing Chhiri Tendi to begin porting at an early age. Sometimes at night, when Chhiri Tendi would toss and turn awaiting sleep's gentle kiss on the forehead, he would hear his father crying in the dark. His mother would scold his father, telling him to be a man, to stop weeping, to go to sleep. "What kind of man am I?" Phurbu Tawa would respond. "I've killed a person in cold blood! I can be a man if I stop crying, but a terrible man. Why stop?"

Shortly thereafter, in rapid succession, both of Chhiri Tendi's parents died. With his mother it was due to natural causes. She was milking a yak and fell over dead. Chhiri Tendi's heart fell from a great height at the loss. His father died four months later. Walking home from a neighbor's after a bout of drinking, he was attacked in the night. He had a knife wound in his gut. Around his neck was a dead, stuffed cobra. A note was found inside his shirt. I questioned Chhiri Tendi's translation of the note from the original Nepalese because it is a doltish sentiment conveying little sense, but Chhiri Tendi claims the translation is perfect: "The Nepalese Cobras *are* fear." Likely, the authors meant to suggest they were the personification of terror and caused fear, not that they were the personification of fear. Whatever the point, the message was left on Chhiri Tendi's father.

Chhiri Tendi wanted nothing more than to exact brutal revenge for the murder of his father, but he also knew that in the exacting, he would become the thing he, his father, and his people reviled. Perhaps some day he could serve justice to these thick-witted revolutionaries. That "some day" would likely be when the Cobras returned to kill him. Yes, he would avenge his father at that time, but he would be sure not to draw blood in the process.

Chapter Twelve: A Team Divided

Hoyt climbed step by labored step up the awful scree. He kept looking back at his fellow climbers; one of them would falter soon. The weather was unbearable. Wind and snow pelted the team like enemy fire. The annual monsoon was not yet finished with its unbridled abuse of Asia, and Hoyt's team was feeling the extent of it now on the southern side of Fumu, even if the northern side remained in full, glorious sunlight. It had been overcast but otherwise pleasant when they set out from Base Camp. Then after three hours on the mountain the sky opened up and loosed its wrath.

The pairing of weather and terrain was dreadful. The scree was notorious for its "giving" character, offering up boulders as gifts for the inattentive. Most individuals who brave the scree receive these gifts in a manner fatal; some decapitated, others taken for a ride back down to Base Camp. Now with the visibility at nearly zero, rocks could be heard coming, but could not be seen until they were immediately in front of the victim. "We hear the giant 'bang bang' of a boulder rolling down the hill," wrote Hoyt. "The sound gets louder and louder, but we see nothing. Then it materializes in front of us, the size of a damned elephant. It goes barreling past us and disappears, back into the whiteness. Then it happens again a minute or so later, and then again. Some of them are close enough to touch. Not easy to keep calm given the situation." The team had even decided not to tie off to one another. God forbid a boulder should catch a rope and pull several men down instead of one. Hoyt felt if they made it to the planned location of Camp One at the top of the scree without losing a man and turning tail, it would be a bloody miracle.

One thing was certain. As planned, acclimatization would indeed not involve the scree. Once they were up, they would stay up until they were done with their expedition. The falling rocks and lack of footholds made climbing too risky. Chhiri Tendi had agreed with this plan, as had the other more experienced climbers on his expedition, Drake, Wilde, and Thornton. They would set up Camp One at the top of the scree and begin acclimatization there.

And still more rocks came rolling down the scree.

Hoyt climbed in front, likely still smarting from the loss of a brother and separation from his wife, neither of which he had time to ponder at this moment. He had also stopped writing about these topics in his journal. By the time he was ascending Fumu, his tone was shifting between gentle and gruff; cracks emanating warmth were appearing in his cold, hard surface. He sometimes wrote sympathetic words about those around him – even feeling sorry for Chatham after the violence in the cave, and then swinging back to vitriol condemning Chatham: "He is as unpleasant as sand in the teeth and his handiwork with falsehoods is almost mesmerizing. If lies could be considered a form of wordplay, then Chatham is the Shakespeare of our time." He wrote kind words about the young climbers, Thornton and Ferguson, lauding them for reliability far exceeding their ages. He would then say they were mere children who knew nothing but acted as if they owned the world. Hoyt still had no good words to say about Yuudai. And in addition to Yuudai, there was yet another topic still capable of bringing about the old Hoyt ire fully formed and unrepentant: "I dreamt last night I found Junk alive but lying on the mountain," Hoyt wrote. "I started kicking him repeatedly and he did not try to get up or fight back. I simply delighted in kicking him like a child delights in playing with a scab. But with every kick, I felt the pain. And I continued to kick anyway." In his writings, Hoyt was certain Junk was making better progress due to optimal weather conditions and an easier route. It was September first, the same day Junk was beginning his first ascent up the Rakhiot Glacier. The two men were actually in a tie.

More rocks came rolling down the scree.

Chatham was not deterred by the weather, nor by his third-degree burns, nor by the contusions on his head. He continued to prattle on to those near him about potentially made-up exploits in exotic destinations. This time it was a narrow escape from premature burial in the Great Pyramid of Khufu. "He says his escape came down to teeth," Thornton wrote in his notes. Chatham claimed he was rescued by his top left incisor, which had come out during an accident opening a hidden sarcophagus in the lower chamber. When he saw the exit of the pyramid closing on them, likely due to tampering by angry locals, he allegedly had the clarity of mind to throw the tooth under the rock. The little space made by the tooth between the door and the bottom of the entrance was enough for them to jam a piece of their equipment in and lift the door. "I am quite confident that story never happened" Hoyt wrote. "The man's stories are mere flights of fancy. In addition, his climbing abilities are mediocre at best. He is too slow. In sum, Mr. Chatham has offered nothing to this endeavor, save the hot air he expels."

More rocks.

Yuudai climbed near the back with Chhiri Tendi. All of the American expedition members remained adversarial toward the quiet Japanese fellow. Wilde would berate him for taking too long to organize his pack before leaving camp, a crime that would have gone undetected had it been any other person. Both Wilde and Chatham bumped into him whenever they overtook him on the way up and also when they sauntered by him in camp. He was doing a smashing job of climbing and not getting in the way of others, so no one could find fault with him there. But no matter what he did, he remained the son of the man who had killed Hoyt's brother and a citizen of a nation at odds with the United States. William Hoyt was not of the school that believes camaraderie is essential to a climbing expedition. Only allegiance to the leader and skill were required. He did not participate in the overt animosity toward Yuudai, but based on his journal entries he clearly detested the man.

Possibly sensing he could do nothing to change the situation, Yuudai climbed, read books, smoked cigarettes, and said nothing. He preferred to stay near Chhiri Tendi and the other Sherpa because they held no grudge against him. To the Sherpa, Yuudai was just another member of the team. They were not necessarily friendly to him, but they were not cruel to him either.

Rocks rolled by them, too close for comfort.

Everyone was feeling the effects of the brutish weather. Wind gusts made a concerted effort to knock them down. Snow whipped sideways. Chhiri Tendi was already experiencing frostbite on the fingers of his left hand. Hoyt had a touch on his forehead and nose, and his amputated toe's stump stung him no end. It would be well after dinner by the time they made it up the scree, even though they had started the climb before sunrise.

An absolutely giant boulder was heard cracking free of its supporting earth and coming loose up ahead. It banged and rolled and banged again. It was coming closer. The dark outline of it was seen barreling toward them mere seconds before it arrived, easily twenty feet in diameter and moving at the speed of a freight train. The men did not have time to yell or to ponder their pending flatness. It was upon them.

And then just as suddenly as it had appeared, the boulder was compromised by a smaller (but certainly not small) boulder in its way. The big one cracked and turned west. One small remnant of it, the size of a musket, continued to move forward. It bounced at Wilde who reflexively ducked, resulting in the rock hitting Chatham square in the mouth. The man was immediately taken off of his feet. He rolled down the incline several yards and came to rest face down. He was moaning. When turned over by Yuudai, he was all gums and blood. "So much for your heroic teeth" yelled Hoyt down to him. Wilde laughed out loud. Soon more of the Americans were laughing out of pure *schadenfreude*. Ferguson. Drake. Even Chatham himself, possibly in shock, began to laugh. "I was not laughing" Hoyt wrote. "I did not mean it as a joke. I am not what one might call 'funny.'" He had also surrounded himself with an expedition of individuals who were either just as nasty as him or had taken on his nastiness due to proximity to him. The usual camaraderie one finds in an expedition was not present here. Not at all. The laughter continued in the dead whiteness. Yuudai and the Sherpa looked on.

Then the laughter was interrupted by a noise coming from higher up the mountain. This was a new sound. It was not an eruption at the top of the mountain. Nor was it another boulder bouncing its way toward them. It was indeed coming toward them, and it was massive, but the sound lacked the intermittent banging of a rolling rock. This sound had a loud, consistent, grumbling quality to it. Fumu, nastier and more unstable than these men, was clearly about to make a joke of her own.

Out of the blizzard, a giant slab of the ice and snow from higher up the mountain – easily the size and shape of Big Ben moving roof-first - came sliding toward them, digging deep into the scree as it went. It was nothing short of a glacier moving at high speed. Had it not been caked with debris picked up from the scree, they would have never seen it coming until it was right on top of them. They ran laterally to avoid its path, some men going left, others going right. The monstrosity barreled by them, improbably high and long, all the while kicking up stones and emitting a deafening din.

And then it was gone. Hoyt and his team were fortunate because the slab reached the bottom of the scree without hitting Base Camp (nor did it hit Junk's camp for that matter). It also did not hit any climbers despite its girth and speed. But now some of the team stood on one side of a freshly cut deformation – a valley running down the fall line of the mountain - and the others stood across the new valley from them. Neither group could see the fellows across from them because of the snow. Yells could not be heard properly. The valley was not deep and the walls were not terribly steep, but the freshly-cut stones comprising it appeared full of wanderlust; ready to give way the moment a boot touched them. Hoyt would be damned if he would let a soul cross the valley. "Follow the cut upward!" Hoyt yelled, hoping to be heard.

Apparently, there was another unfortunate effect of the landslide: Thornton, the young linguist, deft climber, and exceptional documenter of the expedition thus far, was temporarily blinded. Rocks kicked up by the passing ice had hit him in the face. The man had now covered his eyes with one arm and was swinging the other arm in front of him making sure not to bump into anything. According to his writings, it was then that Hoyt realized Thornton was walking dangerously close to the fresh valley as he moved up the scree toward him. He responded to the crisis with his failsafe emotion: anger. This response was likely reasonable in his mind because he was potentially going to lose his first climber and he needed every able-bodied man in order to defeat this hill. He yelled as quickly as he could 'Damn it, Thornton, stay to the right!' "

These words caused Thornton to immediately turn toward, and fall into the freshly-cut valley. He rolled head over heels into the whiteness until he could not be seen at the bottom.

In his tent at the top of the scree that evening, Hoyt wrote:

Dearest Journal,

The day's events have taught me a cutting lesson about my nature. I care about myself more than anything else in my purview with the exception of God almighty. These people around me, from Drake to Chatham to the jap, all of them are but spheres orbiting the star that is me. When a meteor (in the form of, say, a stuck yak or a rolling boulder) sets them off the course I have dictated by gravity, I am enraged because they are not serving me as they should. What an unpleasant thing to be...an angry sun.

The cost of my self-centeredness came to a head today on the mountain. Thornton wandered blindly, moaning in pain from stinging dirt in his eyes. I yelled at him – quite angrily mind you - to stay to the right so he would not fall into the valley. We needed every climber we had. His hurt eyes may have been something we could remedy, but broken bones or death from a fall would make him unsalvageable as a climber. I told him to stay "to the right."

And there is the problem. My right was his left. I was aiming down the mountain and he was aiming up it. I did not have the capacity to take his perspective, to see the world from another point of view, to remove myself even momentarily from what the German intellectuals would call my own 'umwelt.' And now Thornton has a shattered pelvis and a broken arm and is being carried down the mountain by the four Sherpa we had on our side of the ice slide.

The team had several problems since the ice slab incident. Thornton was out. The weather would not relent. And the team had been divided, with one group having both radios. After Thornton and the Sherpa had left for Base Camp, the team on Hoyt's side of the valley consisted of Hoyt himself, Yuudai, and Chhiri Tendi. They would have to fend for themselves with two tents, ample climbing equipment, but only a few days' worth of food.

Hoyt had tried to make radio contact with the others immediately after the Sherpa had left with Thornton. He told the person on the other end his location and the planned location for setting up Camp One that night. Chhiri Tendi had walked up behind Hoyt holding the other radio at that moment. Close proximity did not require the antenna to be extended. Chhiri Tendi looked at Hoyt and then said into the mouthpiece, between deep breaths "What are you wearing?" Hoyt held back from hitting the inappropriately comical Sherpa. "I abstained from exploding. The mishap with Thornton was teaching me I had to change my ways somehow." Chhiri Tendi's opinion was that he probably deserved to be hit.

Hoyt, Chhiri Tendi, and Yuudai hiked up the scree, avoiding falling rocks as best they could. We can only assume the climb had now become harder psychologically because of all of the uncertainties that had been added to the equation. What if they did not find the other group? They would be stuck at the top of the scree with limited food until the weather abated. And once it did, if they could not see the other members of their expedition somewhere along the top of the scree, then they would need to give up on the climb and retreat to Base Camp or else risk succumbing to fatigue from hunger. "What's more, I am stuck with two members of the team who I dislike intensely. Even Chatham with his now ghoulish visage and interminable chatter would be better than this harlequin and this silent, malicious oriental. Regarding the latter, I am convinced he is going to cut my throat tonight because the rest of the Americans are gone. This is his chance to kill the leader of the enemy. He can do it in the night and then hide my body, lying to Chhiri Tendi about seeing me wander off into the darkness, mad with a mix of altitude and despair brought on by my team's fate and my brother's death. He can continue the lie when he sees my fellow expedition members again. And then when he returns to Japan, he can finally expose the truth and be welcomed as a hero." Hoyt's prediction turned out to be incorrect as they all slept through the night, their exhaustion a warm, feather bed.

By five in the morning when they awoke, the weather had not changed. The wind whipped outside of their tents and snow piled up. Waiting it out seemed to be the only choice and so that is what they did. "I am trapped here while Junk advances" Hoyt wrote. "Frustration builds in me by the second. He is no more than a grown urchin, unsuited for the glory of the mountains. The only positive aspect of my current predicament is that by slowing down our ascent, we counter the effects of altitude we had risked by delaying acclimatization. Other than that, I am in my own personal Hell."

Yuudai and Hoyt did not say anything to each other the entire time they were holed up above the scree. They remained in their own tents. Ever the vigilant Sherpa, Chhiri Tendi communicated with both of the other climbers, inquiring as to their physical and emotional health. "I knew my job" Chhiri Tendi said in my interview with him. "And it was not just to carry the customer's equipment. It was also to give advice. And I could give the best advice if I knew everything, from the team's physical ailments to the dreams they were having at night. If anything seemed even slightly off, I would recommend we get the fuck off the mountain."

There was nothing to do but sit in the tents and pass the time. The men read books, smoked, wrote, drank coffee, ate canned meats and chocolate, and shivered. When the next night came, sleep did not come with it. After all, they did not have a day of climbing under their belts. They tossed and turned and shivered through an evening of deafening wind and knowledge they were low on food. They could risk at most two more days before they would have to accept defeat and climb down.

Out of what was likely boredom, Chhiri Tendi made an unusually risky decision. Having more experience with these types of unpleasant situations, he felt better than Hoyt or Yuudai. He decided to venture out into the storm and look for the other members of the expedition. He would bring one of the radios with him. If he could find them, then they could all reunite and form a single Camp One. This would buy them all more time to wait out the storm and possibly continue the climb. Give me one day, he asked.

Chhiri Tendi struck out eastward along the top of the scree at approximately noon on September third, with the weather now even worse than it had been during the climb up. Hoyt and Yuudai remained in their individual tents, waiting for Chhiri Tendi to either return or radio them with news. Neither came. Night fell and they did not see or hear from the sardar.

Now Hoyt was convinced Chhiri Tendi was dead. In his frustration, and possibly due to the effects of altitude on logic, he also became convinced Yuudai had set into play all of the events that had transpired so far on the mountain. "The man could not have planned this better. We are alone now. Even Chhiri Tendi is gone. Now he is certainly going to drop the blade." On that third night above the scree, sleep did not arrive yet again for Hoyt. He tossed and fretted. Yuudai was going to murder him. And even if he was spared by some whim of God, the world he would live to see was an embarrassment. He had not even made it to Camp One and already the team was in disarray and the expedition in serious jeopardy. Did Hoyt really want to live through this? Did he want to experience a world in which Junk stood triumphant, soaking up the spotlight of history, while he wiped egg off his face in the shadows?

Yuudai entered Hoyt's tent at five in the morning. A delirious Hoyt jumped out of his sleeping bag, fully clothed to shield from the cold. He pulled off his scarf to expose his neck. "Take me!" he yelled at Yuudai. "It is over! Better death than defeat!" Yuudai looked on quizzically. When no death arrived, Hoyt composed himself and put his scarf back on. He asked Yuudai what he wanted. In broken English, Yuudai spoke. "No Chhiri Tendi. What to do, Mr. Hoyt?"

What to do indeed. He had dilly-dallied long enough. It had not been a complete day since Chhiri Tendi had left, but it had been long enough given the storm. The decision Hoyt had to make at this point was no decision at all. Mountain climbing at its core involves a certain amount of recklessness in the sense that you are doing something quite dangerous and *you do not need to be doing it.* But good mountain climbing requires Eros to counter Thanatos – a Rational Self to counter the Death Drive. This sensibility is usually innate. It is difficult to forge on the mountain; After all, if a climber does not know when to walk away from a climb, he does not live to *become* the reasonable climber. Hoyt was born with a sensibility that held fast in high pressure situations. This anchored his otherwise dangerous love of climbing in a bed of relative safety.

But apparently, all of that is rubbish, because Hoyt decided to continue the ascent. The snow was still coming down at an unholy clip and the wind had not let up. The Junk competition meant too damned much to Hoyt, and he was convinced if they simply struck out east as Chhiri Tendi had done, they would cross some evidence of the rest of the team. When the slab of ice had divided them, the others had been off to the east of the cut, so it made sense now above the origins of the ice, the other team's camp was likely only a hundred yards away or so.

Of course, if it was that easy, then what had happened to Chhiri Tendi?

Roughly ten minutes after leaving Hoyt and Yuudai, Chhiri Tendi had come across a wide trail of relatively fresh tracks in the snow. He checked his compass. The tracks were heading due west which was far astray from their planned route. Chhiri Tendi followed them for what seemed like an eternity. Darkness began to fall and his digits became like ice. His nose felt as if it was made of marble. When the darkness was complete he continued to struggle through the snow and wind. "I was convinced I had stumbled across the footprints of spirits whose job it was to lead me to the afterlife; because there was no way they were tracks of our team. They were too off course."

But it was in fact their tracks after all. Frostbitten and frightened, Chhiri Tendi came across the tents of the rest of the team at approximately 8pm on the evening of the third. Drake and Wilde welcomed him into their tent to get warm.

Drinking tea, wrapped in a blanket, Chhiri Tendi said nothing for a few minutes. Then he recalls inquiring about their circumstances.

The team openly admitted they were going to try for the summit regardless of Hoyt's presence. In a rare display of profanity, Wilde summed up their reasoning thusly: "Hoyt is an asshole. We all know this to be true. Why wait for him or search for him? He can climb down if he's lost. Any responsible man in reasonable health would do that. And we've busted our humps to get here. We are not going to turn around now!"

Chhiri Tendi was not supportive of this stance, so he changed the subject. "You are off course. Did you know that?"

"No, we didn't." Wilde said this while giving Drake a rather nasty look.

"That would be my fault" Drake responded. "You know I am a tinkerer. Well, I have completed work on a new invention that will help us with any technical sections of the mountain we may need to climb." Drake pulled something out of his sleeping bag. It was circular, about eighteen inches in diameter, one inch thick, and wrapped in rags. Removing the rags, Drake now held a black disk that seemed rather heavy. It had two handles opposite each other along its circumference and one small knob halfway between the handles. The middle of the disk contained some dials and what appeared to be an antenna. Drake continued. "I call it 'the magic rope.'"

Chhiri Tendi was confused and unimpressed. Why was this oversized dinner plate the reason for the party being off course? Drake did not help: "The magic rope is made of sixty concentric bands of reinforced titanium, one of the sturdiest and lightest metals known to man. Each band is connected to its neighboring band by fifty hair-thin but powerful springs. With a turn of this small knob, each band of the rope will slide upward from the closest outside band. This means that, at full extension, the magic rope becomes a forty-foot tall pipe." Now Chhiri Tendi was interested. Wilde had a look on his face like he had heard this ten times already. The wind screamed outside.

"So the climber holds onto the handles and is lifted up the difficult portion of the mountain?" Chhiri Tendi asked.

Drake responded "Precisely. And not only that, but I have added a small device in the middle detecting pressure in the air surrounding the outermost band. Using this, it can detect within a small margin of error whether it has reached the top of a ledge. Or at least, it can tell when it has reached a large enough space for a person to find purchase."

"But how can it stay balanced? You have a grown man forty feet up in the air holding onto a pole that is not planted into the ground below."

"Fair question. I have not solved that issue. People will have to hold the 'rope' at its base while someone is ascending. And then when the penultimate man has reached the ledge above, he and the others on the ledge can hold onto the rope and the last man can be pulled up by the retracting rope held by the people above!" Drake said this last part with his arms gesturing toward the device on his lap, like a magician's assistant pointing to the bouquet of flowers just taken out of what seemed like an empty hat.

"Let me tell you the first problem of three with that device" Wilde chimed in. "Even if it does work, *it is not mountain climbing.* It is taking an elevator at a department store. My wife can do it. We might as well have taken our spouses with us on this trip." Drake rolled his eyes.

"Secondly, it will not work. And thirdly, Mr. Drake took..."

"That's *Doctor* Drake thank you very much!" Drake retorted.

"Thirdly, Doctor Drake took apart all of our compasses in order to make this magic rope contraption work. He convinced the group that the benefit of this Mary Shelley monstrosity was greater than the cost of no compasses. He argued that the odds of us getting lost before we stumble across you, Hoyt, and Yuudai – who would still have compasses - were slim to none. So much for that."

Chhiri Tendi recalls, "Drake bowed his head and was silent."

The silence spread to the entire group and then Chhiri Tendi broke the tension. "We need to get in touch with Hoyt and Yuudai right away and let them know our situation. They'll want to find us." Chhiri Tendi took out the radio. It was an early model handie-talkie, standard United States army issue, turned on by extending the antenna. But that was a problem. Chhiri Tendi saw that the radio seemed to be missing its antenna.

"My fault again" Drake said sheepishly. "I needed the antenna too. I took it off the radio before the team became separated."

The dreams of a mountain climber are laced with panic. He will picture toast and jam in his kitchen far away, steam rising from a cup of tea, a kiss on the head from a yawning, awakening spouse - her somnambulant feet shuffling along the floor - and perhaps a pet licking his hand. The sun is shining outside. His newspaper shows a headline unreadable in the world of dreams. But as all headlines are, it is tragic. Man's aggression against Man. A border violated. The ire of a population unhinged. This is all it takes to make the dream change. Everything in the room succumbs to instant freezing. The dog's tongue is stuck like cold metal to his palm. Where his wife had kissed him now stings. The coffee no longer evaporates but instead cracks along with the mug. His toast and jam are now grey slabs of till. Fear sets in. Then, like the coffee, the entire scene cracks and the climber is awake in his frigid tent.

There was no wind outside when Hoyt and Yuudai got up on September fourth at six in the morning. Everything had died down. The temperature was colder than usual, as if Phaethon had again driven away with father Apollo's sun-chariot. But other than the temperature, the horrid weather had passed. They got dressed, ate a small breakfast, broke camp, and struck out eastward along the top of the scree.

Along the way, they saw the place where the mammoth chunk of ice had likely cut loose. It seemed to have broken off all the way up at the Eastern Ridge, thousands of feet up. Where the ridge met the sweeping snowfields at its base, there were drifts literally one hundred feet deep. A section of one of the drifts seems to have collapsed under its own weight and carried with it the super-compressed snow in its belly. So compressed was the snow that it had become ice. The rest of the snow drift fell several hundred feet down the mountain, but the ice had gone farther and faster, blasting away snow and earth as it came down. Even though snow had continued to fall in the blizzard for hours after the incident, the trail of damage it left was still evident.

The sun shone down, truly one of the treasures of the southern route. The temperature became much warmer. Visibility was endless. After only an hour of hiking perpendicular to the fall line, Hoyt and Yuudai came to a point in their route where they could see several miles ahead of them. It was clear from that vantage point they were not going to come across the rest of their team if they continued to move in that direction. Wherever the others were, it was not east. Hoyt told Yuudai they were going to continue ascending. The risk was likely obvious to both of them, but of course Hoyt was desperate and willing to face almost Certain Death. And chances are he did not lose sleep over putting Yuudai in harm's way. What's more, Yuudai did not seem to be the type to speak up. So up they went.

At the point where they stopped moving east and started climbing up again, they were almost perfectly aligned with their original route. Plans originally had them following the route as far as they could, up the snow fields to the base of the Eastern Ridge. Then they would turn west, crossing Rauff's Maw and continuing until they rose high enough to mount the Eastern Ridge. There the ridge would lead them to adventure's end at the summit. That plan would not change unless they ran out of food and fuel. "I hate to admit it," Hoyt wrote in his journal, "but I am gambling just like that manqué on the other side of the mountain. When it comes to Junk, *nomen est omen*."

The ascent up the snowfields was technically easy, but it was physically challenging because they were hungry and gasping for air. They had not acclimated yet, and they both suffered from splitting headaches and nausea. The slight cases of frostbite they had suffered in the storm were not causing them too much discomfort, as they had tended to those spots with hot water immediately upon arriving at their Camp One. Unburdened by a massive team, they arrived at the base of the cliff whose roof was the Northeast Ridge, and decided to down climb to Camp One that same day. Tomorrow, they would do the same thing again. And the day after that, they would return to the base of the Northeast Ridge and set up Camp Two. From there, on the morning of the sixth, they would set off for Rauff's Maw. They would be completely out of food and fuel by then. If they did not find the rest of their party at that point, they would have to make haste for Base Camp, or die trying.

The rest of the expedition decided to continue up the mountain even though they were far off course – too far west to leverage the easy passage of the snowfields. No, the route they would take was a snowfield harshly interrupted by a forty foot wall of granite. They would again have to forego acclimatization because such a technical climb could not safely be repeated again. The only good news was that if they succeeded in getting over that wall, they would be west of Rauff's Maw, and therefore able to skip it. This could potentially shave days off of the ascent.

With Hoyt absent, Wilde took charge and mandated a day of rest. If they could not acclimate again, he felt that holding their ground for a few more days was the next best thing. "Our numbers have dwindled too much. We cannot afford to lose a single man to altitude sickness," he said. They set up camp at the foot of the granite wall on the evening of September fourth and remained there for two days.

Little did the team know Ferguson would take this opportunity to prosthelytize about healthy living. Ferguson cursed the canned meats, pipes, and alcohol they had on the expedition. He was surviving on a diet consisting almost exclusively of yams and almonds. "It keeps the intestinal flora verdant and the remainder of the bowels pristine." Somehow he had managed to jam pamphlets into his backpack and now took this opportunity to pass them around. "I will take on this diet when I give up caring" wrote Wilde in his notes that evening. Ferguson offered to give a quinine suffusion to anyone who wanted it once they returned to the States, but the rest of the men politely refused. Realizing he was not winning over converts, Ferguson asked if he could at least prepare supper that evening. The team acquiesced and the Indian cook was given the night off. Yams, beans, and walnuts were cooked in a skillet and sweetened with a liberal helping of brown sugar. The team was surprised and pleased. Supper turned out refreshing and delicious. The next day he continued lecturing about a healthy diet. He infused the discussion on the second day with talk of abstinence from sexual relations. He alleged the right diet would dull those urges, bringing about psychological harmony. "Not me" Chhiri Tendi responded. "When I see a yam, I go crazy. If you're alone on the

trail, a well-cooked yam can be a respectable replacement for a lady."
Ferguson promptly lost his audience.

The team awoke on the sixth after two days of rest, ready to take on the wall. Drake was excited for this moment, for Wilde agreed the team could give his invention – the "magic rope" – a try. There was no denying it was designed for the sole purpose of surmounting obstacles just like this one. They came to the very base of the wall. Wilde wrote: "Drake took off his backpack and unzipped it with bare hands, steam pouring from his nostrils. Out of it he pulled the black disk. Its concentric rings looked like the grooves of an unusually thick musical recording, the knobs and dials in the middle being the recording's label. Drake took the disk and placed it on a relatively flat area. I asked what would happen next."

Drake said one person would lean down and grab the handles sticking out of the sides. Then Drake would turn the small switch next to one of the handles, thereby freeing the springs. The device would gently begin to expand. Once it was at the height of the climber, others were to stabilize it at its base and the climber with his hands on the handles would continue to rise. And rise. And rise. At some point, when they arrived at the top of the cliff, the magic rope would "sense" the top and stop expanding. Or it would expand to forty feet, whichever came first. At that point the climber could use whatever maneuvers or equipment they had at their disposal to reach a safe outcropping.

Chatham spoke up. "I'll go first. I'm already damaged goods." Everyone agreed with this idea.

Chatham squatted down and grabbed the handles of the contraption. Drake turned the knob. The contraption did not gracefully, gradually extend. It was at full extension – forty feet – instantaneously, the event ending with a loud *snap*. The force with which it bolted into the air was awe-inspiring. It hit Chatham's face with such aggression he was sent airborne and back. The group was surprised he was not decapitated. He lay unconscious, face-up in the snow about fifteen feet from the black totem. Everyone was in shock, ergo no one went forward to balance it. And so it came down like a tree in a storm, and landed on Chatham. This actually woke the man up. He was moaning and his face was bloody for the third time on this adventure. "Hot" he yelled, as the friction from the extending metal bands had heated up the device considerably. Wilde, Drake, and Ferguson rolled it off of Chatham. Drake turned the knob again and the device sprang shut. Wilde wrote "I went to pick it up and I felt the burn through my gloves. Closing it had heated it even more and condensed the space in which the heat existed. It was actually smoking and glowing red. I yelled and threw the thing as far as I could. It landed and sank into the melting snow like the head of some small red trickster demon, returning to Hell until summoned again."

Silence spread throughout the group. They were stuck at the bottom of the cliff with one man (again) badly hurt. Drake exclaimed, "I have another magic rope in my backpack!" Wilde slapped him with his still-smoking glove.

Facts had to be faced. They were not getting up this mountain without doing some rather technical climbing up this wall. Wilde also decided they would pull Chatham up the face in a sleeping bag tied to ropes. "His injuries are all superficial. Cosmetic. He will be better by tomorrow." Apparently he was better sooner than that because Chatham did not stop talking about his past exploits while they pulled him up in the sleeping bag. "This reminds me of the time I was spun up into the web of *arachnida prepostera*. She was seven feet in diameter and nastier than a bear in spring thaw!"

The team made it up the cliff using more traditional methods, and the going was brutal. They decided to stop for the night only one hundred feet from the previous camp. The distance was paltry, but with the cliff behind them, the accomplishment was solid. Ahead of them lay a relatively easy, straight, but rather long shot to the Eastern Ridge, with the Maw to their right the whole way. There would be no need to cross it until they were making their way down.

Chhiri Tendi recalled looking around for Hoyt and Yuudai the whole time they progressed. "It was unfortunate that even with such sweeping vistas, there was no sign of our fellow climbers." Chhiri Tendi had to assume the two men had used common sense and climbed down to Base Camp; and Hoyt was nothing if not bloated with common sense.

The sun had set an hour earlier. Hoyt and Yuudai had just split a can of sardines, their second to last meal (the next morning's breakfast would consist of biscuits, marmalade, and coffee...and then that would be about it). Fuel for the Rob Roy was also dwindling. They were not sure if they would have any in the morning to make coffee or tea. And Hoyt felt once they were out of coffee, all bets were off. Even the competition with Junk would no longer matter.

The adventure looked to have come to naught. Hoyt would be climbing down in defeat within twenty-four hours. Junk would take the prize and Hoyt would live out the rest of his life in reclusive humiliation. "I will retire immediately," he wrote. "I will take a vow of silence, eating nothing but stale, leftover bread from my former company, washed down with water hand-scooped from the East River. Or perhaps I will go crazy like my mother, ranting about the Jews using mind control to steer President Lincoln's decisions in office." No matter which path he chose it did not matter, because inside he would already be dead.

Tomorrow was quite simply do or die.

Yuudai walked out of the tent at about seven at night. Dinner was done and it was time to have a go at sleep. It was then a chink in Hoyt's emotional armor gave way. He followed Yuudai out of the tent:

"I had the intention of telling Yuudai I appreciated his dedication and his willingness to follow me into the unforgiving, frigid Unknown. I was also going to offer him an out. If he wanted to return to base camp first thing in the morning, he had my permission. That was when he turned around to face me holding a gun. I thought 'What a fool I am to have let down my guard for even a moment; to convince myself this man – or any man for that matter – was worth any sort of warmth from me.' He was going to shoot me and likely make up some story about an inglorious ending, something about me screaming for my mother at the last minute or renouncing Jesus Christ as my savior (sic). *But despite these feelings, part of me wanted him to pull the trigger. 'Go ahead' I cried. "End this suffering! My heart, soul, and belly are on the verge of emptiness. Do it! I am ready to cross the River Jordan!'"*

To Hoyt's surprise, Yuudai aimed the gun into the air and fired. A red flare rose hundreds of feet into the sky above them, lighting up the side of the Eastern Ridge as they climbed. When it finally arced, fell back to earth and fizzled, the silence must have been palpable and filled with one thousand awkward thoughts. The two men quietly went to their separate tents and retired for the night.

The rest of Hoyt's team did not recall ever seeing the flare that night. The location of their camp should have provided them with an uninterrupted view of Hoyt and Yuudai's location. Chhiri Tendi has no explanation for this, except perhaps they were all in their tents at the time.

However, other eyes did see the flare. First was Junk. His fellow climber Zeigler wrote that "Junk saw something shoot up – just barely -

over the Eastern Ridge. It seemed too low to be a magma eruption, although it lit up the sky in a similar fashion. Junk probably would have danced around in the dark had there been enough air to support such behavior. Instead, he simply blurted out a loud, forced 'Ha!' and commented that the 'abstemious, joy-retardant faggot' appeared to be having problems. No action was taken to set up a rescue. Zeigler was unsure in his writings whether no action was taken because Junk hated Hoyt that much, or because their distance from the flare and the existence of the Eastern Ridge made rescue impossible.

But still even more eyes had seen the flare. About eight of them in total. These eyes were much closer, only a few hundred feet further up the base of the Eastern Ridge from Hoyt. These eyes were angry, insane, and situated in the heads of men who wore stuffed cobras around their necks.

Chapter Thirteen: What Happened To Mcgee

Junk finally took pen to paper on September 7th. He did this for three reasons. First, seeing as practically everyone else on the expedition was writing, he felt it was about time he did the same. Should not his own perspective be documented once this journey came to an end? What if Hoyt was keeping a journal, which he undoubtedly was? Second, the lack of air was making him feel sillier than usual. As his brain reverted to a more childish state, he found himself to be more playful and creative (at least in his opinion). The urge to produce became overwhelming. Deep sea divers will sometimes experience rapture of the deep. Junk was experiencing some kind of rapture of the skies. Thirdly, he was smitten. River Leaf had captured his heart. Junk was quite explicit in his explanation as to why. "River Lef [sic] doesn't laugh at my jokes. I told a classic about a polack and mick fishing with the Pope and she din't [sic] even crack a smirk. She talks only when there's a thing needing to be said, unlike me, who finds the CO2 in my lungs a good enugh [sic] excuse to say something. She commits acts of extreme heroism or extreme violence if the need arises. Mother would've loved her. They're 2 uf [sic] a kind." Altitude may have jumbled Junk's prose, but through the mess we can clearly observe that River Leaf had become Junk's muse.

The commencement of his journal coincided with the expedition striking out from Camp Two, half way up the eastern lip of the Icy Bellows, on their way to Camp Three where the lip meets the Eastern Ridge. The journey from Camp One at the Rakhiot Glacier to Camp Two had been painless. The wind from the Bellows had been relatively calm for no understandable reason and the lip had not presented any technical challenges; no steps, no narrows, just a gentle walkway to the skies. This next stretch to Camp Three would not be so simple. The lip became rather nasty right away. Two steps, the first about twenty feet high and the second slightly taller, blocked their route. The air would also be thinner. Other than these challenges, the route remained relatively wide and gentle and certainly less challenging than the southern route which Hoyt had chosen, with its scree and its maw. Nonetheless, Junk had to admit the Rakhiot Glacier and Qila Pass had taken far more of a toll on his campaign than he had expected. Perhaps the steep slopes and unpredictable rocks of the southern route would have been preferable. Then again, they had seen Hoyt shoot off a flare. Not all was right on their side either.

Junk may have been cheery, but the other Americans were tired and despairing over their losses. Taylor, Fenimore, and Morrow. All gone. The remaining team members were suffering from altitude sickness or frostbite or both. Cole's frostbite had spread to his nose and other cheek. If he did not attend to the problem soon, he would have to begin climbing down. McGee was dizzy and nauseous from the altitude. His fear of heights had gotten the better of him, slowing him down to a snail's pace. The world dropped off sharply on both sides, and that is enough to make anyone feel they are performing a high wire act. To someone with acrophobia, that terror is multiplied many times over. McGee must have also worried for his heart which had not experienced such persistent exercise ever before. River Leaf was moving more slowly and seemed to finally be feeling the effects of her surroundings. Everyone was talking less and the words that did come out were garbled. The thinking beneath the words was equally garbled. Even the more experienced climbers were starting to make bad judgments as they rose into the realm of twenty thousand feet. Junk himself had left his entire backpack behind after a brief rest and had to down climb several yards to get it. Supplemental oxygen would have to be utilized soon.

The Sherpa were another story. With the porters remaining at lower camps, only the five high-altitude Sherpa and ten other Sherpa remained. They seemed lucid and game. Had they not been there to tend to the Americans' every need, the expedition would have come to an end as soon as it had started. Pasang Dolma toiled under the weight of other people's equipment but did not show signs of exhaustion. Occasional heavy breaths were the extent of it. "The rest of us may fall over dead, but Pasang Dolma will be able to cary [sic] my corpse to top [sic]" Junk joked.

Junk likely had different feelings about the four nasty Sherpa. If everyone else were to die, those men had a look like they would happily use half the American bodies as kindling while cooking the other half. They were undoubtedly gifted at their jobs, climbing and porting without rest, but their social etiquette would not do should they ever find themselves at tea with the world leader. They ate alone. They conversed alone. They kept entirely to themselves except when their services required them to engage. In fact, they rarely even spoke to Pasang Dolma despite the fact he was their sardar. Pasang Dolma seemed to have regrets about his selection of four high altitude Sherpa. They had not acted this way until Base Camp so he could not have known he had chosen poorly.

Despite the glum, exhausted, and badly deprecated state of his team, Junk remained ebullient. In his journal, his letters became bigger and more crooked. "We've suffered [sic], but we're still moving. The mountain of my dreams is with me, and the girl is more than half-conquered." Clearly, his ability to make sense was waning.

They arrived at the first step. Technical climbing such as this could be easily managed by these individuals at sea level. It is quite another story to do it miles up in the atmosphere with scant air and frostbite lurking. The only positive was that Hoover's expedition had left ice screws in the step years ago. The team tied off and began to ascend. Junk went first attached to Pasang Dolma. He was followed by Cole and Zeigler. Progress was slow and careful. McGee waited at the bottom for his turn, likely panicked. Junk took the time to stop, turn around, and smile down at his old friend. "Remember. One million dollars!" As you may recall, Junk had bet McGee one million dollars that McGee would not make it. The words acted like a magical incantation (even if Junk did not have the funds to pay off). McGee settled down and began to focus on nothing but making it up the step. He began climbing quite self-assuredly, not looking down and not stopping for anything. River Leaf followed behind, tied to McGee, and then the Sherpa brought up the rear.

When Junk had reached the top, he squatted down and admired the view. They were high now. They could see Everest clearly. Its southern face, which had smashed Junk's hopes of retaliation only two years previous, loomed before them. To the east of that was Lhotse. Far off in the west was Manaslu, a 26,000-foot behemoth. Beyond Everest and Lhotse lay the Rongbuk Glacier and Tibet. Taking all of this on, Junk must have had the sense that Hoyt's statement regarding Fumu's height was right. But only time would tell. Given this was a privately funded expedition with no scientific studies being conducted, they had no instrument to measure the height of a mountain. Their naked eyes would have to be their instruments.

They all reached the top but they were exhausted. McGee lay on his back breathing heavily. According to Cole's writings they all knew at that point McGee would never make it to high camp. The question was: Would he have the foresight to climb down, or would he foolishly stay the course? Cole quietly inquired whether Junk would ask his friend to begin climbing down. "Never" came the response. Junk felt his old chum was stronger than the mountain and that he would surprise the whole team. River Leaf was next to ask. It was no use. There would be no change in plans. McGee would see high camp.

No one asked McGee for his own opinion. They knew he would follow Junk to the end of the world, or even to the top of it.

Before setting off for the second step, which lay about one hundred yards further up the lip, Junk said to his team "Whoever decided to call these things 'steps' was rather tall." He was probably in the mood to make quips because of the foul moods around him. The team continued to put on their packs and prepare to trudge on yet again as if they heard nothing at all. Junk wrote that night. He used phrases more staccato and awkward than usual, likely due to altitude:

> *"Then I heard it. Some kind of rare bird ascended to this great height? Perched on someone's head? The most glorios [sic] song I ever heard. Short... only a few notes. I turned to find the source of the sound. River Leaf looking at me and covering up a smile. Her cheeks plump garden tomatos [sic]. Goggles hide her eyes, but it doesn't matter. It was clear. No bird. No bird call. It had been a laugh. River Leaf had had a second of weakness and had laughed at something I'd said. The fact she didn't laugh before had made her attractive, but that I could break her down...boy oh boy the challenge!*
> *Yes, she laghed [sic] at material of shitty caliber. But not because she has a bad sense of humor. She just knows any joke told with almost no air and a stomach full of fear is something of a feat."*

Junk hiked next to River Leaf and tried to carry on a conversation with her as they approached the second step. Single words had to do. He started it off.

"Scared?"

"No."

"Tired?"

"No."

"What then?"

"Alive."

This was apparently enough conversation for Junk to be happy. Even if she was no longer smiling, he knew the potential was there and that was dandy by him.

The team stopped again at the foot of the second step. The thing was tall, steep, and covered with ice. Even the granite rocks protruding from the frozen whiteness were covered in a slippery sheen. Perhaps there was a way around. Junk, Cole, and Pasang Dolma tied off to one another and went along the eastern side of the step, out over the edge of the ridge. Using ice axes, ropes, and ice screws, they carefully made their way a few feet along the steep drop-off, thousands of vertical feet over the scree and moraine below. No alternate route presented itself. They climbed back onto the ridge. Moving to the other side of the ridge, the side facing the Icy Bellows, they tried again. If the other side of the ridge had been no better than climbing the step, then this side was far worse; an impassible overhang covered in partially-melted snow from the day's sun. No option was left but to go straight up the second step.

A decision was made to set up Camp Two A so the team could rest up for what they hoped was the last bit of technical climbing before the summit. Tea was made by the Sherpa and canisters of dinner were consumed rather joylessly. Only Junk remained animated. He made yet another critical decision that they would stay at this new camp for a few days and perhaps even climb down to the first lip. Zeigler, who was generally a rather timid fellow, balked. He wanted to get things moving. Each day they lingered was another day that a storm could come and end their designs for victory. He generally did not like their current position, very exposed on the lip, at the mercy of the wind and cold. However,

Zeigler was a good climber and knew the decision was ultimately Junk's. They would stop and rest.

"Sun is setting, Bellows wind beginning to screem [sic] and it's goddamned cold" wrote Junk. To be certain, night time on the lip around the Bellows can be brutal. Tents need to be set up leaning slightly off the outer edge of the lip or else the wind will tear them to shreds. But if one pitches the tent too far away from the center, one can end up on a cornice that comes loose in the night, sending the tent and its inhabitants on a journey several miles downward.

McGee had gone totally silent at this point. Every laboured breath was being used to stay alive and focused. Playing cards, smoking a cigarette, and even taking a sip of scotch were things of the past. All attention was on simply existing and ignoring discomfort. Junk shared a tent with his old chum. If he was worried about McGee's fate, he did not let it on to anyone. He must have sincerely felt McGee's overall toughness, compounded by the allure of a one million dollar payout, was enough to see the old street thug through.

Cole was in an uproar. The altitude had made him as forgetful as the next man, and somewhere along the way he had lost several books, scientific papers, and "important sketches." He demanded he be allowed to down climb, even if it meant going all the way to Advanced Base Camp to find it. Chances were good he would not have to climb down too far since he recalled looking at the documents only the night before. However, he may have to go off the side of the ridge and recover the materials if the wind happened to have blown them in that direction. Junk was adamant Cole could not leave. All hands were needed. They could not spare him nor the Sherpa resource he would require. "But those things are my security blanket" Cole complained. "I cannot be up here without them." Junk calmed him and explained they were all giving up their comforts on this climb. Junk wrote that night "Told Cole that on a climb of this size, expozur [sic] to the elements is not just physical, but emotional too." Cole listened to reason and acquiesced.

The lanterns in the tents of the Americans went dark and the team fell into a troubled, bitterly cold sleep; a sleep portending the troubled, bitterly cold day to come.

The only tent remaining active was that of the four ill-natured Sherpa. "They're more chatty than usual tonight" Junk wrote before retiring. "Wish I could understand what they're saying. I also wish I could fire them. A little tricky here. Shame. They seemed really nice on the approach to Advanced Base Camp (aside from one spitting incident), but became obnoxious once we really needed them on the assent [sic]. I'm going to pay them less than promised when this is done. I'll also give Pasang Dolma more than promised. Other than picking those four dopes, Pasang Dolma has been aceptional [sic], as have the porters and cooks he hired. I sleep now and hopefully dream of River Leaf."

The team tried to sleep late the next morning but it was impossible. Everyone was awake before dawn. The wind had picked up to such a degree the noise was deafening and the air inside the tents was frigid. Climbing up the second step in such conditions would be risky. Cole recommended they climb down to Camp One until the weather improved; such a plan would also allow McGee to begin his way back down to Base Camp (Cole probably felt this would also give him an opportunity to look for his own lost academic reading material). Junk assured Cole that he was underestimating both the fortitude of the big Irishman and his motivation when fueled by the promise of big money. Certainly not happy with the suggestion but always the respectful chap, Cole listened to his leader.

Junk decided that if no choice offered a better situation, then continuing their ascent was the best option. "We cand wade for the wedder to me like it was on Chabbaquiddick!" Junk yelled at Cole. "We're a the tob of the world now! Time for our meddle to me tesded!" The oxygen-deprived, slightly confused leader also "reasoned" climbing would warm them up more than sitting still or climbing down.

An advance team consisting of Junk, Zeigler, and Pasang Dolma would do the second step and make their way up the remaining lip (Cole would stay behind to aid in the healing of his frostbite). Upon finding a safe location for Camp Three, they would return and get the rest of the team. The hope was that they could be back by one in the afternoon, and they could get the rest of team up before sunset. Should they be slowed down by anything, a Camp Two B could be established immediately above the second step.

Everyone ate their tins of breakfast to the din of wind and eruptions near the summit. They finished their tea and the advance team suited up. Light appeared on the eastern horizon and illuminated the second step looming over them. Ice screws from Hoover's expedition were nowhere to be seen, probably buried under the excessive ice and snow. Junk went first. Whereas they were usually separated by several yards, Junk set the first and second ice screws almost on top of each other. They would take no big risks here. Unlike his usual mode of operation, Junk demanded this step be taken conservatively and by the book.

And so it went. With much difficulty, the three men ascended the step despite high winds, oppressive cold, and scarce oxygen. At the top, they hiked along the razor-thin ridge as it gently began curving to the southwest and up to the Eastern Ridge. If it is possible, the wind became worse. There was nowhere to set up tents if they ran out of strength. Zeigler began complaining after only an hour of hiking. He could not feel his feet and breathing was simply too difficult. Junk was dazed but felt physically fit. He wanted to continue. Pasang Dolma said he was alright and would do whatever Junk asked of him. That night Junk wrote, "We played it saf (sic) and went down. Try tomorow (sic)." Their decision paid off, for as they began to descend, Zeigler caught sight of a small saddle only one hundred feet above them, near where the lip met the northeast ridge. Odds were damned good it would provide enough space for a camp. That would be their destination tomorrow.

With as much care as they could summon, the three men descended the lip and made their way down the second step. Upon reaching Camp Two A, Junk shared the good news with the team that the lip presented no more technical challenges after the step and that a protected location for Camp Three existed in the form of a saddle. But he also decided oxygen would need to be used earlier than they had hoped. He said, "I can't count to two for Christ's sake." The team was relieved to hear this news. Even McGee mumbled "Thank fuck."

Unless the weather worsened, the entire team would resume the ascent the next morning. Junk wrote, "I'll sleep well tonight. Optimistic. Even though the rest are sad sacks. River Leaf's asleep in her own tent. What I'd give to walk over there and offer my warmth. Perhaps another night."

They slept until first light. The wind had calmed slightly over the evening and still few clouds were evident. Stars still shone in the western sky. This was their chance. Everyone was rested and ready to go. The day off seemed to have restored McGee's vigor and Cole felt up to the task. The Sherpa moved quickly preparing the packs, grumbling all the while about God-knows-what in their foreign tongue. The only English word Junk could detect was "fools". Pasang Dolma distributed breakfast containers to the team (The ten remaining low altitude Sherpa would stay at this camp). The team was not short of food which was a blessing. That is the kind of miscalculation that plagues many an expedition and can foil an otherwise perfect assault on a summit.

Cole tried to cover his face as well as possible including his frostbitten nose. However, covering the nose is a problem because the moisture in one's exhalations collects on the covering material, thereby causing it to freeze. Junk had not planned well for maladies like these. There was no one on the team with medical experience at all. Cole himself was probably the most knowledgeable individual about such things, but was too invested in reaching the top to make a rational decision. He was also oxygen-deprived. Cole "decided" to keep going, even if it meant losing his nose and cheek when he got home.

Junk went up the step first, followed closely by Cole and then River Leaf. She climbed without complaint and never stopped for longer than a few moments in order to calculate her next axe-strike. McGee was next and Zeigler offered to follow behind him, cheering him on and providing suggestions if needed. The Sherpa carried up the rear. As the team ascended, rumbles from the summit would mix with the wind, making for a disharmonious experience.

McGee stopped half way up. "I'm done" he uttered in a voice so quiet only Zeigler could hear. He needed to go down. The height was too great. He was terrified. "I'm afraid of heights" he called out needlessly. Junk queried the people on the step below as to the nature of the delay. Word was passed up the line that McGee had given up. "Bullshit!" Junk responded. "Get your ass up here, Fatty Arbuckle! We'll talk about your running mascara when you've reached the top of this thing." The others were in shock at Junk's behavior, but clearly the expedition leader knew his friend well because McGee started moving again.

They reached the top of the second step without a mishap. Perhaps they would have been overjoyed were they not so exhausted. The grouchy Sherpa no longer stood out in their demeanor because everyone on the top of the step that day was miserable. Even Junk's daydreams of love were not enough to keep him chipper. He moved slowly and said little. Yelling at McGee on the step had probably been enough to make him winded.

Looking around, the landscape was slowly changing. The sound of the summit - sporadic cataclysms like God sounding a tympani drum - was now as loud as the wind and strong enough to move the Earth beneath them. The expedition had also reached their first streak of black ash, a three-foot-wide line scarring the lip diagonally in front of them. Whatever fireball had caused it had likely come from near the peak of the mountain and then hit the lip, careening off into the eastern sky and the moraine below. Such an event could happen again at any moment.

Junk made the decision they would again set up an intermediary camp. The wind was still abusive and his team, made up of several amateurs, was spent. "Original plan of for [sic] camps was to [sic] optamistic [sic]. This will end up being six camps, all of them justified." Food was still not an issue, but the extended time on the mountain would require some conservation efforts. That would likely not be difficult for the team as appetites tend to diminish with altitude. Even the repulsively corpulent McGee was looking more slender than normal.

Each individual responds to altitude differently and so far their minimal acclimatization efforts had been sufficient for everyone. Altitude sickness had been absent up to that point. But now Zeigler was complaining of debilitating headaches. They began as small pains in his temples at the base of the step, but were now causing him to double over, hold his head in his mitts, and squint his eyes hard. Each time the mountain erupted, he moaned. Pasang Dolma recommended they take Zeigler down immediately to Camp Two. Junk agreed this was the prudent thing to do. He told two of the grouchy Sherpa to gear up and bring Zeigler down before nightfall. They could sleep at Camp Two and then make their way up the next day. Zeigler could also come back up if his condition improved.

"No" one of the four unpleasant Sherpa replied.

Such a response from a Sherpa was unexpected to say the least. Disobeying a direct order from a sahib – at least an order as rational as this one - was unheard of. Junk was quick-tempered in this rarefied atmosphere, and yelled with slurred phonemes "Get walgin' you horthe'th ath!'"

According to Cole's journal from that evening, the Sherpa's response was crystal clear, as if he had access to some personal, unseen reservoir of air. "No. All he needs to do is rest here and that will help him. We must keep moving forward before we come across a storm. The wind is high, but the sky remains cloudless. The 'Angry Parent' cannot be expected to stay calm for much longer. We will stay here tonight. We will continue the climb tomorrow but Zeigler will remain." This response must have put Junk into a bad situation. He could not dismiss the Sherpa. He knew they were required for him to conquer the summit, especially if he wished to do it before Hoyt (assuming Hoyt had not already beaten him). The Sherpa had also tapped into Junk's urge not to slow the expedition down any further, even though he knew the only cure for altitude sickness was descent. Simply staying put was no elixir for Zeigler's ills. What's more, Junk could not cast aspersions on the Sherpa because they were essentially pulling the same stunt he himself had pulled years earlier on the Everest expedition: Usurping the whole operation.

To everyone else's surprise, Junk simply said "Bah!" and walked into his tent for a nap. He was too tired and the counter-proposal gelled too well with the urges lying coiled in his gut. He was compromising Zeigler's life and his own leadership because of his aspirations for conquering Fumu before Hoyt.

River Leaf entered the tent moments later, causing some commotion among the rest of the team. These were, after all, a group of healthy men, which is to say their minds had been steeped in raunch since the arrival of body hair. The idea of a woman alone with a man in one of the tents seemed rather scandalous. But the ado did not last long. The team was tired and needed to rest. Junk wrote that night: "In the tent, River Leaf said litle [sic] to me. 'Zeigler needs to go down' was all. Nothing else was needed. Her words were like an incantation. I rose and began planning for Zeigler's decent [sic]."

As it would happen, Cole *wanted* to take Zeigler down. It would give him an opportunity to look for his lost materials. The decision was therefore made: Cole would take Zeigler down to Camp Two and one of the Sherpa would join him. One Sherpa accepted but only after a long pause and raucous chewing out in Nepali by Pasang Dolma. The decision was a bold one for Junk to make. With both Zeigler and Cole down the mountain, two of his strongest climbers would be unavailable to him. He would have Pasang Dolma and that was about it. He was unlikely to rely on the other remaining Sherpa for anything after what had occurred only moments earlier. No progress up the lip could be made until Cole and the Sherpa returned.

As Cole prepared to help Zeigler down, he reminded Junk this would be a perfect time to let McGee go as well. Junk refused. His friend would make it. Cole and Zeigler walked out of their tents and into the blasting wind at noon on September 9th, prepared to climb back down the two steps on their way to Camp Two, where Zeigler would have a respite from the paucity of air at the higher camps. Junk and the rest of the team would wait at Camp Two B, hoping to have Cole back by nightfall. But before the descending party could even make the step, the disagreeable Sherpa began yelling in a rambling manner back to Pasang Dolma. Junk wished to know what the man was saying. Pasang Dolma responded "Nothing. A string of terrible excuses why he cannot go down. Fear of heights? The way down is actually the other direction? What silly things to say!" Pasang Dolma began yelling again in Nepali, undoubtedly telling the unpleasant Sherpa to stop with his nonsensical excuses and begin climbing down.

No one had even been paying attention to McGee who was puttering about camp in a daze looking for his misplaced hat (the tired, rotund, confused Irishman was in fact wearing his hat). He had his backpack on, possibly confused about the plans and thinking he was going down along with Cole and Zeigler. According to various team members' notes, what happened next seemed to occur at a slow pace, like a reel of film being presented one frame every second. An exceptionally powerful gust of wind blasted through the camp. Only the members who were about to climb down were tied off. Everyone else simply held their ground, bending down in order to minimize wind resistance. McGee did not. His solution was to walk into the blast, standing straight up, taking the full force of it. This solution was working for him. However, the gust died as quickly as it was born. His overcompensation now had no opponent, and he went stumbling forward, half-running and half-falling. It was not long before his awkward scramble ran out of space.

McGee yelled bloody murder as he went over the edge. It was then everyone turned and moved to see. They all watched in horror as McGee took multiple tumbles down the steep ice. His fall was arrested only modestly by the raised, icy trail of a deceased avalanche crossing his path. This had the result of putting McGee into a slide. Helpless to do anything "we wached [sic] as, quite alive and aware, he sarted [sic] a high-speed glissade down the Belows [sic]" wrote Cole in misspelled, beaten writing that fumbled across the page.. "Limbs flailed. Hed [sic] snapped violent with each flaw in the slope. The scene was nauseating. Ashamed as I am to write this, it would have been less nausating [sic] had he fallen and died right away. Easily ten seconds after the calamity had begun, McGee, now only a dot in the distance below us, reached the botom [sic] of the Bellows thousands of feet down, and disappeared into the Oculus. We were tramatized [sic]."

The exhausted climbers snapped out of their mental slumbers. They had the sudden capacity to yell and go into a chaos of activity. The ailing Zeigler simply went down on one knee and buried his hands in his mitts, muffling his cries. Others like Cole started pointing to possible routes down the Bellows and yelled at the Sherpa to prepare ropes and ice screws. River Leaf did not have a plan but in desperation pulled out her ice axe and made to the edge of the lip as if ready to descend.

Amid the chaos, standing silent and motionless was Junk. He was a statue, still staring at the place where his childhood friend, his brother, his business partner, his confidante, had fallen. "The look on his face wasn't one of horor [sic] or grief as I would've imagined," Cole wrote. "It was one of calculation."

The mad activity of the camp continued a few moments longer and then an ear-splitting eruption near the summit drowned out all sound. Everyone stopped what they were doing and held their mitts to the sides of their heads. When the noise resided, Junk took the silence as an opportunity to say "Listen to me" in a calm voice. How was their fearless leader going to respond to the loss of his old chum? What came out of him must have been a surprise to all. "We are not climbing down there to get him. Continue with what you were doing. Cole, get Zeigler down to Camp Two. Everyone else, we will sit tight until Cole gets back." This command did not have any obvious effect. All eyes were still on him, possibly awaiting some explanation for his unexpected plan.

The surprises continued. It was not Cole who challenged Junk, nor was it Zeigler. Nor Pasang Dolma. Nor the four disobliging Sherpa. It was River Leaf. Standing twice as tall as she ever had before, storming across the lip toward Junk as if not the faintest breeze passed by, she came within inches of him. "What is wrong with your heart? What is wrong with the whole of you?" This was likely all she could muster.

Junk replied. "The assault will *not* be called off! Odds are Patrick's dead. Would you want to climb down the Bellows and then the darkness underneath to retrieve a corpse? Would Patrick have wanted us to do that? And what if he's alive? You have no idea what a million dollar bet will make a man do. Especially him. If he's alive, he'll find a way out and meet us at Base Camp. Bet he's planning it now. I don't share much with William Hoyt, but like him, I have Faith. True, it's not faith in a bearded man in space pulling the strings of Destiny. It's faith in a fat Irishman stuck in a hole."

Denial. The only possible explanation was denial. Junk probably could not accept a loss of such magnitude and his mind had concocted some happy ending in which this all works out with McGee in one piece and a victorious return to Boston. "No doubt abot [sic] it." Cole wrote. "It was denali [sic]."

River Leaf said testily, "This is not the streets of Boston, Aaron Junk." "That's true" he replied. "The weather in Boston is far worse!" She stormed off into her tent without another word.

Cole followed the orders of his team leader without question and helped Zeigler down to Camp Two with the aid of one of the dyspeptic – but now utterly angry – Sherpa. Junk, River Leaf, and the Sherpa waited in their respective tents for Cole to return. When sunset came without any sign of him (nor any sign of McGee escaping the Oculus), they made dinner and settled in for yet another wakeful night on the lip. Progress, it seemed, would have to wait.

Audible to others, River Leaf left her tent just before the last light had faded. The wind had laid down its arms with the end of day but still the air was frigid. When Junk ventured outside, likely to investigate River

Leaf's actions, he was witness to a night commencing clear. However, clouds in the distant west looked foreboding.

River Leaf was wearing all of her gear and was walking to the edge of the lip. Junk asked her what she was doing, although it was probably quite obvious to him. And indeed, and certainly to Junk's dismay, her intention was to climb down the Bellows in search of McGee. At the very least, she would make it to The Oculus and call down to him. If in the hole she saw a climbing route and maybe some sort of floor or ledge below, she would descend into it despite the frigid air inexplicably blasting forth from it at all times. If the hole was a long black void with no visible bottom, only then would she give up. Without being asked River Leaf added that she had no intention of returning to the expedition. With or without McGee, she would make her way north, up and out of the giant bowl they called the Bellows, down the Rakhiot Glacier, and then leave the entire Qila Sanctuary on her own.

Such actions were unheard of on mountaineering expeditions. No team member disobeys their leader and no team member simply walks away from the campaign. But those thoughts were not the ones crossing Junk's mind. He wrote that evening:

"Distraught. Might be the altitude, but I want to cry for the first time in my lif [sic]. So lovely. So strong. So delicate. But so short the courting. She was leaving. To lose her only hours after falling for her. My pain from McGee I could hide, but not this. I begged her not to go. If McGee's alive, he'll make it. She wouldn't respond to that. I think I love you. She wouldn't respond to that. Don't you want to make it to the top? She responded to that. And she said mor [sic] than she ever had before. I never had any interest in making it up there, she said. I was just going where you told me because I was lost and had nowhere to go ever since leaving

my family. I went where I was taken. By anyone. Not any more.
There's nothing up there, she sad [sic]. Nothing but ice, fire, and
wind. For you, she said, there's also a victory. And your reasoning
to not retrieve McGee seems convenent [sic] in light of that future
victory. You've turned away from your oldest friend for a win with
nothing good or right about it. I'm done following you to stupidity
and deth [sic], she said. i will go where I wish now. I said but you
have no home. Where will you go? I've been called an Indian my
whole life, she said. So perhaps I'll try my luck in Calcutta."

    With this, River Leaf turned and jumped off the side of the lip. But why? Why would an Indian squaw face certain death in order to rescue a corpulent paleface whom she had only known for a short time? We cannot be sure, but it seems that she was simultaneously being pushed by Junk's horrible behavior and perhaps being pulled by the bonds she shared with McGee. They had been the only two members of the expedition who had no right being there. Their reasons for climbing Fumu had little to do with a taste for adventure. Their short time together had been intense and the presence of one another must have been a kind of comfort.

    Another possibility was that she was a woman, and in being so, she harbored sensitivities that favored the nurturing of helpless souls. Women have been known to act boldly and ridiculously when their children are threatened. Lift automobiles. Prostitute themselves. Punch out wolves. Is it such a logical leap to think that the childless River Leaf might risk everything to save this helpless man who looked much like and oversized baby and had been in her proximity for months? We cannot be sure.

    Whatever the reason, River Leaf was on her way down the side of the Bellows, dropping through a chute between two jagged rocks. With grace, she placed her ice axe into the snow and began a gentle glissade into the darkness. She was gone. McGee was gone. The flame of euphoria that must have brightened Junk's life over recent days was extinguished; snuffed out in perfect time with the close of the day.

Junk would wake up at first light to the return of Cole and the surly Sherpa, but no Zeigler. "He couldn't do it" Cole said. "The pain of altitude sickness passed, but he's still spent. He's in the care of the Sherpa at Camp Two now, and he'll likely go to Camp One tomorrow." So this was the team. Junk, Cole, and five Sherpa. It would have to do. Junk wrote, "Looked into the Bellows to see if there was any sign of River Leaf or McGee. Nothing. Gone gone gone. Before she left, she had asked what's wrong with my heart. Don't know. Starting to wonder wether [sic] it has a flaw running through it, cutting through valves and dooming me to loneliness." He was empty now. The personality that had once romanced the City of Boston was nowhere to be found. All that emanated now from this shell of a man was the naked instinct to go up.

They set off from Camp Two B on September 10th at seven in the morning on their way to Camp Three. That camp would reside on a saddle along the Eastern Ridge, protecting them somewhat from the wind that had plagued them all along the lip. They would be at 28,000 feet then; only one thousand vertical feet away from Camp Four and another one thousand feet from the summit.

The intensifying rate of suffocation had become too much at this point. Even standing still was now an ordeal. Junk and Cole put on their breathing apparatuses which sped up their ascent considerably. They had a surfeit of oxygen canisters at their disposal due to the slow attrition of fellow climbers as well as the fact the Sherpa did not feel they needed such assistance quite yet.

Clouds had rolled in and hidden the way in front and behind them. They could see only about fifty feet in any direction. No precipitation was coming down yet, but everyone knew it was only a matter of time. The thinned ranks walked up into the grayness, step by laboured step, straining ever closer to the neumenon that is Fumu's summit.

Chapter Fourteen: Vespers

Minds and journal entries were failing on both sides of the mountain. The sources of information which allowed the writing of this book were drying up as elevation increased. Chhiri Tendi was able to fill in many of the blanks from the Hoyt expedition in the interviews he so kindly granted me years later, but many other finer details must be surmised. Some facts about the overall adventure are certain. Hoyt and Junk were in a dead heat almost all of the way up from their respective base camps. Both parties were approaching the Eastern Ridge at the same time but from different directions. Both teams were running low on supplies, but not dangerously so. And both parties were experiencing crises of leadership, one physical and the other spiritual.

In the case of the Hoyt expedition, things were going utterly pear-shaped. Their leader had not been seen since the scree. Fear was in surplus. The temperature seemed to drop with every step up. A gauze of clouds - streaked red with the blood of Fumu's magma - now settled on everything. The team had begun using bottled oxygen, but a large percentage of the canisters had been lost in a small landslide the evening before. They would have to conserve and still possibly run out before the push for the summit. God could not have spoken louder or enunciated more eloquently: Misfortune was imminent.

Early morning on the seventh, they walked along the "happy side" of Rauff's Maw which was to the west of it and therefore closer to the summit. Their confused wanderings on the scree had reaped the serendipitous benefit of depositing them onto a route initially more difficult than the planned one, but then less strenuous hike along the Maw and soon the Eastern Ridge. Although progress was slow, it was steady.

The knowledge that a storm could roll in at any moment was enough to move them along.

The only positive in their lives at the moment had to do with diet. Some of the team members had switched exclusively to food prepared by Ferguson. With each meal, they listened to his Seventh-Day Adventist prayers and then ate deeply of the cleansing, nourishing sustenance. Even if it did not stick to the ribs as much as, say, tins of pemmican, Ferguson's meals did rekindle the men's feelings of well-being and general optimism. Wilde, who seemed the least likely to be attracted to novel things of any sort, had converted the quickest and the most absolutely. "I eat as if eech [sic] bite adds a day of life."

Wilde would need all of the health he could manage. He was leader of this motley team until Hoyt returned or to the very end, whichever came first. Everyone was respectful and supportive of their temporary leader, but even so, Wilde seemed out of his depth. His usual stern bearing showed signs of weakness. His eyes darted about as if perplexed, trying to make decisions about the route. Being too conscious of the pressure to make a good decision, he often did not. No one called him on such things; likely because no one wanted him to give up.

Exhaustion had ended most conversations. Chhiri Tendi was the one exception, still producing quips and tawdry riddles. The now mentally-deficient Americans did not laugh at his humor – which contained an improbable ratio of curses to proper words - but the other Sherpa did, and that was enough to goad on Chhiri Tendi. He walked in the back, barking out his expletives at a rate seeming impossible given the lack of air. Those in earshot up the line, including Drake and Chatham, and the four other Sherpa, were exposed to Chhiri Tendi's banter all day. Those further up – Wild and Ferguson - were spared. "I could not stop," Chhiri Tendi recalls. "I was nervous. And as I told you before, that is what I do when I'm nervous." The circumstances being what they were, any jitters on the part of the team were well justified.

Above and unseen, slightly off to their left, was the summit, closer than ever now. The sporadic din of distant eruptions was certainly close enough now to bring a rumble to their stomachs. Black ash streaked portions of the snow field upon which they walked as if the mountain had adorned itself in war paint in preparation for battle. Despite these visual distractions, out of the corner of his eye, Chhiri Tendi came across something stuck in the snow near the edge of the Maw. No one in front of him seemed to have noticed.

"At first all I could see was a small black tube jutting out of the ice. It did not look like a chunk of the black ash that occasionally crossed the landscape; it had harder angles than that. Definitely made by men. I walked over to it. I kicked it and it didn't budge so I took out my axe and broke the ice around it. Now the thing gave way. I picked it up. It was a gun. A God damned gun! The metal was rusted from exposure to constant freezing and melting. But otherwise it looked pretty decent. I checked for bullets and indeed there were five fuckers in there. I decided not to announce my find as the Americans would want to discuss its origin, the reason for its being deposited here, what to do with it and so forth. That would slow us down. I planned to tell the others when we got to Camp Two, but then forgot as other events on the way down became more important in my mind."

There can be little doubt that what Chhiri Tendi had stumbled upon was the pistol of none other than the Nazi Wolfgang Rauff. The Hoyt team's location along the Maw corresponds quite closely with the location of the disaster as recalled by Rauff's Sherpa. But if Rauff fell straight down while holding the gun, how did it wind up along the side of the Maw and not in it? The answer is unclear, except that perhaps the kickback of the gun removed it from Rauff's hand and placed it on firm ground behind him. That would also explain why Rauff's gun shot – the one that brought about his expedition's demise - did not find its target. Regardless of how it arrived at its current location, it was now the property of Chhiri Tendi, who placed the object in his backpack and did not think about it again for a time.

They approached the base of the Eastern Ridge, the future location of Camp Three, much earlier than expected. It was not even noon. As abhorrent a thought as it was, the team knew acclimatization was necessary. The thought was not only abhorrent due to lost ground, but also because the team would be submitted to more of Chhiri Tendi's comedy act. "Had enough of Chhiri Tendi's comments about women's bosoms" Drake wrote that night. "Now actually squeamish at the thought of bosoms, something I thought impossible." They dropped much of their equipment that would be required for Camp Three, rested, and then turned to descend back down to Camp Two despite their urge to remain.

They followed the Maw as they descended, looking out for the other side, for they knew once the other side came into view, it would mean the Maw was narrowing, and that would alert them to the proximity of Camp Two.

Chhiri Tendi finished up his rant with a rather saucy comment about the women from his home town of Thame. An actual laugh was heard that did not come from one of the other Sherpa. But then again, it did not come from the Americans either.

It came from across the Maw.

On the heels of the distant laugh came another voice, shushing the first. "My heart raced" Chhiri Tendi recalls. "It must have been Hoyt and Yuudai making their way around the Maw. No one else on the team had heard it. I yelled out into the grayness which caught the attention of the others. 'Hoyt' I cried. 'Yuudai!' There was no reply." Chhiri Tendi told the team he had heard a laugh from the across the way. They thought he was being silly. How often had anyone seen Hoyt or Yuudai laugh, they asked. And how likely was it those two sourpusses would be laughing now given the situation? The team reasoned the more likely explanation was that Chhiri Tendi was desperate for an approving audience and had gone temporarily delusional.

Only slightly more than one hour after leaving Camp Three, Camp Two appeared out of the clouds below them. "Exhausted" wrote Wilde that night. "Breathe little esier [sic] here. The air is a lover returned and I am soothed by her gentle kiss." They ate their meals of either yams or pemmican and turned in early with the hope of awaking before first light and getting more mountain below them. They slept deeply. This would be the last time they acquired such rest on this adventure.

Hoyt and Yuudai had been without food for two days. They had enough cooker fuel left to heat snow for drinking water, but that was all. Now they climbed at a clip reflecting their deprivations. The aging American, suddenly certain this climb would be his last, had decided dying on a nearly hopeless climb upward would be better than surviving a return to Base Camp. Yuudai, who seemed to place duty over all else, stayed with Hoyt. He did not complain. He did not make recommendations. He remained silent and followed. At moments, one man would fall down with exhaustion and the other would help him to his feet. Hoyt wrote, "Yuudai tripped. Ice crack. Delayed getting up. He'd passed out. I tug the rope to wake him up. He gets up and walks again as if nothing happened."

It was September the eighth and the day was ending. They had been climbing along the base of the Eastern Ridge since waking up, long, sad rests followed by short spasms of advancement. Given the nasty conditions, the only indication of day's closing was bleakness getting bleaker. Grays turned to deep blues. And then blues to black. No snow was falling yet, but the wind was picking up and visibility was minimal.

Unbeknownst to the two climbers, they were not far from the location where the rest of their team had placed equipment for Camp Three. The team members had down climbed to Camp Two for the night, but canned meals and fuel awaited, as did oxygen. Should they continue another three hundred feet along the wall, they would find the equipment and many of their problems would be solved. Hoyt and Yuudai continued to climb in the darkness as if sensing that possibility.

They came to Rauff's Maw. Unlike their colleagues, Hoyt and Yuudai approached from the east of it. They would need to cross in order to progress. But Hoyt had planned well. The Maw narrowed at its top and bottom, and they were at its top now. A small pass existed between the chasm's topmost point and the wall supporting the Eastern Ridge. They were heading now through this narrow pass. And it was through there that materials for the actual Camp Three awaited unbeknownst to them. In the dark they stumbled and gasped, moving ever closer to relief, to ambrosia, to reunion with the others.

The beginning of the Maw was now only feet away, down the slope to their left. The Eastern Ridge wall was to their right. This path between the two obstacles was roughly ten feet wide and made of smooth, unflawed ice with an occasional pile of wind-blown snow that had likely dropped down the cliff from the Eastern Ridge. They could not see the Maw in the darkness, but if they could, they would see a yawning chasm dropping down nearly one thousand feet into a bottom obscured by the curvature in her walls. Even if the time had been noon on a brilliant summer day, the bottom of the Maw would have remained dark, silent, and vigilant for offerings.

The snow began. It blanketed them and the ice at their feet in an instant. Most certainly out of energy and filled with doubt about the likelihood of survival, Hoyt collapsed and gave out a terrible moan. He wrote that night, "Fustration [sic]. Despration [sic]. Father was right. Makes me mad. Toes sting. "

On the ground, he began to pray out loud. It was not a humble prayer. He did not pray for his life. He did not pray for Yuudai's life. He prayed for Junk's death and an explanation for his current circumstance. His prayer rose in volume until it was calamitous. A wailing. A keening. A temper tantrum. Hoyt's old anger was still alive, barking at the Heavens for answers and urgent, savage justice.

No matter how cathartic the prayer must have been to Hoyt's soul, its impact on the outer world was devastating. A cataclysm, heard but unseen, with "the din of one hundred battlefields" to use Hoyt's words, was now coming from everywhere, easily drowning out Hoyt; a corresponding quake in the ground took Yuudai off of his feet.

Blinded by darkness, Hoyt and Yuudai had no idea what had just happened all around them, except that it felt and sounded apocalyptic. When all was quiet again, Hoyt, torch in hand, rose and walked forward cautiously. He came to a spot where the ground simply disappeared in front of him. Shining his torch downward, he saw no noticeable bottom. He followed the ledge of this new drop off. It kept curving to the left. Before long he had made a complete semi-circle and was back at the wall of the Eastern Ridge, but now behind Yuudai. "By the bowels of Christ!" yelled Hoyt. "We're trapped!"

They decided to wait for daylight to fully assess their predicament and plan an escape. Conditions and space prohibited the construction of a tent. They were left with no choice but to bivouac into snow freshly fallen around them. Given the limitations available to them, they also had to place their new home right at the base of the wall. With snow coming down hard, the chances of a cornice coming loose on the Eastern Ridge and landing on them were astronomically high. Even if harm did not come from above, they had no guarantees the ground upon which they stood was intact. "We sleep in our grave" wrote Hoyt.

Once the structure was completed and they were inside, they found one unexpected comfort. The stone cliff supporting the Eastern Ridge made up one wall of their temporary home. It contained a slight crack, and out of that crack came a gentle warmth, possibly from some unseen volcanic vent. It tempered the biting air ever so slightly. Hoyt and Yuudai were still starving and lacking any energy, but curled up in their warm, down sleeping bags near Fumu's exhaust, they had a brief respite from the cold.

Hoyt wrote hardly anything that night. Without question he was too weak to summon the will. Aside from the quotations mentioned earlier, he also wrote "Bless Yuudai. Saved food. A feast of pemmican."

When the morning of September ninth arrived, the storm broke just long enough to present our heroes with a horrible sight. Hoyt's sonorous prayers combined with the new snow had apparently caused a widespread breaking up, and collapsing of, the ice fields. The Maw was now more of a valley with gentle slopes made of crumbled ice chunks and snow. What the Sherpa called "The Cat's Eye" had dilated even more. The only part still holding fast was the six square feet upon which Hoyt and Yuudai stood. They now resided on a balcony hundreds of feet in the air, supported only by a tall, thick pillar of welded tuff. Their route was utterly obliterated. To carry on with the campaign, or even to retreat, they would have had to climb down an icy overhang followed by hundreds of feet of sheer, crumbly cliff. At the bottom, they would then have to climb up a sloping side of the former Maw. Of course, climbing down the cliff would have been nearly impossible even for a man in perfect health. There was nowhere to go. They were trapped; trapped actors in a theater in the round; performing a tragedy to an audience of nothing.

Down at Camp Two, the rest of the team looked up at the collapsed Maw. It was now more of a massive gulch with sides rising at approximately forty-five degree angles. Their route up to Camp Three, and Camp Three itself, were simply gone in the wreckage, buried by a slope of debris. At the top of the slope was a newly exposed spine of solid earth leading up toward the Eastern Ridge and summit. At the bottom of the slope were more nondescript chunks of ice, and then another slope rising up to what was the other side of the newly-expanded Maw. They had no idea whether the man who had brought them to Fumu was stuck under the debris somewhere. But again, as none of them had much love for the man – nor the Japanese fellow with him – no tears were shed.

Wilde would not be deterred. The collapse had certainly thrown a spanner into the works, but it did not preclude victory. He had an alternate plan almost immediately. Instead of retreating, they would attempt an even more aggressive route to the summit. "We are going straight for Camp Four, today" he wrote. "Yes indeed. The penultimate camp. Today!" It was to their benefit the collapsed Maw had exposed a solid rib of rock heading almost directly from where they stood to the mammoth spine that is the Eastern Ridge. The rocky route did not seem to contain any tricky steps. It would certainly be a farther jaunt than Camp Three, but the inviting nature of the new path assured the men they could go the distance before nightfall. Wilde yelled "Breakfast and then we can't waste another moment!" Wilde and Ferguson gobbled down one of Ferguson's signature breakfasts of yogurt and yams. Chatham, Drake, and the Sherpa ate the more traditional climbers' breakfast and suited up for battle. The team donned their supplemental oxygen equipment for the first time, seeing as today's assault would bring them higher on the mountain than ever before…and by a long stretch. The four Americans and Chhiri Tendi began to climb up the new route, leaving the remaining Sherpa and Camp

Two behind. Five men left. They were to be the "happy few" who would take turns attempting the summit only days from now.

It was not Chhiri Tendi who talked up a storm on the route, nor Chatham, whose wounds had finally quieted him. It was now Drake's turn. He talked Chhiri Tendi's ear off. The inventor was refreshed from a night at lower camps and felt like passing the time in discussion, or monologue depending how one looks at it. "Why did I have to be tied by rope to this one," Chhiri Tendi recalled. "The talk was non-stop. He was jawing about something he called a 'picture radio.' He envisioned that some day, technology would bring us to a place where we could transmit pictures through the air just as we do with sounds today. A box made by a man cannot do such a thing, I said. Only gods can transmit visions to people through the air. When a Sahib starts talking like that, you suspect the altitude has rogered his earhole and damaged his brain. Boy, did I turn out to be wrong. I watch Gunsmoke all the time now, and I doubt any god is sending me that crap. But to be honest I was hardly listening to Drake that day."

Chhiri Tendi was too busy thinking about searching for Hoyt and Yuudai. The other team members were not concerned about their irksome leader and their unwelcomed Japanese guest, but Chhiri Tendi felt like he was failing in his job if he did not look for them. His eyes kept darting to the remnants of the Maw, looking for signs of movement among the collapsed slabs. He detected nothing.

The brief break in the clouds ended. Again the world disappeared, consumed by snow. Any increase in speed they may have obtained from the terrain was cancelled out by the weather's bad turn. The rocks beneath their feet became treacherous almost instantly as they were covered in a thin but growing layer of fresh snow. The only positive was the protection from avalanches provided by the ridge.

Soon the situation got worse. Wilde and Ferguson, the two who had dined on the yam feast that morning, began to fall ill. Both men would take turns dropping to their knees, doubled over with stomach cramps. Moments after the cramps commenced, the two had made a terrible mess of their trousers. Drake and Chhiri Tendi caught up to the two sickly men. Chatham was already standing over them, imploring them to turn around. They refused. "It will pass" Ferguson was heard to say between stomach spasms. Chhiri Tendi responded, "Yes, and it will keep passing. You are going to dehydrate."

The wind and snow increased until they feared a blizzard. Exposed skin was destroyed. Vision was wiped out. Footsteps became small and rare acts of falling forward. Despite the chaos, they could still hear intermittent eruptions getting closer. At one point, shortly after a disturbingly close eruption, a red, glowing ball the size of a rhino flew into view only feet away and hit the slope, skidding along and leaving a sooty streak as it went. Where it came to rest, God only knew. Perhaps it would make it all the way to Camp Two before stopping. Shortly thereafter, a lava bomb the size of a teapot struck Chatham square in the chest, the explosion burning a hole in his coat and further scorching his face. In response, he did what any reasonable man would do. He howled in pain, dropped flat on the ridge, and stuck his face into the loose, new snow. When he had caught his breath, he turned over. Again, the hideous gargoyle refused to turn back. All his lip remnants could generate was, "-uck all! I go uh!" The sentiment was clear even if the words were not: He was proceeding no matter what the cost.

The weather had almost brought them to a complete halt when Chatham yelled from the front of the line "We -eer!" Indeed they had made it. They were standing on the Eastern Ridge; the confluence of the northern and southern routes; the last turn before the summit. The storm prevented them from seeing anything of interest. Realization of their location only came from the fact they were no longer going up and that the earth dropped off in front of them, likely a straight shot down into the Icy Bellows and the Oculus at the bottom. To their left, unseen but certainly heard, was the summit, less than one thousand vertical feet away, booming and raging and throwing things. Drake wrote that night, "Half expcted [sic] to see an arrowed sign, broken ratling [sic] in the wind spelling in crooked letters 'Here be dragons.'"

Wilde moaned. He sputtered to the others that they should go back down several yards and set up Camp Four there. The wind on the Eastern Ridge itself was too great. They had to find some protection even if it was minimal. The frigid wind was damaging them, causing widespread frostbite right through oxygen masks and clothing. That night, all four Americans wrote separately in their journals of discolored toes possibly beyond saving. Chhiri Tendi told me in our discussion "I knew the toes on my left foot would have to be removed when we returned to civilization. The thought was not so much scary as it was sad. I liked my toes. They were good friends. And I remembered my mother, rarely a warm person, playing with them as a child. I would miss them."

They climbed down off the Eastern Ridge to set up their camp of two tents. There was no protection to be found anywhere. The wind whipping over the slope was just as aggressive as the wind at the top of the ridge. With no option left they chipped away at the ground, grinding up ice chunks and using them to build a berm. They slaved away, almost unconscious with exhaustion. The ancient ice did not give easily under their axes. Their arms ached above their numb fingers. Each strike against the ground sent pain traveling through their bodies. Wilde and Ferguson stopped work almost immediately because of the abdominal cramps wracking their beings. Chatham (an invalid himself), Drake, and Chhiri Tendi did the lion's share of work. When the berm was approximately five feet tall, they stopped and set up the tents leeward.

Once inside, Chatham, covered in wounds and frostbite from the ascent, fell asleep immediately, oxygen tank and mask still on. Chhiri Tendi had to pull it off of Chatham's burnt, frostbitten face. The depth of Chatham's slumber must have been profound, as dragging cold rubber away from burnt skin only caused a low moan. After aiding his fellow climber, Chhiri Tendi got into his bag, but did not sleep. His air-deprived, exhausted mind could not stop pondering Hoyt and Yuudai's fate. "What kind of Sherpa was I?" Chhiri Tendi asked. "Actually, what kind of *man* was I? There were two members of my team missing. Sure they may have climbed down, but knowing Hoyt's stubbornness, they didn't." Sleep never came. Physical and mental anguish stayed with him.

Drake was also sharing a tent with them that night because constructing a third shelter in such raw weather seemed excessive and potentially deadly. What's more, the added warmth of another body in the tight space could only help.

Meanwhile, life in the other tent was as grim as a hospital ward for the terminally ill. Wilde and Ferguson were taking turns soiling themselves and throwing up out of the tent door. Sleep would not come for them either. In its stead, Unconsciousness finally arrived and relieved them of their pain. Calls out to them from the other tent went unreturned. Drake ventured over to see if Wilde and Ferguson were even alive. They were alive, but completely unresponsive to the sound of their names and a firm shake to the shoulder. All they did was shiver. Drake gave up trying to revive them because the stench was overpowering, and he had resolved that he could help the two sick men better once he had some sleep under his own belt. But as a last gesture before leaving – possibly the only kind gesture anyone on the team had ever shown, he changed the two men's trousers for them, cleaned up their unmentionables, and disposed of the mess out in the raging storm. The two men remained in a vegetative state the whole time they were being attended to. Thanks to Drake, they now had Dignity along with temporary Peace.

The wind and snow continued to pummel the tents, threatening to collapse or bury them at any moment. The din of the weather and the summit canceled out everything else across all senses. The outer chaos and inner conflict taunted Chhiri Tendi. As night fell, he made a decision. "Even if it killed me, I was going out to find Hoyt and Yuudai. I couldn't sleep anyway and I sure as hell was not going to waste any more effort trying."

He suited up and walked out into an unwelcoming world.

Hoyt looked out over the darkening grey and then retired to the cave. He did not know the date. Time was no longer a property of the universe. There was only space, and very little of it. "Dearest Journal, Waiting for death. Won't be quick. Warm in here and puddle to drink. May starve over weeks. Scared." William Hoyt was actually scared. That is, he may have been scared many times in his life, but he was actually confessing to it in print.

As the snow in the cave melted from the warm vent in the rock, more of the vent became exposed and more warm air entered. It widened at the bottom so that the *rate* of warm air coming into the space increased. Of course, this temporary luxury would soon give way to tragedy in the form of shelter collapse.

"Mr. Hoyt. I thought of something." Hoyt must have concluded that the words were uttered by voices in his head. After all, Yuudai had not initiated a conversation since the airplane ride to Fumu. It came again; "Mr. Hoyt." Yuudai was now rifling through his backpack with a ferocious urgency. Then he was pulling out a massive piece of fabric, white silk divided into sections by some machine's stitch work. Hoyt was

- 313 -

hallucinating from his deprivations. "A marshmallow?" he wrote in his journal. "If so, big enogh [sic] to feed us forever!"

It was not a marshmallow. It had several ropes streaming off of it, leading back into Yuudai's pack, which was now half of its original size. As Yuudai unfolded the fabric, it took on a familiar form. A parachute. "I saved it after our arrival," Yuudai uttered in hoarse, quiet, fluent English. "Just in case." He went silent again and simply stared at his expedition leader.

Hoyt was now alert. His world had just changed. Possibilities must have permeated into, and ultimately flooded, the hulls of his previously empty thoughts. He wrote later, "Heart beated [sic] agin [sic]. Fath & hope restord [sic]. God is grat [sic]!" His story would not end here. He could still prevail. The delightful turn was all due to Yuudai, this archangel sent from Heaven by way of the Orient, who now held in his hands the key to their prison cell. In his joy, Hoyt let out a quick "Ha!" and then promptly covered his mouth and excused himself for the outburst.

Yuudai continued to pull out the parachute. It was attached to a smaller backpack now being birthed from the larger backpack. Yuudai took the chute and carefully stuffed it into the smaller backpack so it would be ready for use.

The problem must have been obvious to both men the moment they individually became aware of the parachute's existence and utility. There were two men and there was one parachute. But perhaps at first neither man had been willing to let his thoughts travel to such a dark place. A discussion began. It never became heated or selfish. Voices remained calm. They considered the possibility of sharing, one person holding fast to the other who wore the chute, but they ultimately agreed such a move would end in two deaths. Another plan was hatched in which one man would jump wearing the chute while tied to a rope secured to their current perch on the other end. The man remaining above could then climb down the sheer cliff aided by the rope. This idea was also rejected because they did not have even a fraction of the rope they would require. What's more, if they had that length of rope, they would not have needed a parachute in the first place.

Hoyt recommended they draw straws. Yuudai refused. "Some day, when we both survive this, I will tell you about *bushido*, Mr. Hoyt. *Bushido* is the way of the good soldier. Bushido is my code. I cannot take the parachute. Go" he said. "I will find some other way. The team needs you. Go."

The author wishes he could write that Hoyt refused to do any such thing; that he would rather die alongside Yuudai than take the good man's only parachute from him; that he followed the teachings of the Good Shepherd and such an act was unconscionable. Hoyt wrote: "Took it, patted him on shulder [sic], thanked him."

In the blackness of the wee hours, Hoyt donned the pack and walked out into the storm. Yuudai followed him out briefly to check the weather, and then without any discussion (the weather would not permit it), Yuudai retired to his Den of Slush.

Hoyt probably did not hesitate, concerned if he *did* hesitate, he would lose his nerve. Any further thought would have led him to the realization he was going to land empty-handed. No tent, no food, no climbing equipment. He jumped into the blackness.

The parachute deployed gloriously but the wind made the subsequent ride down hell. "Parashoot [sic]. Wheeee!" Hoyt wrote later. We can only assume from the product of his nuanced pen that the drag on the chute was intermittent, causing violent drops followed by updrafts sending him far from his starting point. He landed on a pile of ice blocks, partway up the western slope of the former Maw. This landing point was a good thing if he was going to attempt a death march to the summit instead of retreating.

"That is how I found him," said Chhiri Tendi.

"I was climbing down the slope and then he passed me going up, not under his own power mind you, but dragged unconscious over broken seracs and rubble by a parachute caught in the crazy wind. I turned tail and began to follow him back up. I was wracked with pain, from my throbbing head to my frostbitten toes. I couldn't see much of anything through the snow even though morning was breaking. And I was following a meat marionette. 'Is this some bizarre spirit guiding me to the Land of the Dead?' I thought to myself. The world could not have gotten stranger or bleaker."

Chhiri Tendi finally caught up to Hoyt, grabbed him by the legs and stopped him. They lay for some moments in that pose, not moving at all and becoming buried in fresh snow. Fumu's summit raged above them, making an ungodly racket and belching glowing red disagreement into the skies.

Once Chhiri Tendi had enough strength and will to look up, he could not believe his eyes. In the increasing light, he spotted a lone tent peg inches from his face. With a shift of focus, he saw tins of food scattered among the dirty ice and snow. A tent, collapsed and covered in snow but otherwise intact, lay just to the right of his feet. There was equipment everywhere. More was likely buried under the snow. Either by luck or by the grace of God, they were lying in the middle of the remnants of Camp Three, the ill-fated outpost that had fallen victim to the collapsed maw.

With new-found energy Chhiri Tendi set up the tent. He came across an oxygen mask and tank while sifting through the flotsam and affixed them to Hoyt. When the tent was completed, he pulled Hoyt inside and shoved food into his mouth. "I didn't know at that point he had had access to water so I also tried to hydrate him" recalls Chhiri Tendi. He had found a sleeping bag and took some time placing Hoyt inside of it. After he had boiled tea and drank it down like a shot of brandy, Chhiri Tendi slipped into his own sleeping bag.

"Yuudai's gone," Hoyt mumbled from inside the bag. Chhiri Tendi recalls registering Hoyt's words and promptly falling into a dreamless sleep.

When they awoke, the entire day had passed and now darkness was coming. The weather had abated somewhat. Still the sky was overcast but the wind was calm and the snow had stopped falling. Hoyt was awake before Chhiri Tendi. He had fallen asleep with his mask on. When the oxygen in the tank was used up, his own gasps woke him. A night of air had also revived him. He was not in the least bit interested in catching up on the events of the morning with Chhiri Tendi. "I'm ready," he said. "Let us sally forth!"

Chhiri Tendi was more than happy to do so. They ate, got dressed, and ventured out into the cold dusk. Within a day, the expedition would be a single team again, reunited at Camp Four high upon the Eastern Ridge. But they would be one man short. "I will speak well of Yuudai to the others" Hoyt wrote that morning. "And by way of a letter passed to the mercenaries in Calcutta assigned to pick up Yuudai, I will let his father know of his selfless act."

Chhiri Tendi and Hoyt hiked with newfound vigor. Their bodies had sustained permanent damage, including frostbite and ghastly bruises from falls on the maw's uneven remains. But these unpleasantries were drowned out by adrenaline coursing not just through their veins but through their very souls. Ear-damaging explosions were heard from the top of the mountain. Like trumpet blasts on a battle field. One of these blasts was followed by a coda of black rocks rolling down the slope behind them. "The rock hissed. Smoked," Hoyt wrote. The noise from on high became so disconcerting the two men took wads of notebook paper from Hoyt's pack and stuck it in their ears.

Before it was completely dark, Hoyt and Chhiri Tendi came upon Camp Four. Any relief they had felt must have been quickly replaced by horror and nausea. Camp Three had been ruined, but Camp Four and its inhabitants had been utterly annihilated. What greeted them was a composition done in blood, snow, marrow, and tent canvas - a scene so abhorrent the likes could only be found in an old penny dreadful or the Grand Guignol. It was impossible to obtain a body count unless one was willing to deal in fractions.

Chapter Fifteen: The Oculus Part I

River Leaf peered down into the darkness. If the night around her was pitch black, then the hole beneath her was even more so. When she lit her torch, it did not help. She could only lean over the hole and aim the beam for so long before having to back away. The arctic wind emanating from the Oculus was simply too much for a person to bear even in small allotments, especially a woman. It shoots out of the ground with the aggression of the Conqueror Worm itself.

She tried calling down to him, but the noise of blasting wind and the eruptions miles above her overwhelmed all other sound (What mosquitoes are to the Amazon, explosions are to Fumu – a maddening annoyance that simply will not relent). The weather was bitter here at the bottom of the Icy Bellows and River Leaf must have known her time to act was limited. Snow had begun to fall at that point, and this only served to add to the bite of the wind. She sent a flare into the Oculus. Perhaps she felt that such an act might provide a glimpse of the scene below. If she were to see McGee alive in the glow, then it would alert him to her presence and she would press on in her attempt to rescue him. If the light presented her with no sign of him, or a sign of him obviously dead, then she would give up and hike out of the Icy Bellows immediately toward Camp One at the Rakhiot Glacier (a relatively easy hike, surely the shortest and gentlest route out of the Icy Bellows' bowl). The only question was what would she do if she saw McGee intact but not moving? Should she assume he was alive and make a rescue effort, or that he was dead or dying and not unnecessarily risk her own demise?

Likely bracing herself for the cold, she leaned over the hole and fired her flare gun into it. The shot worked quite well. Although the light made evident there was a seemingly bottomless hole below her, there was also a large chamber *ringing* the hole whose floor was some twenty-five feet down. The flare landed on the floor of the chamber. Only feet away from the flare, not even noticing its phosphorescence, sat a very much alive McGee. The vision must have been haunting. He was seated on a rock, motionless, bathed in red flare light. He was holding up a human head.

River Leaf may have been moving quickly to get the rope ready or she may have been recoiling from the cold blast. Whatever the reason for her sudden activity, it caused the ice beneath her to give way. The Oculus consumed her. She fell, but like McGee, the chamber floor broke her fall so she did not disappear down the throat of the dead volcano. Landing on her pack may have been the thing that saved her, for she did not break anything.

McGee had been writing in his journal since falling into the Oculus in order to – in his parlance – "not go nuts." His awkward gibberish was enough to paint the picture:

> *"River Leaf fell from the sky. An angel sort of. Here I was alredy [sic] dead, but she came to return me to life. She got up after falling. semmed [sic] ok. But scared and sad mabe [sic]. I didn't move cause I think mabe [sic] I was still in shock. I looked at Hoover's head. 'Zack Hoover. I knew this guy, river leaf.' He had been a chum of junk's back in the states. They new [sic] each other from climbing. I also became his friend. He was funny and as crazy as we were. We chased tail together. He got me into some swank parties. I liked him. Now here's his fucking head."*

We can only shudder and imagine that the cold air in the cave and lack of elements had preserved the head well. Perhaps its white mouth was still forming the words to tell Chhiri Tendi they were indeed higher than

Everest. What a proud moment it had been up on Fumu two years earlier. The sort of moment in which a man is certain he is unstoppable. Infinite. An invincible ego housed in a mortal body. Brought to nothing in the end but a stone in a pit.

McGee's notes – written terribly in near full darkness - suggest that he wept for the better part of a half hour while River Leaf consoled him. We must assume she too was terrified, but the writings tell of a woman who kept her wits about her. Possibly she was too busy taking inventory of their environs, considering every detail for signs of escape.

But any opportunities for escape remained elusive. The flare had long gone out. There was almost no light source at all. The only sensation in that place is the sound of cold air rushing up from the vent and out of the Oculus. River Leaf lit her torch and had a look about. They were in the mouth of the long-deceased volcano. This had once been Fumu's summit tens of thousands of years ago, back when she was twice her current height. Then an eruption occurred of such magnitude that the lava chamber beneath Fumu had been entirely spent and the Earth collapsed down into the chamber's vast space. The cold air still rushing out from below is inexplicable to this day. In theory there is nothing down there anymore to be expelled. Even if there were a deeper hidden volcanic chamber, then the vent should have been spitting out hot air. There is obviously no such thing as cold lava, but this place must have given off the sense such a thing did exist and was ready to spring forth from below at any moment.

Belgian adventurer Jean-Claude Bastiaens, who explored the chamber several years later, wrote that "its shape makes one feel as if he is inside a giant, hollow ice tulip. From the vent hole at our feet, the floor fans out about eight metres in all directions. It then curves gently upward to become the walls. As the walls rise, the circumference of the room decreases until it became the Oculus at the top."

River Leaf tied her ice axe to her rope and attempted throwing it through the Oculus, but that did not work. Her one throw that did manage to reach the surface found no purchase and fell back down into the vent. She pulled it up and tried no more. The Icy Bellows above them was made of maddeningly smooth snow and ice. The axe would never find anything upon which to catch. Then she tried climbing up the walls and slowly-rising ceiling of the cave, hammering in ice screws as she went. But despite the fact River Leaf was as light as dandelion snow, each screw would fall out under her weight. She sat next to McGee who had not moved at all. "The only moving I did was shivering. I was cold and I think in shock" he wrote.

So as not to waste the remaining power in the torch, River Leaf turned it off and they sat in the dark. There could be no doubt, McGee said to River Leaf, that Junk had refused to rescue him. That was good by him. He would rather die than end his friend's journey. McGee also promised her that he would calm down sooner or later, and that when he did, he would help get them out of the Oculus. "I just needed [sic] to let things sink in," he wrote. "Then I'd be redy [sic] to win my million dollar bet."

How River Leaf responded to this is not easy to envision. She may have been disgusted by the endless bluster of the foolish men entering her life. Or perhaps she felt remorseful for questioning Junk's judgment. He had only done what McGee had wanted. The fact it worked in his favor was only a lucky boon. What River Leaf felt about this we will never know.

River Leaf extracted two sleeping bags from her backpack and laid them out on the ground. Had Junk not purchased two sleeping bags for River Leaf back in Darjeeling, the end would have come sooner for either the squaw or the fat Irishman. But that good fortune aided them tremendously now, and the two unlikely adventurers lay down for the remainder of the night. They were awake the entire night. Their hopes of tackling the problem well-rested would not come to be.

When daylight did shine down from the Oculus and their living quarters turned deep blue, McGee was weeping again. River Leaf made a half-hearted attempt to cheer up the old street tough. She pointed out that they were at the true summit of Fumu at that very moment so McGee had actually beat his best buddy to the top. That had to be worth doubling the pay out. McGee wrote: "Nice of her to try and make me laugh. But a laugh wouldn't happen [sic] as I was to emberaced [sic]. I just blubbered again, 'I will find my bravery, River. I swear. Soon. I swear.'"

Chapter Sixteen: Cannibals!

Upon returning to base camp several days later, Drake wrote in graphic detail about the events befalling Hoyt's team just below the Eastern Ridge:

"I am writing this all down so soon after the event because, despite the pain it dredges up in my heart, I wish to never forget it. For if I forget, then that only creates an opportunity for me to remember anew, and that I could not bear.

"Chatham and I slept fitfully on the night of the tenth. It was the height of the storm and Camp Four had provided no protection from the wind. When I awoke at dawn, three things were immediately evident. Firstly, Chhiri Tendi had left. Wherever he had gone, he had taken his equipment with him. Secondly, Chatham was wide awake and sitting up in the corner of the tent, his eyes showing naked fear even through burnt, deformed eyelids. He was shaking uncontrollably. Thirdly and finally, there was a sound coming from outside the tent the likes of which I had never heard before nor do I ever hope to hear again. It was the sound of a man screaming. But the screams conveyed an unfathomable quality of distress, the kind of distress one only hears in the most vocal of infants as they are pulled from the birth canal. I mouthed to Chatham 'What is happening' to which he shook his head violently as if to reply 'I haven't the slightest" or maybe "This is not happening this is not happening this is not happening.

"I peeked one eye out of the tent and saw before me the worst sight of my life to date. There were four men, none of whom I had ever seen before, eating someone alive. I could not see whether the meal was Wilde

or Ferguson and the scream could not be used for identification purposes. Three men held him down while another was chewing into the flesh of his arm. They had already removed other body parts - feet, testicles, fingers – and had thrown those away onto the snow behind them. Blood was everywhere. Then they moved, but for a moment, and I saw it was Wilde upon whom they feasted. Ferguson's body lay right next to Wilde, already destroyed, missing eyeballs.

"If this sight were not baffling enough, the strangers wore white attire from head to toe, probably as camouflage. It was a strategy similar to that of the Germanic Harii warriors, albeit exchanging black for white. Of course, the white camouflage of their uniforms was now splattered with maroon. Topping off this ensemble was the one object on their uniform that was not white: a cobra tied around each of their necks like ascots. These were no doubt some sinister form of heraldry, the origins of which I did not care to understand.

"Making the scene more surreal still was the weather. The storm had broken and the sky was a deep blue. Only the summit remained grey. The sun had risen and the wind was unusually calm for 28,000 feet. Had I cared to look at the lovely, sweeping vista, I would have been able to see the Himalayan peaks to the south, the flat stretch of the Terai beyond them and at last the dense, lush forests of India on the horizon. But given current circumstances, the view was not to be. What was happening only ten feet away held far more gravity.

"I closed up the flaps and moved to the back of the tent next to Chatham. What was there to do? Nothing? Nothing. Perhaps something, but in my panic the ideas just did not come. I intentionally do not carry knives on climbing campaigns (they tend to give a climber unpleasant options when tied to someone who has gone over the edge of a precipice) and I had no other weapon at my disposal. Nothing came to mind. Nothing, that is, except the scene of unholy carnage I had just witnessed

outside. I held back vomit. The altitude was also sapping my ability to make any decisions whatsoever. The look in Chatham's eyes suggested he was in the same predicament. Our brains did the least amount of work possible: regulating basic body functioning, and they did not even do that job well anymore, sending every system into a poorly organized frenzy of activity.

"The screaming outside became a tired, half-conscious moan. The moan then included a bubbling sound as fluid blocked air passages. Then a crescendo in which the moan returned to high pitched scream one last time, a loud snapping sound, and then merciful silence. Ferguson and Wilde were gone...most of their bodies and all of their souls.

"'Hello' came a voice from outside. It was friendly and accompanied by laughter from colleagues. I could not place the accents. English was not his first language, but he was certainly fluent in what appeared to be British English. 'Good morrow. Where is the one they call Chhiri Tendi?' I couldn't speak. 'We know you're in there. We're not fools. Is Chhiri Tendi in there with you? These two meals were white eyes. Not Chhiri Tendi. We want him, and then perhaps we'll leave you alone?'

"I knew then what I had to do. I had to make a run for it. I would race out of the flaps of the tent as fast as my straining lungs could take me, ice axe in hand, and glissade down the slope. My pack was next to my sleeping bag. I filled it with as many things as I could think of and started putting it on my back. Chatham was not moving so I signaled to him to please do the same. He simply shook his head. There was no way he was going to muster the courage to move, let alone leave the tent! The man outside began to speak again. His voice was closer now.

"'How rude of us not introducing ourselves! We are the Nepalese Cobras: Cannibal Division.' With that, a huge, curved blade cut through the tent only a foot from my face and then disappeared.

"I continued to pack, hoping to get away from these savages. I suspected I had enough to survive at least down to the cliff that my failed 'magic rope' had gotten us up. There I would need to move quickly to set up a rappel. Perhaps they would not chase me that far? Maybe they would let me go? No way of knowing.

"From outside, I heard some complaints in what sounded like Nepali. Groans mixed in with the words. Some of the cannibals were not well perhaps?

"The knife slashed through again, turning the wall into ribbons. 'This man Chhiri Tendi owes the Nepalese Cobras. Owes us in blood. Owes us in cries for mercy.'

"I had been warned about Fumu's cannibals before. Several teams, including Malick's, had returned with tales of their brutality. But I had considered the claims so preposterous as to be figments of climbers' exhausted imaginations. I had also heard rumors [sic] of the Nepalese Cobras, a small, crazed group of insurgents, spawned from the noble and unparalleled Gurkha infantry, hell-bent on banishing or killing all interlopers in Nepal. I could not believe Chhiri Tendi was at odds with these monsters; certainly not an enviable position in which to be. Then again the position Chatham and I were in at the time was no better.[7]

---

[7] The cannibals' manifesto, found years later in a cave and written in human blood explained their *raison d'etre*: "We have learned a harsh lesson over the centuries; that complicity in the designs of other nations will be the downfall of the great nation of Nepal. For these other nations are cannibals. They cannibalize land, culture, resources, wives, children, fighting strategies, languages. And what they do not eat, they spit out. We are their trash. We are their refuse. We are not worth a farthing to them. They leave us hungry and penniless on the side of the road after devouring our resources. Such behavior will no longer stand. From this moment on, let it be known that we are the ones who eat."

Subsequent research on the events at the Hoyt camp that day revealed that the cannibals had been following Hoyt's porters since Calcutta, just as they had done so many times before with countless teams of Western Men and their coolies. Their modus operandi had been to track colonialists as they entered the Kingdom without welcome, wait until they were at their most secluded and their most fragile, and then kill them.

"'Chhiri Tendi is not here' I yelled out. 'He left to find our expedition leader. He went west.' I lied to save Chhiri Tendi, maybe the bravest thing I've ever done, but it did not matter because my words were ignored by the men outside. I heard more groans. Some of the cannibals were in pain. The speaker kept talking to them in another language. Nepali perhaps. Then he said to me 'Your fellow adventurers in the other tent. Were they....fresh?' I told them the men were in fact not fresh. Both suffered from food poisoning. Then I lied. I said we were suffering from food poisoning as well. My bravery, my concoction of lies, was really no more than semi-consciousness; dream states aiding waking thoughts. I looked at Chatham cowering in the corner, his face a monument to unsightliness. Its paisley blotches of blue and red skin flaked and rose up in a scatterplot of welts. A perfect simulation of putrefaction. 'We've also caught some kind of flesh-ravaging scourge,' I yelled to the cannibals. '...an airborne syphilis we think!'

"The moans outside increased and the leader seemed deeply concerned. His fellow men were collapsing. They were throwing up. The food poisoning had hit them at an alarming rate. 'The meat of the Americans has made my brothers sick! I cannot save them! I have no way to get them down the mountain! This is Chhiri Tendi's fault! Give him to me now!' I swore to him Chhiri Tendi was not in the tent and that we had

Back in Calcutta, the cannibals, disguised as Calcutta denizens, had asked a group of porters about the location of their charges. The porters had responded truthfully, for they had nothing to hide, that some Americans (Hoyt and team) were waiting for them at Fumu. In the course of the discussion, the fact arose that one of the Sherpa signed up for the expedition was none other than sardar Chhiri Tendi. What luck for our cannibal ghouls! The Cobra's – of whom the cannibals were but a subset - had promised long ago to someday exact revenge on the son of the man who had killed their leader years before. The attack on Hoyt's team therefore addressed two Cobra goals in one climb...kill colonialists and exact revenge on Chhiri Tendi, a local enemy of the Kingdom.'7

One curiosity to address: The cannibals pre-date the Cobras. The cannibals have been mentioned in accounts of Fumu expeditions going back almost a half-century, well before the Nepalese Cobras existed. I can only assume the two had existed separately up until a point and then joined forces. The "Cannibal Division" may have been absorbed into the Cobras.

food poisoning and pestilence and that he should not touch us and that he should go away if he knew what was good for him. He did not buy my story and began slashing at the tent furiously with his weapon.

"I had no other choice. I grabbed my tent-mate who was now too far into shock to resist. With a surge of energy, I stuck his head through one of the slashes in the tent's roof. 'Feast on this' I bellowed. Upon seeing Chatham's ghastly visage, the attacker yelled in terror. The yell became less piercing because the man seemed to be half-falling and half-running away from the tent. The ruse accomplished, I let Chatham down. He fell back on the ground, eyes rolling back, his exhaustion having turned into a kind of defensive slumber. I would not be able to help him.

"The window of opportunity was now open. With my pack now on my back, I pushed out of the tent flaps. I almost tripped over three people on the ground, dressed in bloody white, doubled over in agony. I stepped on one of them with my crampon, unintentional but well placed. It sunk into his neck. His blood shot up in three separate, parallel fountains, each corresponding to where one of my boot spikes had punctured flesh covering his jugular.

"Their leader had not run away. The Chatham trick had only fazed him. He lay just feet away, near the corpses of my colleagues, on the ground and looking angry. When he saw me make a wearied run for it, he bolted up – as if he had access to all of the oxygen in the world – and ran at me. 'You are not going anywhere!' he yelled.

"Then he was upon me. He grabbed onto my backpack and, moving faster than me, pushed me down and forward. I landed face first in the snow. He straddled me and punched me a few times in the ribs. Then there was a pause in the blows as he unsheathed his knife. 'No' I thought. 'The end has come.' He fell forward on top of me and my pack so his head was over my head, his legs closed around my legs. One hand pulled off my hat and grabbed my hair, pulling my head up out of the snow. His other

hand reached around and placed the blade of the knife to my throat. I felt him playfully sink his teeth into the top of my head while making a growling sound. I screamed as a chunk of my flesh pulled away. Then he hissed, 'Beneath armored, prickly skin, Humanity is the sweeeeetest fruit.' Those words haunt me to this day."

"I prepared for the blade upon my neck. But that was not to be. I felt a spastic, convulsion in the small of my back. It had a mechanical quality to it. I heard metal snapping against metal and springs unwinding. This was followed by a feeling of intense heat in the same location. The hand holding my hair slacked as did the one holding the knife. The legs around my legs did not seem to be there any more. Blood and saliva dripped onto the snow next to my head.

"The metal and heat led to only one conclusion: My assailant's movements had deployed the second 'magic rope' which had been located in my backpack. The man was impaled through his stomach. I did not know this for certain until I turned onto my side and slid out of my backpack. I have never seen a man so dead in all of my life. He was run through by my invention. His gut had been catapulted elsewhere (I luckily never ran across it). Steam now rose from the cavity but was whisked away every few moments by wind blasts.

"All was silent now. The other Cobras were dead or unconscious. I went back into the tent, curled myself into a ball, and wept. Chatham was next to me, still passed out. I covered him with his sleeping bag. I lit a cigarette with shaking hands and drew off of it with abandon.

"My head was not clear. I could not concentrate on anything relevant; anything pertaining to my survival. The altitude and shock had done their damage. I laid down, empty of energy. My thoughts darted to arbitrary subjects like my dead wife, the secretary I had had an affair with at GM, and a balloon I had won as a child at a fair in Lansing that popped and left me in tears. These thoughts would occasionally be interrupted by visions of half-eaten men and guttural sounds of problematic digestion. But through all of these visions, one thread remained consistent – a voice telling me it was time to go down. There was no question at this point. No summit was worth this. It was time to go down. I slowly realized that consistent voice was Chatham's. I opened my eyes and saw him lying next to me. He was practically dead, but he was croaking out the word like an incantation that might have the power to transport, 'Down...down...down.'

"I don't know how much time passed after that before I heard two familiar voices outside getting louder and closer. The talk turned to yells as they came upon the sight of our corrupted camp. When these people came through the tent flaps, I could not identify them because they were replaced in my head by hallucinations. One was the choke mechanism I had designed for the 1938 Buick Y-Job. The other was a carrot. The carrot came to me and called my name. The choke mechanism went to Chatham and shook him. I responded by simply saying "Down." The carrot understood immediately. "They need to descend. They are in shock." The choke mechanism slapped Chatham to clear his head, but the strike to his burnt face caused more than consciousness. It caused him to scream and flail wildly. To my hallucinating mind, Chatham was now Al Jolson. Jolson screamed and convulsed in anguish. I began to cry again.

"The carrot, now an ivory bishop from my childhood chess set, boiled tea outside and returned to administer sips to me. My head came back. It was Hoyt and Chhiri Tendi! They had returned! They were alive... frostbitten on their faces, but otherwise alive. "Are they all dead out there?" I asked. "Yes," came Chhiri's comforting answer, 'whoever or whatever the fuck they were". Catching my breath as best I could I explained the events of the morning. I did not realize it, but the entire day had almost passed. The sun was setting outside. I grew terrified. What if more of these monsters were coming?

"Time was now of the essence. Chatham was very sick and I was not much better. The lack of air and the bitterly cold temperatures were slowly killing us. Hoyt knew this and set about tying up Chatham in his bivvy sack. Once ropes were secured around him, Hoyt handed the end of the rope to me. 'Chhiri Tendi and I are going to continue to the top. You must go down with Chatham.' He seemed disinterested in doing the noble thing and giving up the climb to aid us. He pointed the way down the mountain (as if I didn't know which way was down in this rather clear dusk) and went about setting up his tent for the night amidst the puddles of frozen blood.

"Down we went, Chatham moaning while I lowered him. I was trying to let out the rope for him with hands reduced to useless ice claws. I descended through the night, not stopping for rest. I would let out the rope and drop Chatham into the darkness, hoping each time the ruined man would come to rest on some sort of ledge before the entire rope had been exhausted. We were lucky. He always did come to rest on something. When we came to the cliff where my "magic rope' had failed (we missed Camp Two entirely), I lowered him down with the utmost patience and care. When the rope slacked and I knew Chatham was at the bottom, I rappelled down . The sun rose. We saw Camp One. The Sherpa there waved to us and I collapsed in relief.

"All of my efforts with Chatham had paid off. He was still with us. The surfeit of air at this lower altitude had filled him with fresh life. He started to talk to the Sherpa telling them the trip down the mountain in the sleeping bag reminded him of a mudslide he had once experienced in the jungles of Peru. For once, I was thrilled to hear his voice.

"The Sherpa tended to us masterfully, seeing to our frostbite and wounds as best they could. Looking down at myself, I realized my return to society would not be pleasant. At least half of my body was ravaged by frostbite. Surgery would be required to remove much of me. The

cannibals had not touched my flesh, but Fumu had eaten her share. I will be a cripple.

"Now I sit here at advanced Base Camp at the bottom of the scree, two days after the slaughter. I look up at Fumu and see the clouds are rolling in yet again. I cannot even imagine what is happening to Chhiri Tendi and that bastard Hoyt right now. For Chhiri Tendi, I pray for only good things. May he reach the top unscathed and then descend safely. For Hoyt, I pray the mountain's ridges pull up from their earthly shackles like great arms and strangle the man to death."

Chapter Seventeen: The Eastern Ridge

September 11th. Misery held sway on the Eastern Ridge. Junk and Cole trudged forward with inexplicable effort. There was no way of accounting for the energy reserves they were now consuming. Had they tapped into some heretofore unknown inner well of Hope or Delusion or Wrath that made their current actions possible? Were they moving forward now like automata, their bodies advancing out of habit even though consciousness had jumped ship long ago? We cannot know. All that is available to us are the facts surmised from journal entries, local descriptions of the day's weather, and our own personal experiences facing improbable adversity.

What the storm of the past several days had deposited on the Eastern Ridge must have felt less like snow and more like a frigid swamp. It lay in icy drifts up to their waists. Junk, who led the way at this point, would make efforts to clear it with his hands and axe, but this proved too tiring. He needed to essentially fall forward with each step in order to move through it. And even though the sun now shone through clouds of blown snow, the wind made life miserable. It must have permeated their clothing and chilled their cores. Cole's frostbite had gotten worse. His cheeks were black. The fingers within his right glove were immobile. Although tethered to Junk, he trailed behind his leader by a full rope's length. Junk would feel the rope jerk taut as Cole would collapse in exhaustion. But each time, he would get up again and continue.

They travelled as close to dead center along the ridgeline as possible. The north side of the ridge, to their right, was hidden by cornices jutting out over the North Face and the Icy Bellows below. Straying from their route even a touch in that direction could mean a fall of thousands of feet. However, should they overcompensate and walk too close to the sheer cliff to their left, crumbling ice could give way and send them down into the ruins of the Maw, also thousands of feet below.

The din of the volcano now drowned out all other sound. Even when speaking in close proximity, the entire content of one's lungs was required. On occasion, smoking volcanic bombs of all shapes and sizes – cylindrical, bread crust, cored - dropped from the sky or rolled out of the cloud along the ridge. The falling debris left the snow pack dotted with holes, each one ringed with sooty ice, with some expelling wisps of smoke that would get caught up in the high winds immediately upon exit. Sometimes a piece of debris would hit a climber, but so far the pieces that had made contact were small and caused no problems other than leaving marks on clothing.

Pasang Dolma climbed several yards behind Cole. Unlike the Americans ahead of him, Pasang Dolma carried much of the weight of that evening's camp on his back. The weight slowed him down, but not much. He was strong and experienced. According to Junk's notes, the Sherpa showed no indications of exposure to the mountain's inhumane conditions. He did not have any frostbite. He did not suffer from altitude sickness. Granted, he was tired, but he seemed game to go forth. The same could be said about the four nasty Sherpa. Pulling up the rear, they never relented. There were no pauses in their stride, only monotonous progress. They may have had the personalities of demented, cantankerous old gammers, but they were vital to the goal of establishing high camp.

And high camp was where they were headed. It would place them just below the permanent cloud of the summit, where the ground would be equal parts snow and ash whorled together like marble.

If Junk was despondent over the deaths of Morrow, Taylor, and Fenimore, and the likely deaths of McGee and River Leaf, we cannot know. More likely his brain was not capable of such consistent thoughts at that point. The same could be said regarding Cole and his lost academic writings. His focus must have been exclusively on taking the next step and forcefully ignoring his growing frostbite. Even though the entire team wore supplemental oxygen at this point, thinking through things rationally was still difficult.

Rationality would have helped because at approximately 11 am, a choice needed to be made. The ridge split in front of them into two ridges that paralleled one another rather closely. From the writings of Hoover's team a few years back, they knew the ridge to the right would end abruptly after one hundred yards or so. The ridge to the left provided a straight shot to the cloud and the summit therein, but that ridge was steep and narrow. It was in between the two ridges that the other choice laid. It was the beginning of "Hoover's Route". You may recall that it starts out pleasant enough, gradual, smooth and protected by ridge walls on both sides. But then it whittles down to almost nothing, merely a narrow ledge scarring the north face like a varicose vein. That was the ledge where Hoover had had his head jettisoned into the blue. Walking such a ledge would be risky, not only because it was as skinny, fragile, and as vicious as a scorned mistress, but also because the wall above it rose at 100 degrees, meaning the climbers would have to lean out over the void. If the men *could* get past that ledge, then the route theoretically met up with a massive couloir which provided an easy, staircase-like path into the cloud and then the summit.

So there was the choice. Junk could choose straight and visible, but steep. Or he could choose meandering, gently sloping with one nasty ledge followed by *terra incognita*. No journal entries exist from this portion of the climb, but one must assume the choice he ultimately made was not considered too deeply. For as we now know, the condition of brain cells at 29,400 feet is frozen, slow, and depleted of sparks; certainly not conducive to rumination. Junk had lived, eaten, and breathed long shots his entire life. Now he chose the safe bet. He went for straight and steep, which in this case was the known quantity...at least up to the point of the permanent cloud. The "decision" made, the team pressed on, digging into the deep snow straight ahead of them, moving closer to where they would place Camp Four.

At about 6 pm, with the sun setting, the men dug in and set up their tents, canvas flapping violently in the high wind. They would try to sleep for six hours, and then Pasang Dolma, Cole, and Junk would leave the grim Sherpa behind and make for the summit. If all went well, they would be atop Fumu by sunrise. Then, triumphant, they would turn and make their way back to the distant world of laughter, women, and draughts – a place that must have seemed mythical and impossible to souls stuck in such a raw Hell.

No one could have possibly slept that night through the cold and the caterwauling of the mountain. Ejecta shot forth from the earth's deep places, barreling into the sky then landing on and around them. Small holes were scorched into the tent, allowing cold air to blow in. Sleep must have been even more difficult to come by because, in a way, they were already sleepwalking through their waking life. Sleep would not be recognizable as something different, made of unique stuff. Any dreams would have included climbing and ice and loud noise, and rising from slumber would have included the same.

Junk made one brief entry that night in his journal. The garrulous socialite wrote: "Leaf. McGee. Mom. Hoyt. End of this is nigh." He also added "I feeling light [sic]." He may have meant that he felt lightheaded but was too exhausted to finish the thought.

Some time just prior to midnight, Junk and Cole heard yelling from the Sherpa's tents. Pasang Dolma was incensed about something, throwing a wobbly which was directed at the other men in his tent. The hot-tempered Sherpa raise their voices at their leader. That they were rebelling against the orders of their sardar was odd enough, but odder was the fact that they no longer seemed to be speaking Sherpa. The new tongue was foreign to the Americans, still possibly of Nepalese origin, but new. The yelling stopped as quickly as it had started. "After what seemed like a long spell, we heard Pasang Dolma's voice right outside of our tent" Junk wrote later. No fear of being heard by the Sherpa, "he told Cole to run. Cole? Why Cole? Why not me? We both scrambled to get our boots, packs, and oxygen on."

Cole was first out of the tent. When Junk came out, he looked upon a ridge lit up by a full moon in the southern sky. Its angle was low enough to the horizon that Fumu's cloud did not obscure it. The scene must have felt like a dream; a dream wrought with unfamiliar symbolism. Men cloaked in white with dead cobras tied around their necks. The men's faces are the faces of people Junk knows, but playing a different role in waking life. They were the faces of the four unpleasant Sherpa. Why are they dressed like that? Why had they removed Cole's oxygen mask? And why are they holding a curved knife to Cole's throat? To Junk's right, he sees Pasang Dolma walking down the ridge, descending into obscurity. "We let him go" one of the men in white yelled over the sound of eruptions. "He is a fellow countryman. We showed mercy and let him live. Maybe he will be willing to join our ranks some day." Ranks?

Later that day, Junk would have an extended window of time to write down the events of the evening, and he did so in a rather thorough manner, aided by supplemental oxygen:

"All I could mumble in my confusion and exhaustion was the inevitable question 'Who are you?' Their response was unsettling in its strangeness, length, and eloquence[8]. The one man holding the knife to Cole's neck spoke, or rather yelled, over Fumu's racket:

---

[8] Editor's note: Interestingly enough, Tersely's book would later be called unsettling for the exact same reasons.

"'We are the Nepalese Cobras: Weapons Division. Our mission is to develop the weapons capable of liberating Nepal. We will cleanse it of the bacteria permeating its every facet, from government to school to steppes to mountain top. We mostly fill our days attacking British soldiers, stealing their weaponry. We had been in Calcutta last month for two reasons. First, we intended to meet Nepalese citizens in India who were involved in India's nationalist movement. They would be likely sympathizers with our cause. Although they generally agreed with our grievances against the West, they thought our methods – and our uniforms - were too garish. Too bedizened. We had no luck recruiting there so we killed several of them. Second, we were waiting to ambush a British minister named Galloway who was reported to be on his way to Nepal from England. We had heard he would have an entourage of soldiers guarding him. These targets were sure to get us on the front page of Indian papers. But as we waited in a portside tavern, we overheard you, Mister Junk. And we heard you, Doctor Cole. We had struck gold. Not only did we have Americans to rend, but we had an American who knew how to make a weapon that incinerates entire cities! The ultimate weapon. The weapon that can make Nepal not only independent, but feared! What needed to happen was patent; We disguised ourselves as Sherpa, spoke Sherpa, and threw ourselves at Pasang Dolma. The Cannibal Division of the Nepalese Cobras had taught us a thing or two about climbing, and we were trained in the Gurkha battalions to fight at high altitudes. You know the rest. We have feigned peonage ever since. Cole, your documents are not lost. We have them and will return them to you once we have begun our trip down the mountain. You are coming with us to Kathmandu. There, you will help us build an atomic bomb.'

"The guy kept talking and talking. Who goes on like that while holding a knife to someone else's neck? His bass-heavy voice was just forceful enough to be heard over the eruptions.

"And still *he went on, about how, yes, he did spit on the man-children's monastery, because Mano and his people had proved unwilling to join their cause. He found the man-children's pacifism offensive. Even after threatening to kill one of these man-children, and even after following through on that threat, the others just cried. They were useless to the Cobras. He found them to be an embarrassment to the Kingdom.*

"As this freak of nature jawed away, I became distracted. There was someone climbing in the moonlight. He was above us on the ridge, slogging toward the cloud. A tall guy, maybe 6 foot three or so. No one from my team. And then it dawned on me. It dawned on me like the coldest sunrise imaginable. That was Hoyt there. That was the bastard who had dared me here, the man responsible for every horrid event of the past month. And here I was getting a midnight lecture on geopolitical strategy from a lunatic. Take Cole, I thought. Take him but let me go. Seeing Hoyt so close was too much for me. Any consideration I may have had for my old, dear climbing partner was rendered inaccessible by the temptation.

"My captors did not seem to notice Hoyt making his way up the ridge. They were too focused on me. Cole seemed to be fading without the help of his oxygen. His head kept nodding and eyes rolling like so many drunks I had seen around Fenway. Hoyt! Hoyt! I just wanted to follow Hoyt! Stop talking, I thought. Go away. Kill me and end my suffering or leave me to complete my personal war. Hoyt was disappearing from sight. He had stood out as a dark figure against a bright ground of moonlit snow. But as he approached the cloud and the snow mixed more and more with black lapilli and scoria, he could no longer be easily seen.

"Another person appeared on the ridge between us and Hoyt. But he was climbing down to us. He moved quickly. He held out something in his hand. I would later find out this man was Chhiri Tendi, a well-known Sherpa who had aided Hoover in his efforts to reach the top of Fumu. I had no idea why he was approaching. Perhaps he didn't know of my

- 340 -

rivalry with his sahib and wanted us to join forces? Did he see there was a problem from so far away and now was coming to aid us? No. All of these theories were wrong. When he came close enough that I could make out finer details, I saw he was holding a gun.

"The Cobras finally saw him but did not flinch. When the approaching man took off his oxygen mask, the lead Cobra grinned. He spoke in Nepali to Chhiri Tendi, his sentences riddled with insincere laughter Chhiri Tendi did not seem as jovial. He looked angry. He also looked terribly frostbitten.. He had the gun aimed at the garrulous Cobra with the knife, but his aim was far from true. His arm moved haphazardly due to fatigue and wind."

Chhiri Tendi remembers holding the gun at these men who had killed his father. They did not seem scared, and Chhiri Tendi knew why. They knew his father had been tortured by the violence in himself; that he could not live with the knowledge that he had killed a man. Being aware of this, what were the odds the son of Phurbu Tawa was going to resort to similar violence? He was not going to pull the trigger, and the Cobras knew it. He is a Sherpa, a people who fancy themselves pacifists. But in the Cobras' opinion, 'pacifist' is just another word for 'coward.' "Put the gun down, Chhiri Tendi. You are not going to pull that trigger."

Chhiri Tendi responded, "Well, as an alternative, perhaps I'll stick this gun so far up your ass that the next time you gag on your lover, you'll shoot his testicles off." The Cobras all laughed out loud. The leader complimented Chhiri Tendi on his humour, saying that it was delightful but unable to help him now.

The lead Cobra said he was so confident in Chhiri Tendi's unwillingness to shoot them that he would remove the knife from Cole's neck. He pushed Cole forward several feet. The Cobra leader was now wide open. Chhiri Tendi did nothing. He was frozen – not with cold, but with indecision. Kill the men and continue the shame of his father, or spare the men and fail to avenge his father? Might there be another possibility? As Chhiri Tendi's mind churned, the Cobra leader said "We are going to leave now and take Cole with…"

"You're right" Chhiri Tendi interrupted. "I cannot kill you. Instead, I leave your fate up to the mountain." With that, he aimed the gun at the ridge immediately in front of the Cobras' feet and pulled the trigger. With a loud report, and despite years of frozen hibernation[9], the gun fired and the bullet disappeared into a kicked up cloud of snow and ash. And as quickly as a single beat of a skylark's heart, the cornice upon which the treasonous Gurkhas stood broke and fell away. The four aggressors disappeared down the north face of Fumu, yelling bloody murder until distance, wind, and eruptions conspired to swallow their cries whole. As quickly as the threat had arrived, it was gone.

After only a brief moment of taking in the scene, Chhiri Tendi threw Rauff's gun off of the ridge to the south where it descended toward the Maw, returning whence it came. He was upset, but not so upset he could forget his job and his charge. He turned and began catching up with Hoyt. He moved with fresh speed up the ridge, undeterred by the pack and oxygen on his back. The adrenaline suffusing the heart upon approaching victory cannot be underestimated. Frostbite, hunger, thirst; they all step aside when we know our goal is near. Chhiri Tendi was a new man, ready to follow his leader into the Unknown. "Many questions were about to be answered," Chhiri Tendi told me. "I felt that on the ridge. I felt excitement like I had never known. My failure on the Hoover expedition was about to be wiped clean. The top of Fumu would finally be revealed to us." He was off like a coney in the vegetable gardens of springtime.

---

[9] That the gun fired was by no means a miracle. The Germans know how to build reliable weaponry, and the guns they built during the World War II era were designed to fire regardless of inhospitable conditions.

Junk stood still and silent for a moment, eyes fixed on the place where the Cobras had been. Cole stared back. Had the Cobra leader not let go of his hostage, the hostage would have fallen as well. Cole's shocked expression betrayed that realization. The two continued to stare at each other, Cole with his mask off, Junk with his mask on.

"Thank Saint -austina" Cole shouted over the cacophony. Junk observed that his colleague could not get the initial "F" of the saint's name out due to frozen lips. "She has shown –ee -ercy!" He was laughing and crying at the same time. He was looking everywhere, considering his reprieve and taking in the sight of the world that was still his to enjoy. "I -ust say" he yelled through the tears and laughter, "that could not have turned out -etter!"

And with that a massive geyser of lava shot straight up where Cole had stood. The spew arced thirty feet above the ridge. Chhiri Tendi looked back at the event and saw Cole's detached arms hit Junk, as if trying to pick a fight despite lack of management. As for the rest of Cole, he was simply gone, incinerated, instantly cured of frostbite, and lost in the brilliantly lit night sky. Junk dove into the deep snow, as did Chhiri Tendi even though he was already easily thirty yards up the ridge. Bright red liquid spat out, not quite as high anymore, but still voluminously and in a wide span. Junk rolled about, trying to dodge volcanic bombs as they landed and hissed around him. He dug into the snow behind his head, hoping to hide as much of himself as possible. Lava poured over the edge of the north face but did not drop far before solidifying and turning to black rock. Then the lava stopped, and what was left was a fat and perfectly conical hornito with black smoke belching out of the top.

Junk's horror passed quickly; one might say too quickly for a sane man. He did not look back at his camp or the remnants of the explosion or the severed arms of his friend. Chhiri Tendi heard him give out a roar and begin to approach. Junk waded through the deep snow - passing Chhiri

Tendi without even a sideways glance to acknowledge the Sherpa's presence - on his way to Hoyt, the summit, and almost certain Death. Chhiri Tendi followed suit but was losing ground by the moment. The two Americans ahead of him were moving at a shocking clip, as if transported by a sleigh hidden beneath the snow. It did not help matters that Chhiri Tendi was weighed down by a heavy pack while Junk and Hoyt were unencumbered. Had Junk reasoned for even one moment through the fog of his dizzy anger, he would have realized Pasang Dolma was no longer with him. Not carrying a pack to the summit was foolish to a degree the mountains do not forgive. He could survive without a tent and cooker, but that assumes all goes as planned, with nothing to bollocks up progress. Should he be delayed even slightly – if he got lost in the cloud for several hours for instance – the mistake of leaving behind his pack could become deadly. Even the water supply he had manufactured earlier using ice melted on the cooker was now freezing in the canteen on his belt. The frostbite continued its own slow ascent up Junk's arms and legs. The master planner of business schemes and expeditions had skipped planning altogether at this, his most crucial hour.

Hoyt could not be seen when the sun came up on the morning of the 12th. He was already in the cloud. Junk was almost there. "The sun was behind me" Junk wrote later. "I knew it would be only a memory in a matter of moments, yet still I did not slow down nor did I turn to look back at her brightness. She had stopped providing warmth long ago anyway. Her light had become a meaningless flirt." And then the sun set upwards, rising over the inverted horizon of Fumu's cloud.

Chhiri Tendi wrote:

"When I reached the cloud several minutes after Junk, I was terrified to enter it. If I removed my mask, would it be breathable? Would I be able to see a single inch ahead of me? I thought of my wife and child one more

time, pictured them taking their late-day walk around the village with me,
a fly landing on my wife's brow and her brushing it away, my son running
ahead with the intent of hiding behind a fence and jumping out to scare us.
But I would run behind him, hands out, turning the prank on him. With
this thought, I left the frigid wind and sunlight behind and walked up into
the cloud. The world around me changed immediately..."

Chhiri Tendi could see several feet ahead of him, and then he could not, and then he could again. The density of the cloud changed moment by moment. The temperature shot up to blistering heat, and then it dropped again, like taking a steam and then jumping into a lake in winter. This made it impossible for Chhiri Tendi to regulate his core temperature. If he disrobed, he would suffer frostbite from the cold. If he kept the layers on, he would slowly cook. The ground around him was marbled, whorls of black ash and stone flowing into snow, slush, and rivulets of icy runoff.

But in the moments when the cloud eased its grip on Chhiri Tendi's vision, the items that truly captured his attention were the fumaroles. Conical towers rose up in impossible angles. Most were narrow, tall, and black. Some easily reached a height of twenty feet. They presented like sinister, giant ant hills. Ones that had been spawned by recent eruptions continued to belch black smoke from their tops. Older formations did nothing but erode at an imperceptible pace. Chhiri Tendi would catch an eruption out of the corner of his eye and witness lava pour down the steep slopes of Fumu. But again, the liquid would only make it a short distance before solidifying into black rock, and then snow would land on it, sticking in colder sections and melting in others. The surface of a distant planet would be more welcoming. Hostility and Volatility ruled here, utterly uncontested.

The pack weighed Chhiri Tendi down, yet he felt a lightness of step he could not explain. In no way should this lightness be confused with joy.

He was *in agony*; much closer to dead than to vibrant. But he felt this lightness nonetheless, making his steps slightly easier even though his body was doing battle with other sorrows.

Clouds blocked his sight entirely. He had no idea where to go. He could not simply follow the ridge back down because the ridge no longer existed. The clouded top of the mountain did not have the luxury of such obvious features as ridges by which to judge location. The top was vague, impossible to map, visible but then disappearing too quickly to estimate coordinates. Even if you could get your bearings between cloudy gusts, the lava flow would change the shape of the landscape around you moment by moment. So really, in the cloud, there was no state for a living organism to be in other than lost.

"All I kept thinking was that I was in the deepest of shit" Chhiri Tendi recalls. "This was really ridiculous. No money or sense of loyalty was worth this. Why did I continue to drag myself forward? I could have turned and at least tried to find my way out. I was pretty sure I would be dead from exposure to chaos within a few hours."

But then all thoughts of that sort went away as the clouds cleared for a moment and he took in what was happening roughly forty feet ahead of him. In the short period of time Chhiri Tendi had to focus his eyes and survey his surroundings before the clouds obscured his sight again, he saw Junk had caught up with Hoyt. The two colossi were fighting at a pace hampered by their pains. Punches and kicks came painstakingly slowly. Kicks resulted in the kicker losing his balance and stumbling backward. Punches landed like sacks of potatoes placed gently on a kitchen counter by the lady of the house just returned from market.

But the brief sighting of the two men fighting was not the most fascinating thing to Chhiri Tendi. No, what was most fascinating was the two men's odd relationship with the ground below them...

Chapter Eighteen: The Oculus Part II

During the day the cave was a deep, haunting blue and in fact quite lovely. At night it became the darkest place on God's Earth. It seemed haunted. Wind blowing up from the massive hole in the middle of the cave made whistling sounds that were communications from the Dead who had shared a common Doom long ago.

River Leaf had set up her tent and shared it with McGee, the latter remaining mindful and respectful of her gender at all times. McGee spent his waking hours despondent, waiting for the end. River Leaf spent hers thinking, looking at the Oculus, sizing up the walls, testing the integrity of the ice floor. She did not seem to have any plan, but she was not going to stop thinking until she did, or until death pre-empted her. "Why does she bother" McGee wrote. "With time thats [sic] left, she should do like me and think about good stuff from her life." But McGee was probably not ruminating on the joys of his life as much as he claimed, for most of his entries from the cave are more of the "Oh my God, we are going to die" sort.

At one point during their imprisonment, McGee wondered aloud whether Junk might make it to the summit. River Leaf apparently did not even allow McGee to finish the thought before snapping "Who cares? He betrayed you." McGee became angry. Just as he could not claim to understand her culture and her take on the world, so should she refrain from judging his relationship with Junk. He completely approved of his friend's decision to press on to the top, so why shouldn't she?

River Leaf may have intended to answer, but the attempt was interrupted by four men falling through the Oculus one by one. The first tried to grip the edge of the Oculus while passing through it. He failed and fell past McGee and River Leaf, screaming into the volcano's dead mouth. The scream disappeared into the distance as the other three men individually landed in their turn on the lip of the mouth, only feet away from where McGee was sitting. One kept sliding right past McGee and made it far enough to slam into a wall of the cave. A shower of ice chunks and snow fell in after them. By the angle and location at which they landed, it seemed they had been moving at a very high speed when they hit the Oculus and dropped through it. Had they, like McGee, slid down the Icy Bellows from a great height and not arrested their fall? That scenario was rather likely.

All was quiet for several minutes. The three fallers who had not gone down the vent moaned, thereby ensuring our heroes they were not dead. According to McGee's notes, the one near the wall sat up first, but did not dare stand too quickly. After a few more minutes the other two sat up as well, arms wrapped around bent legs. McGee and River Leaf recognized each one as they sat up. They were the tempersome Sherpa. But McGee and River Leaf could not understand why the Sherpa were wearing stuffed cobras around their necks.

From a sitting position, in a slurred voice clearly experimenting with English for the first time, one of the fallers began to announce, "We are Nepalese Co-..." but another one interrupted him with a short utterance in Nepali. The interrupter gestured toward the hole that had swallowed their cohort moments earlier. McGee wrote "He shrugged his shoulders and made a look on his face that seemed to say 'On second thought…forget it.'" At that, the person who had initiated the introduction started anew. "We fell."

The Sherpa were all bruised from their falls, but they also seemed to heal quite well and were hobbling about within a few hours. They had some food among them in their packs and shared it willingly with the Irishman and the Indian. Their bilious dispositions seemed to be gone.

Camaraderie now came easier to them. To our heroes, it must have seemed the change in nature came from the precarious situation which they now faced. But as you the reader know from previous chapters, there was likely another reason. These ruffians had lost their leader down the hole, and so the "weapons division" of the Nepalese Cobras was no more. To quote a wise man, "Kill the head and the body will die."

This odd collection of people spent several days in the cave. Plans of escape were regularly hatched and then thwarted. A tent canvas was tied to one of the smaller Sherpa who was to use it like a parachute over the volcano's windy mouth. He was also secured to the rest of the team by a second rope so he would not plummet to his death. Instead of floating upward on the winds, the tent went flat and dropped downward. Ice axes were used to pick away at the cave walls in an attempt to make a pile of ice high enough to allow for escape. The ice in the walls proved too firmly packed after centuries of downward pressure to allow for chunks any larger than a man's cufflink.

As each plan failed and each morsel of food was consumed and the chill began to permeate bone, hopes diminished. McGee wrote: "Boston...the cheers of Fenway...the sissys [sic] with the skinny boats on the Charles yeling [sic] 'stroke'...the ladies gigling [sic] in the Beekin [sic] Hill Tavern...I see it all rising up like one loud ball of stuff, leaving us behind and exiting by the hole above us. I'd wave bye to it if anyone else could see it."

On September 15th, McGee and River Leaf had been in the cave for five days and the Sherpa for three. The group had become quieter. There was no longer much to say. Attempts to escape had ended and everyone rested in their bags or sat on the ground looking empty. McGee was still writing on occasion, an amazing feat considering who we are discussing. "I hope Junk makes it" he wrote that day.

As sun set over the western lip of the Icy Bellows and the light dimmed in the cave, weeping could be heard, not from McGee, but from some of the Sherpa. McGee wrote "Hope is gone. This is our grave." For the first time, River Leaf showed signs of weakness. Like the others, she sat and stared at nothing. Her mouth hung open. Her brain was undoubtedly still trying to generate plans of escape, but the gears of thought were locking up, and dreamy irrelevances were taking hold.

A conversation broke out in the dark that night. It was no longer the type of exchange that focuses on the future, planning and problem-solving and otherwise seeking to improve one's place in the world – the type of conversation that came most naturally to the breed of person trapped in this cave. Rather, it was a conversation focused on the past. Such conversations too have a purpose, but it is quite different. Its purpose is to provide a blanket against the cold. It is the embracing of a child after she has skinned her knee. It is the fire in the hearth lit by the old woman, awaiting the shepherd returned from the fields in February. This conversation was not for bettering lives, it was a palliative before death.

McGee had started it, talking about how much he loved gambling. He loved the way his heart raced when the first roll came out in craps and the joy he felt when it was a seven, especially if he had a lot of money on the line. One of the Sherpa – the one who had a tenuous grasp of English - understood this just enough to say he agreed. He loved to gamble as well. But even better, he liked dancing with young women. There was apparently one woman he especially liked who was taller than him but he did not care. He became very happy when she was around. When she left his presence, his life was just a place to wait until she returned. "And you, River Leaf?" the Sherpa asked to the darkness. He wanted to know what made her happy and what she missed about the world they had left behind. She did not respond. Perhaps she was asleep? McGee wrote:

"I decided to help with the question cuz [sic] I was curius [sic] about her to [sic]. I asked wether [sic] she missed Boston. Nothing. 'Do you miss the Dakotas.' Nothing. She was mute. 'Teepees [sic]? Riding horses? Totem poles?' That got her. She said 'What's a totem pole?'"

Our dear, culturally-illiterate McGee did not know that constructing totem poles is a ritual of Indians of the American Northwest, not the Midwest. River Leaf would know as much about constructing totem poles as would a Lord Chancellor. With nothing else to discuss and a surfeit of hours to kill, McGee explained the concept to her, or at least explained what he had seen in picture shows and newsreels. And it was in this telling that McGee had his epiphany.

As soon as the slightest hint of light touched the cave in the morning, the captives were at work. McGee walked to one of the far walls of the cave. The biggest of the Sherpa climbed up McGee's back and then onto his shoulders where he took a seat. The Sherpa pressed his gloved hands against the low ceiling of the cave to secure his position on the Irishman's back. Then McGee began to walk, ever so slowly, toward the center of the cave. The ceiling height increased gradually above them as they moved. Once the ceiling became too high for the Sherpa to touch with his hands, he called out and McGee stopped walking. The next Sherpa, the one who knew some English then ran up to the men and began to slowly and gently climb up McGee's back. With his feet now planted on McGee's shoulders and resting his hands on the first Sherpa's shoulders, McGee began the challenging task of walking forward slightly without the first Sherpa's hands available to secure them by holding the ceiling. With space above him now, the English-speaking Sherpa scrambled up the back of the first Sherpa, mounted his shoulders and pressed against the roof. Three men now formed an object roughly twelve feet tall. They also stood halfway between the wall of the cave and the Oculus. The last Sherpa began to climb, but the human totem pole collapsed.

They didn't wait a heartbeat before trying again. Within moments, the three men were again one. McGee apparently did not falter. The weight above him meant nothing when compared to the hope of escape, of another glass of whiskey, of another spring day on the streets of the South End. The third Sherpa began his climb and the group fell once more.

Again they tried.

And again.

And again.

Then it worked. The four men were balanced on one another. McGee probably strained but not enough to be of any concern. He would not break. The Sherpa at the top held the roof for dear life with the Oculus only about two yards away and six feet above his head. River Leaf was next and last. Our fair lady hero was not what she used to be. Her demeanor, which most would describe as taciturn, was now being replaced with another kind of silence altogether. It was a flowering idiocy, and that did not become her in the slightest. River Leaf seemed "punch drunk" to use McGee's words. Her mouth hung open and she moved slowly. But she moved nonetheless. She began to climb up the backs of these friends and strangers and the light shining down on them grew brighter as the sun rose. The burden of her body on the others was negligible, starvation and other deprivations having diminished her weight to at most six stone. Her weakened mind did not hinder her progress. Drooling and gurgling like a simpleton, she reached the top of the human totem pole and took her place astride the shoulders of the highest of the three reformed Sherpa. The five of them stood as one, erect in the cave.

Jubilation turned quickly to despair. With all of them atop one another, they still did not reach the Oculus. They were eighteen feet high now but the egress was roughly three feet out of reach. For the first time since anyone on the journey had met her, River Leaf gave out a cry of emotion; not of defeat, not of anger, and not of grief, but something employing all three. It was now definitely over. Their bodies would be interred along with Hoover's head in this frigid, Godforsaken charnel house. For want of one more person, one extra body to reach the Oculus, their fate was sealed.

And that was when a man broke through the southernmost point in the cave wall. Steam poured out of the hole behind him. He was shirtless, bathed in sweat, and by the looks of him, Japanese.

The sweat on Yuudai's body had dried and now he sat shivering. McGee initially approached the stranger with caution. But now he saw that the gentleman was too tired and traumatized to pose any sort of threat. McGee quickly changed tacks and placed a blanket around him. After all, should the relationship prove friendly, and should this man be nurtured back to stable condition, he would become a crucial asset to the group.

Yuudai introduced himself. McGee reciprocated. McGee then fed Yuudai tea and dried meat from Yuudai's own pack. One of the Sherpa attended to a serious, weeping burn on Yuudai's left shoulder blade. It was then Yuudai launched into a tale about how he arrived in the cave. As you already know, Yuudai was not a man one would consider partial to talking. But McGee's description of that moment suggests Yuudai had changed in the course of the past several days.

The tale started back atop the Maw as Yuudai watched Hoyt parachute hundreds of feet down. After losing sight of his expedition leader, Yuudai had retired to the small snow cave he and Hoyt had constructed and shared for a time. The air entering the cave from a slit in the mountain's granite made the cave air wet, but slightly warmer than outside and for the most part livable. Yuudai had gotten into his sleeping bag and prepared for it to become his death bag. The air in the cave and the potable ice drippings were a blessing but also a curse. They would keep him warm enough and hydrated enough to starve and suffer hypothermia over a period of days instead of freezing to death within hours.

The slit in the granite was now very long because the snow was melting near its bottom. And it was no longer a slit. As more of it was exposed, it widened. This sped up the rate at which warm air entered the cave and, in an ever-accelerating cycle, it also increased the rate at which the slit exposed itself. Within a few hours, Yuudai was geared up and staring at a hole in the granite wall large enough to allow a man passage. There was no light in it. What was in there? It could be anything or it could be nothing. It could lead to an escape or it could end just beyond the extent of his eyesight. Shaking from hunger, Yuudai lugged himself and his pack into the darkness.

So began his blind journey through the inside of Fumu. Terrified and practically guaranteed the death of a pharaoh's wife, he stumbled forward. A catacomb of lava tubes presented themselves as alternatives for travel, but without sight, none of the options was preferable to the others. Decisions would have been superfluous. He just kept moving.

When light did appear, it appeared with a vengeance. The dead lava tubes he traveled often crossed live lava tubes and would illuminate the space, the atmosphere would become superheated, and the air would be replaced with poison. He had to cover his mouth with his shirt at such times and sidestep these obstacles. If he could not sidestep them, he would backtrack and try another route. After what he estimated was a day of wandering (he had no way of telling time so this was certainly was a loose estimate), panic set in. He had almost run out of the water he had collected in the snow cave, he had no food, and the lack of light brought on a kind of madness.

Several more days passed. He had stripped of all clothing save his undergarments. He moved forward with eyes closed because they were of no use to him anymore. Such a crucible would have stopped most men within an hour. Yuudai was not most men. Here he was, possibly days into his ordeal, eating crumbs, drinking nothing, and yet still moving forward.

On what he estimated was the second day, he heard water trickling. Yuudai found a vent carrying enough steam to form condensation on the walls. He drank deeply even though the water tasted of sediment. Unable to see where the droplets fell, he licked the walls in desperation. With this dire need sated, Yuudai collapsed in relief. He believes he slept for more than a day in the darkness. Or was it two? Upon waking, he collected as many of the droplets as he could in the darkness, listening for liquid hitting metal and then holding his canteen steady for an hour. Then he started moving again toward God knows what. A cul-de-sac? A sudden eruption of lava through the walls roasting flesh and muscle? An unseen drop-off sending him thousands of feet down? Or perhaps freedom? Maybe he would see home again. Might he get the chance to wed? Might he get the chance to see his father again and make him proud with his heroic return from Nepal and subsequent victories in battle? Yuudai could not know the answers to these questions, but he did know that he would do everything in his power to escape. He would keep moving, leaving the decision exclusively to Fumu.

Yuudai fell down a vertical lava tube. He fell very far, but only bumped his shins at the bottom. The feeling of descending was disheartening even though he knew he had started at a high altitude. When surrounded by darkness, the sense of going downward was smothering. It felt as if he had tripped into a graveyard plot. The end of the journey had come. He would never be found. He was destined to disintegrate over millennia and become one with this mute, eternal strata of granite.

His eyes had been closed because of their lack of utility. But by chance, he happened to open them now. And to his surprise, he could make out a light source only feet away from him; not direct sunlight but light nonetheless. It was a wall, not of rock but of ice. With little room for leverage and almost no strength left in his body, Yuudai used his ice axe to break through the obstruction, striking ice and crying out with each blow. The ice in this location was made cold by the frigid weather on its other side, but softened slightly by the warmth coming from the cave in which Yuudai struggled. It only took three swings for the ice to break, and that was when he met his present company.

Since watching Hoyt abandon him, Yuudai had burrowed through the heart of the world's tallest mountain - perforating it from the Maw on the north side to the Icy Bellow on the south - and lived to see daylight again.

After Yuudai ate, drank, told his tale, gathered his energy, and digested the idea of the Human Totem Pole, the group went back to the work of escaping. Yuudai, who was slightly larger than the Sherpa, took his place on McGee's shoulders. The three Sherpa came next. Then River Leaf. On the first attempt, with no moment of wavering, River Leaf reached up and out of the Oculus. She used her ice axe to hold fast to the blindingly bright outside world, slowly coming to *stand* on the Sherpa's shoulders. With a small jump and a prayer of hope she had learned from her people, River Leaf was out. The totem pole below her fell, but fortunately they fell backwards and not into the mouth of the dead volcano. River Leaf dropped a rope down. She secured herself, making her body almost parallel with the ice on which she stood and pulled out McGee. And one by one, the people rose from the hole. The geysers responsible for killing Morrow a week earlier were a long but gentle climb away. The party moved south toward the towers of steam.

They were on their way home.

Interlude

A nurse on the ward here once told me to "get some rest" after I offered up the fact that the Earth is not round. But it is as true a fact as there is. The Earth is not round. To be sure, a child drawing a picture of the planet will trace around a teacup or toy roundabout. However, these children are only following the dictates of their begetters and schoolmarms. We adults are the ones making the unexamined claims. Ask anyone on the street if the world is round and unless they are cracked, they will concur. Why do they do this? Because it is true? No. Because they *believe* that it is true? Possibly. The cleanest explanation is this: We say the world is round in order to distinguish it from the alternative of being flat. The former is certainly closer to the truth and yet it is still untrue. The mistake we make is that, in fact, there is no either/or distinction. A vast continuum exists between round and flat.

Consider a man's head. We say it is round, but is it? Certainly it is not flat. But the lower jaw protrudes out to form the severe ridge of the chin. The valleys of the orbital sockets compromise the mantle of the skull. The distance from the top of the head to the bottom of the chin is far greater than the distance between the ears. If anything, the head is closer to an oval. Round? Bah.

To use one more example, consider the cobblestone. It is not round, but we may refer to it as such in order to distinguish it from the flat slate in our gardens or the jagged gneiss of the Scottish Isles. But at best, the cobblestone does a shoddy burlesque of round. To be truly round, every point in an object's surface must be equidistant from the center. In all three cases above - the Earth, the man's head, and the cobblestone – we see nothing of the sort. Instead, we see the Language of Convenience smoothing over deep contemplation and hiding the richer, more fascinating truth.

The reader first came across the fact of the Earth's odd bearing when we discussed the Great Trigonometric Survey of India. We learned that the planet is an "oblate spheroid," longer in circumference around the equator than around the poles. But that is only the beginning of the planet's curious lineaments. The thickness of the Earth's crust varies, from up to fifty miles thick in some locations such as the mountain ranges in the middle of a continent, to as little as three miles under the oceans. With this fluctuation in thickness comes fluctuation in the integrity of the planet's surface. I believe I have made my point clearly enough. The nurse on my ward was the one who needed to "get some rest" – or at least – she needed a tutor in geology. The world is as oddly formed as her - an old bint with a dowager's hump.

The shape of the world is a rather uninteresting fact until one considers its impact on Man. And even if the impact does not compare to that of a letter arriving in the mails from a rosy-cheeked admirer, the impact is there nonetheless. You see, gravity at each point on the Earth's surface is quite dependent on the unique conditions of the Earth at that point. For example, because the equator is farther from the center of the Earth than are the poles, a bushman in the Congo is slightly lighter than the selfsame bushman should he decide to plant a flag at the South Pole. What's more, because the equator is spinning much faster than the poles, the centrifugal force playing the foil to gravity is strengthened and the bushman's lightness is only magnified in his homeland. Of course, the same considerations would be at play if he should climb a mountain anywhere in the world; his distance from the center of the earth would increase with the ascent, as would his speed of revolution. He would be lighter at the peak than he would be at the base. What's more, because the air is thinner at the peak, the world's grasp on him grows even weaker!

The thickness of the Earth's crust at a specific location also has a hand in the weight of our bushman. If he should take a steamer to India on holiday, he will weigh more during his voyage at sea than he will at his ports of call. That is because the crust underneath him on the ship is relatively thin. Where there is less crust there is more mantle, and mantle is made of a much heavier, denser rock than the porous crust. The decrease in light material and increase in higher density material beneath his feet makes the bushman heavier.

This house of mirrors upon which we live becomes all the more perplexing when we consider that even the direction from which gravity pulls may change based on surface anomalies. Our poor bushman, wanting nothing more than a peaceful jaunt in his Congolese village, is now being bullied by the world's esoteric and draconian rules of physics. He is made to be heavier, and then lighter, and now he does not know which way is up and which down because the plumb bob next to him suggests "down" is two degrees offset from his current stance. The obtuse globe and its porous crust are conspiring to redirect gravity ever-so-slightly away from the true center of the Earth's core.

But what has all this to do with our current story? Quite a bit, I'm afraid. You see, Fumu is a gravitational anomaly. It is not on the equator, but it is close enough to make an American lighter than he is at home, and its height places those at her peak very far from the world's core, spinning faster than any other human being on the planet. Unhindered by the thick atmosphere at sea level, the person is made lighter still.

Even with all of these variables in play, one should not expect a difference of any more than, say, half a pound in weight. Should the Bushman find himself at the top of Fumu, he could expect his Congolese weight of one hundred pounds to diminish to ninety-nine and one half pounds. Hoyt, at roughly one hundred seventy pounds at the time of the ascent might expect to weigh one hundred sixty-nine and one half pounds. But that is where things become strange. Based on upcoming events reviewed in this book, geologists took a further look at Fumu and found that she is as bizarre below the Earth's surface as she is above.

All volcanoes sit atop a magma chamber; a large pocket within the planet in which the molten lava roils and complains. The chamber is full to the hilt with lava, superheated by the high temperatures of the planet's sub-cellars. The volcano then erupts due to the introduction of more melted mantle into the chamber – or angry gods – depending upon who you ask. The pressure in the chamber builds and then the magma makes an escape upward, where the pressure is less. After the eruption, the magma chamber is empty or close to empty. Fumu is different from most volcanoes in the size of its magma chamber. Two years before the writing of this book, world-renowned geologist Sir George Darling of Cambridge University journeyed to Fumu. Not mad enough to climb the beast, he set up a temporary lab at the southern base. Using myriad instruments and scientific methods over the course of seasons, Darling found something shocking. "Most volcanoes have a chamber housed in the Earth's crust and some go even deeper, with the bottommost reaches of the chamber digging several miles into the Earth's upper mantle. Fumu is like nothing we have ever seen. The chamber is not much wider than the usual chamber, but it seems bottomless." It reaches past the upper mantle, down thousands of miles through the lower mantle and possibly touching Earth's outer core. It is like a long, thin flaw in this diamond Earth, scarring it from surface to core. Why such an unusual volcano, so unique from its sisters? No one is sure. Several theories lie about, untested and otherwise ignored. Darling's theory (the one that got him dismissed from Cambridge and branded from thereon in as a doctor of quackery) was that Fumu is the location where, millennia ago when the Earth was just beginning to cool, the still-wet moon pulled away from the soggy Earth. That separation, that rejection, that outright rebellion by the ungrateful rock never healed for our dear Mother. Fumu stands as the Earth's scar over that wound. Trust me, the other theories are not any better.

If the chamber of Fumu is indeed that vast, then it follows logically that the eruption of Fumu eons before the Age of Man must have dispensed an absurd amount of lava from the Earth's gut by way of what we have been calling the Icy Bellows. Beneath the crumbly, airy crust of the Earth, at the spot where Fumu resides, for mile upon lonely mile, stretching downward into the Unknowable, there exists nothing at all. And with a gut full of nothing at all, Fumu holds the gravitational force of something not much more impressive than an oversized cobblestone.

The effect of this situation upon gravity at the peak of Fumu should no longer be surprising to the reader...

Chapter Nineteen: The Locket

Hoyt and Junk's feet kept leaving the ground. The slightest tightening of a thigh muscle or twisting of the torso would send the men inches into the air. Even with the heavy oxygen tanks on their backs, they would float for fleeting moments. Perhaps if they had backpacks on like their Sherpa Chhiri Tendi, who was now lost to sight in the clouds and smoke, our heroes might have held their ground. But they were not afforded such a luxury. And their new predicament conspired to make their fighting tactics even more pathetic. Punches would miss one another entirely. A knee to the groin would cause the aggressor to stumble. In their exhaustion, they would often stop and collapse against each other like two spent boxers. Depending on how they started the collapse, they might hover above the ground, not touching down for seconds at a time, or they might spin. And when they did touch down, it was several feet lower on the mountainside. Due to the huge void beneath the mountain, the source of gravity was not straight below them, but off to the south a fraction. Should one or both of them continue to float without landing, they would slowly be pulled off the south side of the mountain.

But Hoyt and Junk continued to fight despite their exhaustion and these new laws of physics. They even found the energy to call each other names, like schoolchildren. They did this loudly enough to be heard through their masks by Chhiri Tendi off in the distance, over the din of the wind and lava eruptions.

"Rake!"

"Girl!"

"Street urchin!"

"Choir boy!"

"Peasant!"

"Dandy!"

Their fighting became weaker with each moment. The opponents mostly held each other for balance at this point, with a useless punch to the back coming every minute or so. Slight stumbles turned into brief, floating waltzes. They could no longer get enough breath from their oxygen tanks and their need for the precious gas was increasing with exertion. They were dying. They had not enough energy to summit nor enough energy to descend. They would meet their end fighting and their bodies would be intertwined in conflict for eternity.

Almost motionless now, occasionally slipping a few inches down the slope, Hoyt and Junk were tapping one another's back in the stead of punching. An explosion of lava nearby sent small boiling droplets in their direction. The fiery liquid came to rest on the cheeks of Hoyt and the back of Junk's wool hat. As an indicator of their states, the two did not scream nor jerk in response. They simply groaned and slowly fell down a ledge five feet in height, coming to rest on a patch of untainted snow. Because the patch lay in a slightly sunken position under the ledge, it was protected from the ravages of the weather and eruptions. This trivial feature of the landscape allowed for a pristine spot near Fumu's summit that was allowed to be like other mountains in the Himalaya, snowy, cold, and devoid of fire.

But there was more to this spot begging description. When the two men came to rest a few feet down from the ledge and the axe in Junk's belt pressed into the ice, a large chunk of it gave way. The collapse exposed a snow cave. Affording room for one large man or perhaps two small men, the cave lay just above them on the slope, a God-sent haven, there for recovery or at least peaceful expiration. Independently, and probably not thinking of the other, each man took their remaining strength and pulled themselves up into the cave, the task made easier by gravity's impotence. But their way was blocked by two boots. Boots! Up here, near the top of the Earth! They were of an ancient, European construction, easily a half-century old, black, fastening along the sides, and rising enough to meet a climber's knee. To add to the curiosity, they were attached to a body. Its upper portions were still obscured in the darkness of the cave. Junk and Hoyt would have to pull the fellow out of it if they wished to identify him and then use the cave for themselves.

The task was simple. They pulled on the stiff legs and the body floated out as if on rollers. Time had been kind to this corpse. It was unmistakably George Malick, a giant of the climbing world, a contemporary of other giants Graham and Mummery, lost in Fumu's cloud sixty years earlier. Nonetheless, he was still looking like the dashing man Hoyt and Junk had seen in daguerreotypes; strong jaw, conversation-stopping moustache, and eyes that had not lost their intensity even though clouded by death. Most bodies found in the Himalaya are ravaged by extreme conditions, with clothing torn off and skin bleached as white as the surrounding snow. But the wind, fire, and ice had not been given the opportunity to desecrate Malick's noble bearing. His skin had certainly whitened, and the hair on his face and head had grown unrestrained *post mortem*, silver beard hiding his scarf and bushy moustache obscuring his mouth, but he was otherwise well-preserved in his frigid tomb. His dated clothing was immaculate for a gentleman lost in such a terrible place. The dark loden coat fit him handsomely. His wide-brimmed hat sat atop his overgrown locks and proudly retained its unmarred feather. No oxygen tank or mask was to be found. His climb had preceded such technology, the hearty bastard. Adding to the body's stately mien was its pose. Malick died as if prepared for the end, body straight as a church pew, legs perfectly aligned, and mitts folded neatly upon the lapels of his coat.

Junk and Hoyt were not paying attention to one another any more. They were both in awe of this great adventurer who had come before them. Had he reached the top? Were they too late? With torn, wet mitts and yet another internal store of energy discovered, Hoyt pulled himself up into the cave and grasped Malick's pack, which had for years stood upright at the head of the body like a gravestone. Shamelessly rifling through the contents without consideration of respect for the deceased, Hoyt found Malick's writings. Nothing in the desperate penmanship suggested he had reached the top. It seems Malick had become lost before he could claim victory.

Glowing red ejecta passed through the sky over Aaron Junk's head, illuminating a shiny object clasped in the corpse's mitts. Forcing apart the folded hands, the two men gazed at the ancient totem now slowly spinning and floating on a chain extending from Junk's glove. It was a locket. Junk opened it.

Inside, resting under cracked glass was the faded daguerreotype of a child. By the looks of him, he had been no more than five years of age when the bulb flashed and smoked. The lad sported a blond bob, a smile capable of calming the heart, and dimples big enough to shame the crevasses of Fumu. He sported the black shirt and starched white collar of a British independent school student of the late 19th century. One could almost hear the child squirming in his chair, trying to hold his pose while George Malick and his wife – smiling but out of frame – assured the child the torture would be over soon. The dear thing. One can only hope he was subsequently treated to a handful of black licorice.

The effect of the image upon our heroes was immediate. Junk let the locket go and it floated off with the wind. The men looked into each other's eyes and held one another's gaze for what must have been minutes. Their thoughts did not need expression as they were likely in perfect synchrony. How could they account for a mountain climber's joy as he walks through empty cold space thousands of feet in the air and countless miles from family, home, and hearth? Masochism? Sociopathy? The query leaves them baffled. If there had been an answer at some time, it escaped them now. Mano, the swaddled man, had been right: The ascent was folly. The perils of home, of work, of wives, and of children were where they should be testing their mettle.

Despite any mutual hatred still coursing through their hearts, the two men had stopped fighting and now were racing to take refuge in the cave, wishing to recover some energy in order to climb down. That is correct. They would climb down or die in the process. But first, rest. They gave Malick's body a light shove-off and it bounced down the southern slope like a half-inflated balloon. Then it was gone over the cliffs on the Southern Face. With the opening of the cave free and clear, they scrambled up into it and covered most of the aperture with snow.

Not one hour later, enclosed in the cave, Junk and Hoyt were now freezing to death. Each noted in their hardly legible journal entries that the other's skin had turned pale. Sleepiness overwhelmed them. One would awaken for a moment and shake the other to get the blood moving again. During one of these spasms of activity, a decision was made, and it was a decision that could not have been easy for either man. Since neither had a bivouac sack, the only way to keep warm was to hold one another. For survival, of course. Strictly for survival. Who actually proposed the awkward plan is unclear. Who moved first to initiate the embrace is also unknown. But it is a certainty that over the next several hours, Aaron Junk and William Hoyt found warmth in each other's arms. The oxygen tanks they wore on their backs precluded them from facing the same direction. We can therefore surmise that the shivering men embraced facing each other. Heads on each other's shoulders, floating, spinning, and gently deflecting off of icy walls, they danced a sad minuet to the music of muted catastrophe that was all around them. Nevertheless, they danced this sad minuet together.

Chapter Twenty: The Summit

Retreating down the mountain in search of high camp, Chhiri Tendi stumbled over the small ledge hiding the snow cave. The well-prepared, always professional Sherpa had a pack on his back and so had enough gravity to actually "fall." Upon coming to rest on the roof of the snow cave, it broke open and Chhiri Tendi saw the sahibs within. "They floated around like pickles in brine" Chhiri Tendi relayed.

Seeing they were near mortally drained, Chhiri Tendi used the shelter of the ledge to block the wind and light his small cooker. Within minutes he had melted enough snow to make tea for the others. He gave Hoyt and Junk breaths from his oxygen mask and covered their frozen hands with blankets, also strapping heavy items from his pack to their backs so they would stop floating and migrating south: folded up tents, jugs of water, cans of food, and so forth. As the men sipped their tea and ate some chocolate from Chhiri Tendi's pocket, one of them – Chhiri Tendi did not catch which – muttered "Thank you" loud enough to be heard over the eruptions and wind. Then Hoyt, using slurred words, assured Chhiri Tendi a handsome raise when they got back to civilization. He even went on to apologize to Chhiri Tendi for hiring him for this vanity mission. That the whole damned thing was a mistake and that lives were lost due to him and Junk was too much for Hoyt to stomach. The seated Hoyt touched Chhiri Tendi's knee to ensure he had the Sherpa's attention. Looking up into Chhiri Tendi's eyes, he said with great intensity, "Life, real life, populated with people and compassion, awaits us down the mountain."

Our heroes rallied thanks to Chhiri Tendi. They were sitting up and their eyes no longer rolled in their heads. Alas, their faces were dappled in frostbite and Hoyt would possibly have to lose his nose when (or if) he made it down. But for now the two men had some of their strength back and Hope returned as it had so often on this voyage, likely to disappear again with the Ship of Destiny's next jibe.

Chhiri Tendi sensed that whatever fight had existed between Hoyt and Junk had died along with their appetite for the summit. They seemed to be talking more about how to find their way down. Perhaps they assumed the top could not be found in such a hostile place. Hoyt said as much: "Until greater minds conjure up a machine allowing one to see through cloud cover and instantaneously gauge heights above sea level, and until God has deemed Man worthy of admission to his most divine secrets, the top of Fumu will remain a mystery."

"No it won't" Chhiri Tendi replied as if stating a simple matter of fact. "I was there a few minutes ago."

Junk's eyes became vast. Chhiri Tendi recalls: "His mouth opened wide, so wide in fact he looked as if he were preparing to catch a tossed apple with his teeth." No sound came from him. His face might have turned red had it not been covered in frostbite. This was followed by a hacking cough that continued for more than a half-minute. Next to him, Hoyt sat upright, his back wooden. His facial expression did not change upon hearing Chhiri Tendi's statement, but no soft curves remained there. Every contour – every muscle, wrinkle, and bone - became *tighter*, as if the whole composition would at any moment snap.

Immediately obvious to Chhiri Tendi was that his life might be in danger. He continued. "By mistake, of course. I reached the summit by mistake. I couldn't see! I was looking for you two. Then the sky cleared for a moment. Just a second or so, and I could see I was at the highest point."

Junk erupted. "You became the first man to reach the top of the world...*by mistake?*"

According to Chhiri Tendi's elaborations during our interview, that is exactly what had happened. He had lost Hoyt and Junk in the ever-shifting cloud after seeing them fighting, and wandered lonely for hours. He generally walked upward, thinking that even if Hoyt and Junk were fighting, they were likely to try and fight *up*, toward the summit. Chhiri Tendi was searching for so long he even considered setting up his tent, thinking the sun might set at any moment. But he had lost track of time, as was easy to do in such a place. It was earlier in the day than he had presumed, and so the Chaos in the cloud remained eerily lit. His tent could not be set up anyway because the wind was too strong. In lieu of such a tactic, he took out his sleeping bag in order to rest for at least a moment, lying on his back and clinging to his backpack as an anchor and a blanket. He could not even crawl inside of the sleeping bag because of the sporadic heat, so he rested on top of it...freezing under his backpack. So cold. So hot.

The rock beneath his back felt rough and uncomfortable through the bag. So he let go of the backpack, permitted himself to float a tad, and kept himself buoyed to the mountain by lashing himself to the pack. Time passed and Chhiri Tendi did nothing but repeatedly give in to slumber and awaken with a start. In his waking thoughts, he despaired. Thinking back to his experience with Hoover's beheading up here, Chhiri Tendi realized he had once again made the mistake of leaving his family in order to climb Fumu. He would not make the mistake again. Never on an expedition had he considered leaving behind his sahib to save himself, but now he played with the idea. Hoyt was important, but seeing his wife's smile again was more important.

As if timed by some universal clock, the eruptions stopped for a brief period of time. The wind cleared out all of the acrid black smoke and left only blowing snow. For that moment, the upper reaches of Fumu were not unlike other eight thousand foot peaks. Indefensibly cold. Intermittently clear and then clouded over. These moments of clarity were not clear in the sense of blue skies and views spanning hundreds of miles from the Terai in the south to the Tibetan Plateau in the north, but clear in the sense that Chhiri Tendi could see around him for hundreds of *feet* before the pale sheet of snow veiled the backdrop.

And that was the moment when Chhiri Tendi saw he was at the top of Fumu. It was obvious. The peak was almost ridiculous in its pointy, conical perfection, just as one might expect to see in a child's hand-drawn rendering of a mountain. Its top was so pointy in fact it had been the thing digging into Chhiri Tendi's back when he was trying to rest in his sleeping bag! "I know! It's ridiculous," Chhiri Tendi attested. "But I swear it's true." With the sky clear, he saw that every direction was downward for at least a quarter mile. He had literally stumbled across the top of the world. Then an eruption spewed forth lava to the north and clouded up the sky again with smoke, and Fumu's top returned to its miserable status quo.

Whether Chhiri Tendi should have mentioned this information to Hoyt and Junk is questionable. Despite their claims of moral reprioritization on a cosmic scale, Hoyt and Junk were livid. They looked at Chhiri Tendi with wild, unpredictable eyes. What would they do? No evidence existed that Chhiri Tendi had been to the top, so cold-blooded murder was indeed an option. But perhaps they would spare him if they felt Chhiri Tendi was essential to their return to civilization. Had he not just saved their lives? Was not levity in order? Junk removed all doubt when he transformed into a berserker. He emitted inhuman wails and launched himself at Chhiri Tendi. Perhaps Hoyt held back because he had a little more of a history with the Sherpa. But he watched and likely prayed Junk was successful in whatever designs he had. Chhiri Tendi told me:

"He lunged at me. I was prepared, I was in better shape than him, and I knew a thing or two about fighting. Who cares if he grew up in an

American city? Try lugging paper from one country to another over mountain passes and dealing with armed bandits. Junk couldn't use his hands because they were frozen, so instead he made the miscalculation of trying to knock me down. But he's a short shit. Not much reach. He tried to punch me but he could not get in close enough. My blocks were too good. Idiot. I could have punched him back end things quickly, but it is against my nature. And hey, I had no obligation to protect him. He was not my sahib. Had Hoyt come at me, I would have had a more awkward situation. But Junk? Fuck him. I don't know much about Boston, but if Junk's performance up there was at all representative of the city, it's all swagger with nothing to back it up."

Hoyt and Chhiri Tendi then had a rather awkward staring contest for what must have felt like an eternity. The winds and volcanic concussions did not move them. Junk lay on the ground, winded. Chhiri Tendi felt sad. He had been through much with Hoyt. But Trust was gone. Chhiri Tendi was a dedicated Sherpa guide, but he had Dignity as well. The relationship was over. Chhiri Tendi removed his oxygen tank and mask, threw it at Hoyt's feet and said through gritted teeth, "The top is right there." Hoyt looked back to where Chhiri Tendi was pointing. It was only ten yards away. "When you've gotten to the top," he yelled over the explosions, "look for the fat hornito with two vents at its top." Chhiri Tendi pointed to that as well and Hoyt's eyes followed. The hornito appeared for a moment and was exactly as Chhiri Tendi described. It then disappeared in the clouds again. "That is the direction down to the Eastern Ridge. Goodbye Mr. Hoyt." Perhaps Hoyt should have felt regret or shame, but Chhiri Tendi recalls the man's face remaining grim, angry, confused; not modified at all by the behavior of Junk or any realization that Chhiri Tendi had been a friend and an essential element in Hoyt's looming success.

Chhiri Tendi broke eye contact with his employer and began to walk down the mountain.

"What if I offer you ten thousand dollars to not say anything," Hoyt exclaimed. Chhiri Tendi paused, quite nauseated by the suggestion. He turned and spoke "I'm not saying anything about you two white, pompous, swollen balls or about this whole trip, unless one of you decides to mention it first." With that he turned and walked down into the clouds.

Although details are blurry at this point, Hoyt likely donned Chhiri Tendi's oxygen apparatus and began to walk up the mountain. His body probably defied him with each attempt at a step. Even with supplemental oxygen, his mind was certainly damaged beyond repair. If time was still a concept of which he could conceive, then he may have noticed the world was growing dark. He had been up here all day, since before the sun rose. If he did not get down very, very soon, his life was as good as forfeit.

The world was light and then it was dark, and then lava made it light again. The air was superheated and then frigid and then hot again. Hoyt and Junk were misguided family men and then they were bloodthirsty, selfish beasts trampling over the other on the path to vainglory, and then they were gentlemen again. Who, what, why, when and where they were was anyone's guess now.

Junk grabbed Hoyt by the ankle, perhaps to secure a free ride to the summit. A hand was extended to the immobile man on the ground. Hoyt was trying to say "get up" to Junk but the wind and the explosions and his useless lips hindered his efforts. With great difficulty, probably more than he could bear, Junk responded by putting out his hand. Hoyt took a length of cotton rope and tied it around his waist and Junk's. Now Hoyt commenced to drag his once-and-perhaps-future enemy to the top.

Hoyt gave Junk turns with his oxygen apparatus which was almost spent. Heat and Cold traded off shifts battering our heroes into submission. The mountain seemed to be fighting back with all of its rage at the last moment. The screeching of the wind and the crack of the eruptions had reached a crescendo. All else was drowned out. The sky was dark now with the exception of lava glow through cloud. The world was noise. All matter of ejecta was flying past them: Cylindrical bombs, cow pie bombs, rotational bombs and core bombs all came close enough to be heard hissing as they passed, some actually hitting them, scorching clothing and scalding skin. The surface beneath their boots was comprised exclusively of lapilli, fist-sized lava rocks rendered slick by melted snow. Crampons were useless and handholds were non-existent.

Junk made a sad effort to help with legs kicking out behind him, finding purchase in nothing. But what he could not provide physically Junk provided mentally.

"Hoyt!" he wailed over everything.

"What?" Hoyt replied.

"Drop. Junk."

There was a swollen pause before Hoyt asked, "Are you sure?"

"Yes."

With some hesitation, Hoyt removed his knife and began to sever the rope tying him to Junk. Junk grabbed his hand and stopped him from cutting.

"Whoa whoa whoa. No." Junk rasped. "The *junk.*" This was accompanied by manic pointing at things adorning Hoyt's person. By "junk," Junk had apparently meant to indicate the miscellany that Chhiri Tendi had lashed to them in order to weigh them down to combat weak gravity, including pots, pans, and sleeping bags.

Hoyt cut off the detritus weighing them down. And at some time on September 14th during the early evening hours, William Hoyt and Aaron Junk's bodies gently rose into the air and up to the summit. Two unpleasant, tattered, ridiculous angels ascending to their private heaven.

What is there to say about the summit? The surviving party never wrote of it. We can assume there was no honey, no gold, and certainly no milk despite Mano the man-child's deepest wishes. All the more discouraging, the sun had already set. The sky was as black as a widow's veil so Hoyt and Junk were deprived even the God's-eye view that usually welcomes the climber. In short, we can be certain that not a damned solitary boon awaited them.

In the excitement of racing to the top, the two had forgotten their flags. They took a cross from Hoyt's pocket, a hip flask from Junk's, and a book of unspeakable sketches Chhiri Tendi had tied to them, and jammed all three into a narrow, deep crag at the summit. And with that done, they turned to drag themselves down Fumu.

PART THREE: THE DESCENT / ASCENSION

Chapter Twenty-One: The Tragedy

On September 15th, 1941, the United States was girding itself for inevitable conflagration. One week earlier, the U.S.S. Greer had been accidentally destroyed and sunk by a German U-Boat. Hitler had ordered the invasion of Leningrad. Despite the Neutrality Act, Roosevelt and his generals deemed it legal and imperative to send armaments and other materials to the British fighting in the Pacific Theatre. The World was witnessing the Tsunami of War growing and reaching its crest.

Hoyt and Junk knew nothing of this. They were helping one another down the mountain. They were both crawling. Tied off to one another and in single file, they likely looked nothing like newly-minted victors, but rather like a defeated and captured military column on their way to the camps. Hoyt was in front, and at times he was dragging Junk down. Then Junk would awaken and aid their progress as best he could.

They had had no problem getting out of the cloud thanks to the help of Chhiri Tendi. But now that they were out of the cloud, the relentless cold had returned unfettered. The sun that shone provided no solace. It was too distant and its effect impotent. The frostbite on Hoyt's face had blackened him and swelled him so he no longer looked like an aristocrat but rather like a bushman. His fingers were frostbitten and they swelled up like bangers on the cooker. Swallowing whatever pain his condition presented, Hoyt continued to use those hands to move them forward. The snow was easily four feet deep, so Hoyt had to leverage the routes he and Junk had made on the way up. The oxygen they had received from Chhiri Tendi was long gone. Each breath must have been like a garroting.

They reached Junk's high camp just after sunrise. But what could they do now that they were there? They were too weak to do anything other than sleep in the nearest tent; but things being as they were, sleep at this point only meant death. But sleep they did. If only a single Sherpa were there to attend to them, to pamper them, to save them.

As fate would have it, Pasang Dolma was there to do just that. It seems Pasang Dolma had had no intention of darting off at the behest of the Nepalese Cobras. He had walked down to Camp Three but he had turned around and made his way back up in the hopes of surprising the Cobras and saving his charge. The high camp had been empty upon his return. Any attempt at heroics had passed. But now, only minutes before he had planned to climb down the lip of the Bellows again, this time for real, he discovered Hoyt and Junk returning from the summit. Overjoyed, he lit his cooker and melted snow to make tea. A container of *foie gras* performed the role of breakfast. These comforts went a long way to revive the two helpless creatures. After preparing the meal, Pasang Dolma suggested they all go down immediately. There was no time to lose, as each moment spent at this altitude would continue to chip away at their condition, and Hoyt and Junk were now only slightly further from death after Pasang Dolma's kind repast.

Now able to walk, albeit slouched over, Hoyt, Junk, and Pasang Dolma lashed themselves to one another and climbed down again. However, because of the dire condition of the Americans, Pasang Dolma chose to take the southern route down. It was more challenging, but it was shorter, and according to Hoyt, his team's equipment would still be set up and that would facilitate their descent.

They made rapid progress now, passing the location of the cannibal attack (Hoyt had to avert his eyes) and proceeding down the snowless spine that now defined the western wall of Rauff's Maw. The going was easy and the increase in oxygen was reviving the men. Even the weather was on their side, with the sun strong and little wind. Snow to their left and right melted. The rock upon which they walked was wet, but featured enough to prevent slippage. They still walked with laboured steps, their shoulders still slouched, and they still needed to stop every few feet to rest (and cough, and moan, and grit their teeth, and spin their arms in futile attempts to revive circulation). Pasang Dolma was patient with them. He brought up the rear and spoke words of inspiration. "We are almost at Hoyt's next camp! Food and shelter and Sherpa await!" And only hours after passing Camp Four - the sight of the cannibal massacre – Camp Three came into sight below them, resting on the precipice of the cliff where the "magic rope" had failed.

Nearing the camp, Pasang Dolma finally became restless. He detached his rope from the others and walked briskly ahead. "I wish to prepare the camp for your arrival" he said to Hoyt and Junk. "This ridge is not technically difficult. You should be alright." And with that, Pasang Dolma scurried past the sahibs, waving his hands in the air, hoping to grab the attention of the Sherpa below. He mixed brisk walking and glissading to improve his pace. Within two minutes he was one hundred yards ahead of them.

Now alone and healthy enough to communicate, the two men spoke. They spoke like friends. One asked the other how he would return to the States.

"I am not sure. You?"

"Broke."

This got the two onto the topic of money. Hoyt confessed in a rather relaxed fashion that he had cheated Junk out of the bet at the Presidentials and that he would reimburse him as soon as they reached home. "And should I not make it home alive, there is another source of money for you, Aaron…if I can call you Aaron."

"Sure." Junk replied.

"The cave under the Qila Pass you so sneakily walled up." Hoyt began.

"The cave I-? Oh right. Sorry about that. No hard feelings."

Hoyt winced slightly. "No. Not at all, I suppose. Anyway, you may want to take that tunnel back."

"Why?" Junk inquired. "What's that got to do with the price of eggs?"

"Everything, you crafty old wolf. Everything."

Hoyt told Junk of the gold lining the walls of the ancient lava tube, not to mention the ease with which a team of explorers can walk along its pahoehoe floor. "Much easier than climbing over the pass. Just don't bring any pack animals" Hoyt added.

What information for his mortal enemy to share! Junk's financial worries were over and knowledge of this made Junk walk a little easier, a little more upright despite the damages Fumu had inflicted. However, Junk never said "Thank you" to Hoyt. That may have been too difficult to do. But we can assume both men had an understanding of what had just passed. They were clearly willing to act in a kind manner towards one another at this point, but kind words would be another thing entirely in this, the most masculine of realms.

The sun was nearly going down over Asha's shoulder. The view must have been lovely; to one side of them, a tall, vertical cliff that happened not to collapse with the rest of the maw and now offered a sweeping vista of a world bathed in orange light. On the other side of them, the setting sun and a long blue shadows cast by distant peaks. The men were getting much closer to Camp Three where a good dinner and long sleep awaited them. They could nurse their ailments for a time and then, perhaps as soon as noon tomorrow, they could be at base camp.

Now was Junk's turn at kindness. Hoyt had been speaking about the challenges facing him on the voyage home. "I might not be returning to the United States at all. If I do not have this one gentleman with me when I get to Calcutta, I will be killed by a group of mercenaries in the employ of the Japanese. And that one gentleman is dead. My selfishness allowed him to die. And what is the cosmic recompense for my behavior? I will never make it home to set things right with my wife."

Junk replied, "I may have your lift home." He went on to explain that the pirate Gary Cooper would be waiting for them at the Calcutta train station on November 1st. "That whack job will definitely take on more passengers if we drop a pile of gold in his paws and give him assurance there's more where that came from."

Good deeds were spiraling out of control. An unspoken challenge was in the works. Outdo the kindness of the other man! Who would ultimately check mate the other and perform the ultimate act of kindness? And how wonderful are things when we are asking ourselves such questions?

The thing about descending a mountain is that threats to life and limb are not suspended. Reaching the summit does not herald the end of trouble. The couloirs, cornices, and cliffs do not "shut off" like carnival rides at midnight. If anything, the environment has become even more treacherous because the men are physically spent and less focused on the task at hand.

At roughly three o'clock in the afternoon, not more than one hundred yards from Hoyt's Camp Three, Junk took a bad step. The air was cooling as evening approached, turning the water on the rocks into a sheen of veer glass. Junk's left foot did not come down properly, the ankle bending outward. His legs quickly split from one another until his groin touched rock. He then began an uncontrolled slide sideways. He was wearing no crampons and his axe was tied to his rucksack because there had been no deep ice or snow on their chosen route to camp. But the moment Junk had slipped down off their route the world became nothing but ice and snow. His glissade sent him at top speed toward the edge of Rauff's Maw. True, the sides of Rauff's maw were now mostly gentle slopes of ice chunks since the collapse one week earlier, but Junk had chosen an unfortunate spot to slip where the maw had maintained its awful integrity. One moment he was barreling down a short slope and then the next he was going over the edge of a three hundred foot drop into the remains of the Maw. When the slack in the rope attaching him to Hoyt was gone, it snapped taut around Junk's harness and his fall was arrested. Hoyt, being the consummate professional, had instinctively laid flat on the ground the moment his partner had begun to slide. Hoyt gripped whatever features of the ground he could in the heat of the moment.

Now Junk hung in thin air roughly forty feet below the top of the maw. Both men had given out yells of shock and pain when the event had happened, but perhaps due to the wind, none of the Sherpa at Camp Three heard what had happened. They were all inside their tents, possibly preparing the space for ailing Sahibs.

Hoyt tried to pull Junk back up by scurrying forward on the rocks, away from the cliff. Because the terrain was mostly exposed rock, his axe was useless. He was able to dig it into a crag and pull, but it would always lose its purchase moments later and that would send Hoyt sliding back to his original spot, and in some awful cases, sliding back even closer to the Maw than he was before. He remained still, straining against the weight that wanted to pull him over the precipice.

And there they remained for what must have seemed like generations, but may have only been a few rotations of the minute hand. The sun had now set and the world was growing dark. Over the edge of the cliff, Junk attempted to secure two short, thin ropes to the larger rope by use of Prusik knots – friction knots that could slide along the larger rope and then hold steady when weight was placed upon them. The unused end of one small rope would then be secured to Junk's harness while the unused end of the other would form a loop for his foot to fit through. Junk would be expected to raise his foot creating slack in the short rope, and the associated Prusik knot would then be moved up the main rope. Once it was taut, Junk would then do the same with the knot on the newly slackened harness rope. Then the process would be repeated. Using this time-tested strategy, Junk would theoretically be able to self-rescue.

Even under the best of conditions, the Prusik move is difficult. But at altitude with a beaten body, the move is almost impossible. Junk yelled out in pain as he tried to tie knots with failing fingers. Blowing warm breath onto his hands (he had placed his mitts in his pockets), he tried multiple times to get the rope tied around the carabiner on his harness to no avail. Switching to the foot rope, he experienced quick success.

The temperature dropped to minus 10 degrees Celsius. The time passed and Hoyt remained on the rock above, holding on with everything he could muster. The natural athletic talents that had blessed him since childhood were now on display. Despite cold and increasing wind and the weight of Junk, he did not budge. His eyes were probably affixed to the tents of Camp Three disappearing in the darkness. Still no one came out of them. They must come out soon! They *must* start wondering about the Sahibs' delay.

Junk finally caught a bit of luck. He got the second rope secured to his harness. He lifted his right leg, moved the associated knot up, and stepped up the new stair he had created. He was on his way to safety. He advanced two "steps" upward, shortening the distance between himself and the lip.

Then he dropped. Was Hoyt finally giving in? The rock on which he held fast was after all freezing in the dropping temperatures. Junk heard a voice from above. It was loud to beat the wind, but quite collected. "How are you proceeding down there?"

"Better than before. Hold on a little longer. I'm on my way up."

But Junk's optimism was misguided. The air had become too cold and so the Prussik knots no longer worked. Their strength lay in friction, and friction was no longer possible as the main rope froze. Each step Junk took upward slipped back down. He was back to where he had started, and then Hoyt slipped again.

Climbers are often faced with terrible decisions; decisions of a magnitude usually only faced on the field of battle. One always hopes that the teachings of John Stuart Mill will run through the panicked mind and that it will try to come up with a solution benefitting the most individuals. But rational thoughts rarely fructify in the inhospitable climes of peril. Most often, when faced with mortality, a man forgets all others and can only think he does not want to die. To expect anything more of him is to expect the unlikely.

"Fuck it. Cut the rope" Junk bellowed to Hoyt. He had obviously remembered the knife with which Hoyt had cut off the detritus at the summit. "Save yourself, faggot! Cut the rope!"

"No" came the reply from on high.

"Listen to me. Cut the fucking rope you shit!"

"No."

"You're mother was a good lay! Cut the rope!"

"No."

"That thing you call your wife looks like Churchill. Cut it!"

"No" Hoyt repeated.

"Compared to you, the Hebrews are-"

"I will not cut the rope on you. A good man once told me about *bushido*. The way of the chivalrous warrior. And I am going to follow *bushido* now." A long pause followed. "When you get back to the States, Aaron, tell Wizzy I love her so much and I am so sorry I walked away."

This seemed like a rather odd thing to say given where Hoyt was and given where Junk was. Yet Hoyt continued from above, unseen by Junk but quite audible. "My two boys. My two wonderful, handsome boys. Let them know their father was always proud of them despite his distance, physical and otherwise." Sherpa's heads appeared out of the tents, peering this way and that, but they could not see Hoyt, who was busy holding off inevitable catastrophe for a few more moments.

Then Hoyt said "It is time to cut the cord. Finally. It is time to cut the cord." Junk was terribly confused by Hoyt's words, and not knowing what the outcome would be, Junk let his body go slack in total acceptance of falling.

A yell rose up from above the lip, as if Hoyt was summoning all of the energy left in his body. The rope lifted Junk ever so slightly. Hoyt had just stood up. Another yell from above and then a shadow appeared from on high, off a few paces to the south, jumping with great effort out and over the edge of the maw. Hoyt had apparently struggled to his feet, run sideways along the lip, and then sailed out into the air on the far side of a hook-like outcropping of rock. The effect was powerful and immediate. Being more than a head taller than Junk and also heavier, weighted down with equipment, Hoyt's descending heft pulled Junk up. The rope slid gracefully around the rocky outcropping for the exact same reason the Prusik knots had failed earlier; lack of friction.

The ascending Junk passed the descending Hoyt far too quickly to communicate in any fashion whatsoever. Junk was up at the lip of the maw in seconds and holding onto to the outcropping for dear life.

Hoyt was now dangling far below. Junk could not make him out in the darkness except to see he was not moving, probably resting from his earlier struggle. Junk heard the yell of Sherpa calling out to them and saw torchlight illuminating drifting snow in the sky above. It searched the world wildly for our heroes, but the threshold of the afterlife is not a place easily discovered. Junk looked at the light and hallucinated about movie premiers he had attended in Boston and prison parking lots where he had picked up newly-released friends. He thought of his mother's candle illuminating the dark cold New England morning in their flat, as she rose before dawn to cook breakfast for herself and her son. Familiar creaks on the floorboards, heralding the coming of a new day and a new fight with his mother and the world. All of these thoughts compelled Junk to continue living, and to live well. Jammed up against the outcropping, he took his smaller ropes and tied them around it and then through his harness. He was now secured to the mountain.

Hoyt was moving below him, but the details of his movements were imperceptible.

"Remember what I said, Aaron" called a gasping Hoyt. "Pass those words along. To Mother too. Tell her I love her. Tell her."

"I never really touched her you know" Junk called down. "I married her to get back at you but I never touched her."

Silence from below, then "Can we change the subject?"

"Of course. Sorry."

The cold and wind were unbearable. The voices of the Sherpa and the lights came closer. "Hang on, Hoyt" Junk yelled. "They're coming for us! You'll be able to tell your family yourself."

But it was too late. Hoyt yelled out "Now I fall...and rise. To my triumph!"

And with that there was a snapping sound, Junk jerked a little as all of his weight moved off of the main rope and transitioned to the smaller ropes, and the braided strands of hemp that had led down to Hoyt went slack and began to whip about in the wind.

Junk cried aloud. Arms were reaching down for him and pulling him up but he fought back as if he did not want to be rescued. They were too much for him and he was promptly up on the rocky route to Camp Three. He blurted out every blue word he had ever learned on the streets.

The fuel that had driven Junk was gone.

Chapter Twenty-Two: Return to "Civilization"

By lunch on September 16th, Junk and the Sherpa were making their way from Camp One to base camp at the bottom of the scree. The temperature rose and the men had stowed their coats. Oxygen apparatuses had been discarded en route. They breathed deeply and may have even smelled distant flora in the air.

As you may recall, the two teams' base camps were but feet away from one another. Now, overrun with Sherpa, porters, and surviving expedition members, it had transformed into a small city. Yet sadly, it resembled a city conquered by a bloodthirsty foe. Many people sat about empty of affect and slumped over in shell shock. Chatham was unconscious under a makeshift canopy comprised of sticks and tent remnants. Zeigler sat on a rock looking off across the moraine at nothing. Thornton, still splintered and buckled from his fall on the scree, moaned from inside his tent. Faces and hands were purple with frostbite. So ruined were these visages that Junk could not distinguish many of the white people on the journey from the dark people. Swollen noses, sunburned cheeks, and cracked lips made everyone appear to share the same tragic lineage. Reunions were short and muted as were introductions. No one spoke any more than necessary. So consumed were they in their shock that no one even thought to ask Junk if he had made it to the summit.

When Chhiri Tendi saw Junk approaching, he did not run away. "I did not even think of running" Chhiri Tendi recalls. "What was he going to do? Cut out my gizzard in front of a bunch of bystanders?" Indeed, Chhiri Tendi acted with the etiquette of a Lord. He patted Junk on the shoulder and said "Welcome." He then walked Junk aside and said "I've told no one about making it to the top first, and have no intention of doing so."

The Bostonian did not hesitate. He walked breezily back to the men and yelled "Chhiri Tendi reached the top first. Hoyt and I came later. Now go back to your business." There was a short silence and lack of movement among the men as if a film projector presenting their lives had temporarily stopped working. Then everyone returned to what they were doing.

"And one more thing" Junk bellowed. "William Hoyt is dead. He died saving me. He was a good man. I would like a moment of silence please." No one spoke. Heads were down. After a while, Junk thanked the men and again everyone went back to what they were doing. There had been no tears and no audible gasps at the announcement. You may recall no one had much cared for Hoyt. A moment of silence in which the men could feel shame for not feeling loss was enough to do the trick.

Sleeping was the order of the day, or days, for Junk, Pasang Dolma, and the other Sherpa who had arrived with him. Seeing his tent had been burnt down (by an enraged Hoyt he was told), Junk found another quiet tent and rested. He also tended to his ailments, many of which would be permanent. He would end of up losing four fingers, four toes, and a small portion of his nose (The doctor would be "picking a gin blossom" Junk jested rather darkly).

Everyone began packing up on the 19th, making ready for the long and somber journey home. Only minutes before they were to begin walking toward the Qila Pass, a porter called out. "Look" he was saying in Nepalese. "The others!" He was pointing to figures approaching from the northwest. They walked along an esker riding above the moraine like a man-made promenade. Junk put on his sun goggles to better suss out the situation. The first person to come into view was an oriental Junk had never seen. He did not have the bearing of a porter or a Sherpa. He had a swagger suggesting a privileged upbringing. "Who the fuck is that clown" asked Junk to no one in particular. Behind the stranger were porters from Junk's northern base camp as well as – and this Junk could not believe –

three of the Sherpa who had gone barmy on the Eastern Ridge. He probably wanted to hit these men, but his attention was suddenly drawn elsewhere.

It was not until the people were but yards away that the two last faces were visible. Wearing tattered gabardine and using ice axes as canes, McGee and River Leaf came into view. If he had a decision to make regarding who to embrace first, Junk's decision was made for him when River Leaf changed direction to avoid him.

McGee, looking downright slim and sunburned, cried aloud and hugged his oldest friend with gleeful abandon. Junk may have been somewhat distracted by River Leaf's rebuff, but not so much he could keep from crying as well. They hugged for minutes. Brothers, reunited at last. Nothing was said. It is likely neither man expected to see the other again, but here they were, seeing, smelling, and hearing the one thing in their worlds that gave their respective lives consistency. There was silence until McGee muttered "I was a hero, Junk."

"I'm sure you were" Junk replied, his voice muffled by the shoulder of his friend's coat.

After the embrace was done, McGee added "You owe me a load of money, pal." This was indeed the case. McGee had survived and therefore won himself one million dollars fair and square. Junk was not worried at all. They would be passing through the lava tube shortly and after collecting rucksacks worth of gold, all debts would be settled. With toes deformed and emotions at full extension, Junk led everyone across the moraine, into the lava tube for some unprecedented American plundering, and then out of the mountains on their way to Calcutta.

Yuudai had received no welcome back. He had simply rested his weary bones at base camp in silence and then begun the long hike home. We are fortunate that Hoyt had shared with Chhiri Tendi the details of

Yuudai's heroic deeds with the parachute, otherwise the whole of it would go unheralded.

River Leaf would not speak to Junk no matter the advances. When they passed the monasteries of the man-children, he asked her to join him to pay a visit to Mano. To this she shook her head and nothing more. In a huff Junk decided to just move forward and forego the visit to the odd sage. When they reached Darjeeling, he asked her to get some dinner with him to celebrate their new-found wealth. She had been separating her own clothing from the other equipment at the time. She did not look up from her task. "No thank you" was the flat response.

Chatham was taken to a doctor in Darjeeling. Thornton was also admitted for observation, although his problems were of a more temporary nature; both arms and one rib were broken. Thanks to the quality care of the Sherpa and porters at base camp, Thornton was already on the mend by the time they were on their way to Calcutta.

Chatham and Thornton's medical care in Darjeeling provided the team with an opportunity to bid Zeigler farewell. After descending to Camp Two weeks earlier in order to combat altitude sickness, Zeigler had instantaneously recovered from the headaches and fared well in all other respects. But despite escaping unscathed compared to the others who had climbed higher, the expedition had still left him shaken. According to Chhiri Tendi, Zeigler spoke often on the hike back to Darjeeling of returning to the States and dropping the curtain on his climbing avocation. Like Junk he was no longer a young man. When boarding a train for the Assam province, he waved goodbye. No one would see him again. Relatives in the United States were difficult to find, and when they were found they knew nothing of his whereabouts. The author made a journey to Assam several years back and failed to track Zeigler down. Perhaps the political upheaval of India in the 1940's consumed him or maybe his obsession with climbing got the better of him.

Also while in Darjeeling, the services of Pasang Dolma and the formerly petulant Sherpa came to a close. Of course, because of their insubordination, Junk did not pay the Sherpa, but to Pasang Dolma he gave twice the promised payment. The man had been brave and trustworthy. Had he not returned to high camp after the Nepalese Cobra situation, Junk would not have survived.

Pasang Dolma was finished with the business of being a Sherpa. The Nepalese Cobras had in fact influenced his way of thinking. Although he disagreed with their brutal methods, Pasang Dolma did share and approve of their sentiments. Back home in Nepal, he and the Sherpa formed a new alliance; an alliance that would gain hundreds of members and international notoriety after the war ended. Their modus operandi was to pose as porters and offer their services to Americans and Europeans who had arrived in India from overseas, demanding half of their pay up front. Once their services were successfully sold to foreign adventurers, they would do as they were told all the way up to base camp. And then, the night before the initial climb to the Camp One, they would simply leave. The foreigners would wake up to find camp almost entirely abandoned except for their high altitude Sherpa. One can be sure that the priorities of the climbers change at that moment. Backs are turned to the mountain and planning the route home becomes all-consuming. The devious pranksters would proceed to execute this caper over twenty times throughout the early 1940's. They may have failed to stop the invading hordes from treating Nepal as their own garden of delights, but the message was heard far and wide that not every citizen of Nepal welcomed the white eyes into their Kingdom, and therefore some caution was in order. Ultimately, Pasang Dolma and the remaining Nepalese Cobras fell in with the Provisional Government of Free India. No records exist of them after that.

With Chatham sufficiently bandaged, Thornton given more durable plasters, and a large portion of porters paid and let go, the Americans, their equipment, and the remaining porters traveled south toward the ocean. The train from Darjeeling to Calcutta brought great joy to the Americans as it was their first exposure to the modern age since setting out on their adventure. Junk and McGee were clearly not done with their old ways; they drank, being careful not to burn their cracked lips. They smoked cigars. They played poker with fingers ravaged by frostbite. Despite all of these activities one usually associates with uproarious fun, the scene was somewhat muted. They went through the motions, but did not laugh or shout. No one was patting anyone else's back. Foul language was non-existent. Memories of carnage acted as strict chaperones at this party.

And still River Leaf avoided Junk. If she was sitting conversing with McGee and Junk happened to work his way into the discussion, River Leaf would quickly look around as if something important had caught her eye and then she would walk away with haste and furrowed brow. Drake wrote in his journal:

"Everyone can see that the Indian girl is avoiding this Junk character like plague. I'm not sure what she and the late Hoyt had against Junk. He seems like a pretty decent guy. And he is devil at poker. He took my straight flush with a four of a kind. I don't see that as a reason to hate him. He was a gentleman while he was bleeding me dry.

"Well, back to work on my latest invention. I am done creating things that serve the selfish nature of man. No more magic ropes to the summit. No more computing machines to size up one's coffers. No more war machines for General Motors. When I return to the States, I am going to dedicate myself to the betterment of society. That's why my focus now turns to designing a 'double-barreled cigarette'."

Drake would go on to do exactly that and in 1945 at the end of the war, he actually experienced some success. But when the left lung of a smoker of Camel's "Twice As Nice" cigarettes literally fell off of the esophagus – dropping like an overripe apple from its tree in a killing frost – Drake's luck ran out. The killing frost sent more apples falling, and before he knew it, Drake's employer was swimming in lawsuits. They handled the discord between themselves and Drake in a manner they felt would sever all ties but allow Drake a dignified ending to his long, illustrious career: They fired him on the spot and told the press that the spate of lung detachments was entirely his fault. Drake decided then and there to retire. He lives to this day off of his GM pension in total isolation in the Upper Peninsula of Michigan.

The members of the two expeditions arrived in Calcutta on October 15th, giving them more than two weeks before the scheduled arrival of The Souls At Sea. Zeigler knew of many American expatriates who lived in Calcutta. Before he left them in Darjeeling Zeigler was able to secure lodging for all of the expedition members at their next stop. They mostly spent the two weeks in Calcutta staying in their respective guest quarters and resting, rarely seeing or speaking to one another. Chatham, who was still in terrible condition, spent the remaining weeks in yet another hospital (Thornton was now well enough to move about on his own). No one saw the burned oilman except when visiting the hospital to tend to their own magma burns and frostbite. Junk was not the only poor American sot who would have to go under the knife; both expeditions would leave an unfortunate number of toes and fingers behind in Asia.

Tensions were growing between the Allies and Japan; within India, the Japanese were beginning to align themselves with the Indian resistance. Given the state of things, if any British soldier had seen Yuudai Ubugai walking the streets of Calcutta, the results would have been immediate imprisonment. He had to spend the entirety of his stay dressed as a porter and hiding out in the home of a porter from the expedition who was also a member of the All India Forward Bloc and therefore sympathetic to the Japanese. His isolation on Fumu was simply continuing uninterrupted upon their return to civilization. But slowly that changed. Junk and McGee were staying at a British hotel very near Yuudai's lodgings. Junk began to feel a compulsion to speak with Yuudai possibly because he wanted to learn more about Hoyt through the Japanese soldier. They started spending a considerable amount of time together as the end of October drew near. It turned out Yuudai was a baseball fan and so he and Junk shared stories about their home teams, the Tokyo Kyojin and the Boston Red Sox. The friendship that flourished between Junk, McGee, and Yuudai was only increased by information passed on from Chhiri Tendi to the Bostonians: Chhiri Tendi let them know Yuudai had saved Hoyt's life while passing the Maw on the ascent. Junk hugged Yuudai in response, all the while thanking him for his bravery and honor.

On October 31ˢᵗ, the night before the expeditions were to set sail, Yuudai was invited by Junk to drink – heavily – to celebrate their survival and toast those who had died. The party had been planned to take place at the hotel but that could not happen because Yuudai needed to remain hidden. Instead, it was held at the home of several nearby porters. With the exception of River Leaf, everyone celebrated and stumbled around drunk, arms around the shoulders of new friends. Then in the darkest depths of the early morning, somewhere in the twisting catacombs of Calcutta's poorest district, the expedition members received quite a surprise when Yuudai broke his silence and began to sing. It was "A Wand'ring Minstrel I" from The Mikado. His voice was strong but gentle, as smooth and as warm as freshly-melted candle wax. For once, the others were silent as Yuudai held court. In the case of Thornton and Drake who had seen the murder of Randolph Hoyt at the hands of Yuudai's father, tears fell. The awed silence continued once Yuudai had completed his crooning. He said "My father is wrong. That is a good opera. It is not white men trying to control us; it is white men trying to understand us."

When dawn broke on the first of November, Yuudai, Junk, Chhiri Tendi, and McGee had not yet slept. They arrived at the docks still gassed and singing and having completely forgotten about Yuudai's personal effects or climbing equipment. In the hazy, prematurely hot sun, with the world smacking of low tide and the sound of fishermen barking out orders in Bengali, they bid Yuudai a slurred farewell. "Thank you for saving Hoyt" Junk blubbered.

"Bushido!" Yuudai yelled while stumbling and shooting his fist into the air.

"Bushido!" the others responded.

Yuudai's escorts appeared from everywhere, mercenary men of varying origins and unvarying aggressions. While surrounding their charge, they pulled knives on Junk, Chhiri Tendi and McGee. One particularly greasy fellow pushed Junk up against a rickshaw while another asked Yuudai "Did you make it to the top?"

"Yes" Yuudai lied.

The men let Junk and the others go and unceremoniously rushed Yuudai away. And so ended Yuudai's relationship with our tale. Nonetheless, Yuudai went on to weave his own tale. He fought for the Japanese Army at Coregidor and won accolades from his superiors. But then, when those same superiors began to order atrocities at Baatan and elsewhere, Yuudai refused to follow their commands. He was forced to retire from the Japanese military and his father stopped speaking to him. Once again, Yuudai was the outsider. He moved away from everyone he knew to make a new rural life for himself as a pear farmer in Shikoku. While he was out in the countryside, the cities of Tokyo, Nagoya, Kobe, Osaka, Yokohama, and Kawasaki were firebombed, and the cities of Hiroshima and Nagasaki were turned to glass. Japan surrendered. After the war ended, the Allies remained in Japan to get the place back in working order. And subsequently when the Allies left in 1952, Japan was trying its damnedest to recover from the anguish on its own. Widespread famine shrouded the nation, smashing Yuudai's go at a solitary, agrarian existence. This crisis turned out to be rather fortunate: Yuudai moved to the remains of Tokyo and began a life in music. Small crowds were immediately ignited by his mellifluous take on the American crooning style of Frank Sinatra (This popularity came despite the fact that Mr. Sinatra had just rekindled his career by starring in *From Here to Eternity*). Performances at nightclubs grew in attendance with each engagement. Today he can be heard over the airwaves of the Japanese Broadcasting Corporation. His voice is a soothing balm for a people deeply wounded – a good people who, like so many other good people throughout history, were dragged into the heat of battle along with their wives and children because of a small elite's appetite for conquest. Any of them within earshot is temporarily healed by Yuudai's blending of American jazz, rhythm & blues, and a touch of traditional Japanese *enka*. I was fortunate enough to catch one of his performances upon my recent visit to the Orient. He performed his most popular song *The Train to Her Heart*. Words cannot describe the beauty of that experience. It was standing room only in a smoky room full of clinking glasses. The audience was rapt. When he finished for the night, the applause was more than just deafening and relentless – its din contained a joyful declaration of optimism. Yuudai was finally receiving the approval he deserved for his kind, gentle ways. I chose not to speak to him afterwards, preferring to keep this wonderful, heroic, poetic man a mystery.

"Twas beauty killed the beast." The code words were not uttered by Gary Cooper, but by some other half-remembered swarthy scoundrel from *The Souls At Sea.* The pirate mumbled in broken English, "Captain Cooper sorry, not here for return trip." Cooper was currently sneaking into Los Angeles for the premiere of his hero's follow up film "Ball of Fire." That it co-starred Barbara Stanwyck only trebled the temptation for the captain. The last time the shipmates had seen Captain Cooper, it was just after dusk off the coast of Malibu and they were lowering him and his young lady friend into a rowboat. He was dressed in an immaculately fitted dinner jacket and she in a glittering formal gown many sizes too large for her frame. We cannot be certain whether they were able to sneak into the premiere that night, but according to the following day's Los Angeles Times, "an unidentified oriental man" was arrested for creating a public disturbance after offering Ms. Stanwyck a negligee "for later" and then punching out Gary Cooper when the actor came to her aid. The remainder of the captain's life is a mystery.

The sun was setting as Junk paid off the temporary captain for the extra passengers. He also paid the remaining porters and Sherpa and let them go, thanking them profoundly for their assistance. When it came time to bid Chhiri Tendi farewell, Junk kept it light and to the point. "You're a top-shelf Sherpa, Tendi" he said. "I hope our paths cross again. If you're ever in the States, pay me a visit." As luck would have it, Chhiri Tendi would be in the States permanently, as he decided to move his entire family to the Arizona desert in 1946. "I never wanted to be cold again" he explained. "Plus I liked Junk and McGee and some of the others, so I figured a move to America was a good idea. So far, so good, and I've never looked back." Chhiri Tendi often pays visits to Boston to see the white eyes, but only in the summer and only if Junk agreed to pay for the drinks. Other than those trips, Chhiri Tendi is where he always wanted to be, ever since he saw Hoover's decapitation. "I am with my family" he says while watching his wife and children eat. "Fucking gorgeous, right?"

When the time came several hours later for the ship to cast off, River Leaf was nowhere to be found. Literally tons of climbing equipment had been stowed away. The passengers were waiting on deck. The sailors were playing cards and yelling at each other. In a manner rather patrician, the temporary captain threatened Junk: "Five minutes we leave without girl." Junk was beside himself. He barked out orders to everyone. "Search the docks! Check the bars! We can't leave without her!" The investigations turned up nothing. River Leaf had held to her declaration on the mountain; she was going to have a go at living in India. The ship cast off two hours behind schedule at roughly 11 p.m. Standing at the stern, watching the lights of Calcutta disappear down the Hooghly, Junk was silent. He wrote in his journal later that night, "Hoyt was my enemy, my son, and in the end, for less than a day, my friend. When he died, I kind of died too. But then she was my hope. I could again be driven by someone outside of myself, and this time, for the right reasons. Now she's gone too...the greatest woman...no...the greatest person I've ever met. And I didn't get a chance to say goodbye to either of them." That was the last entry in Junk's journal from the expedition. Not the high note one would have hoped for.

The voyage home was uneventful despite the war going on all around them. The captain chose a route through the Indian Ocean, south around the African continent, and then northwest to Chappaquiddick. The risk inherent in this route had been the hurricane season, but they were spared any such cosmic mischief. McGee took up vomiting again. Junk joylessly played cards with the crew. Thornton kept to himself and read books from Cooper's library; predominantly a collection of primers on film making, the Kama Sutra, and German military weaponry. Chatham remained in his bed the entire journey, saying little to anyone. As it would turn out, Chatham would stay ill for the remainder of his short life. His adventures were over, save occasional nurse-assisted outings to the loo. His body never recovered from the excessive damage dealt by Fumu, save one exception. His mouth fully rebounded. He would spend the next three years torturing his nurses with seemingly infinite tales of cannibalism, lava, and crazed yaks, all of which the nurses passed off as the ravings of a madman. He finally succumbed to his wounds in the spring of 1945, mid-sentence.

Thornton would return to Columbia University to continue his linguistics work. At one point he attempted to write a book about the Fumu expedition, but Junk came after him and threatened him with physical violence should he do it. Everyone else had gotten the word, why not him? Junk wanted absolutely no written or verbal dissemination of what had happened. Junk would tell a few famed climbers about Fumu, and that was to be the extent of it. All of the deceased and missing were to be declared lost on either Hoyt or Junk's respective (and completely fabricated) Alaska or British Columbia expeditions. Families would also be told their loved ones "fell nobly" protecting the others from bear attack. In this way, they would all be left with a sense of pride and with very little motivation to go looking for a body. Thornton never published his book and continued to live the lie like every other expedition member.

The *Souls At Sea* arrived in Chappaquiddick on the evening of December 10th, 1941. Junk and McGee returned to Boston and – after surgery to remove four of Junk's fingers and four toes[10] - more or less continued their lives as if nothing had happened. They were given odd looks at parties, Junk due to his hobbling about on a cane, always favoring his left foot, and both of them due to their cracked and burnt faces. But that was about the extent of the differences as compared to before the journey. Legitimate and questionable business concerns alike flourished thanks to

---

[10] Junk refused to have the surgery done in Calcutta like everyone else. He wished to have the work done by white doctors he knew and trusted.

an infusion of cash from both Junk and McGee. Only a half year previous, many of these businesses had been on the brink of insolvency, but now their real estate holdings company, their craps games, their chain of department stores, all of them thrived. So actually, that was another difference from before. Junk and McGee could still be seen out and about, attending parties, gambling at their own establishments, running meetings with shareholders and the like. But Junk spoke less now, choosing to hold his tongue unless some dialogue was absolutely required. When he did speak, his voice had lost its stentorian punch. The old Junk could only be heard was when he was inebriated and cornering some young filly at a bar; in other words, every night at about eleven. His savage hunger for women had escalated since their return. McGee rarely saw his friend after midnight. And then in the late morning, he would see his friend again, often wearing the same clothing as the night before and a look of utter detachment. None of these women ever appeared with Junk in broad daylight. Come to think of it, almost everything had changed since their return from Fumu.

Not long after their return came the day Junk had dreaded for over a month. He took a train from Boston's South Station to New York's Pennsylvania Station. The cab ride to the Upper East Side must have been horrid; nerves like a muddy bog in the stomach, awareness of looming unpleasantries, and the only solace the promise of a stiff drink on the other side. He arrived at Wizzy's flat late in the afternoon. The door opened just enough for the woman inside to view the man at the threshold, and just as quickly, the door was closed.

Wizzy held a memorial for her husband. Few attended other than his family and several business associates who had something to gain from their appearance. No mountain climbers. No fellow church congregants. Junk stayed away from the services out of respect for Wizzy. McGee lurked in the back for reconnaissance purposes, holding his hat in one hand and blowing his bulbous, pink nose with the other.

All around was war; sibling rivalry writ large. Gun barrels ripe with fire aimed at the skies. Windows blackened at night. Materials of all kinds hoarded. Air-raid sirens at the ready. Bonds offered up as a benefaction to the gods of war. A whole generation of young men noticeably absent from the streets and parks and churches. So was the state of things as the Year of Our Lord 1942 came into being. Every new day could bring the End. The city of Boston was no different than the rest of the world. It was well known German submarines lurked only miles away in the Atlantic and possibly even in the harbour. Every heart, mind, and tongue was busy conjuring images of ruin.

But for Junk, the End was a mere formality. His actions in this world were already meaningless. He wandered the land like a wraith. While most around him feared the curtain coming down for the last time, Junk was already backstage removing his makeup.

One light did shine on this doleful soul but for a brief moment. The light came in the form of a letter, which arrived at Junk's Beacon Hill flat two days before Christmas. According to conversations with McGee years later, it was from Calcutta. We do not know the contents of the letter, for Junk never shared it with a soul; not even McGee. However, we do know that Junk visited the Beacon Hill Tavern that snowy night and bought a round of drinks for everyone.

When Junk finally did shed his mortal coil five years later, it was as it should have been. Whilst romancing Dinah Shore in his Beacon Hill flat, he tripped on the leg of a champagne bucket stand. His head met the stone floor that surrounded his fireplace and he did not get up. When the ambulance arrived, they found him, surrounded by melting ice and a roaring fire.

Postlude

*"The hills are a reclining female figure from whose breasts
flowed life-giving forces, and to them the Lakota went as a child
to its mother's arms."*
    - Luther Standing Bear

With the help of Chhiri Tendi, I visited Mano several years ago. My
first visions once inside the monasteries confused me terribly. Mano and
all of the other man-children were dressed in (rather dated and dusty) adult
clothing. The nature of the clothing varied with the person. Some wore
kilts, others lederhosen, bowler hats, World War I American infantry
uniforms, and so forth. Mano's garb was the uniform of a young Brazilian
tenente from the days of the revolts. Mano had grown since last time he
had donned the uniform; skinny wrists and yellowed socks poked out and
the shirt would only remain tucked for moments at a time. He and the
others were packing pieces of luggage that also looked quite out of fashion
and weathered. When I came into his room, Mano was placing several
weeks' worth of clothing, as well as dried meats and fruits, into a steamer
trunk.

"Some religions have expiry dates," Mano said. "Take Christianity for
example. When Jesus returns, the pope will be out of a job. So it is with
our little nameless religion. We have fulfilled our hopes and we are ready
to return to the world. We have been good children. We have appeased the
mountain."

I asked him how it was that he knew the mountain was pleased.

Mano put his arm around my shoulder and walked me to the open
wall. The day before us was gorgeous. The warmth was overpowering, as
if the entire Himalayan range had let down its guard and was willing to

discuss any topic. The air was so dry, the blue sky so cloudless overhead that looking at the view without squinting was nearly impossible. Through those squinted eyes, I took in two images that seemed impossible but were indisputable. For one, Fumu's summit was temporarily devoid of smoke. One could make out every detail of its ugly, tragic peak; a charred, misshapen lump abused by millennia of its own rage. The second vision was closer, and in some ways more spectacular; in ways terrifying. I was looking now at the base of the ridge between Asha and Lata that crossed my line of vision only about one mile away. Rivers of high-pressured water shot out of dead lava tubes and spilled forth over every inch of terrain. It washed over rocks, trees, barley fields, the legs of grazing zopkyoks, and even the supports of the monastery in which we stood. The sound of the flooding was not overpowering, but instead rather soothing; a calm river flowing beneath accompanied the low rumble of distant waterfalls.

The water flowing all around us was runoff from melting glaciers at the bottom of Fumu. Heavy with sediment, the liquid did not look like water at all, but instead had a bright white caste.

Mano turned to me, pointed outside and smiled.

"Milk."

Acknowledgements

Thanking everyone who made this book possible seems just as daunting as writing the book itself, and perhaps even as daunting as climbing a Himalayan mountain. Well, I suppose that's pushing it. First and foremost I would like to thank my wife Tricia for helping me so often when the words would not come, for going through the manuscript with unholy scrutiny, and for being such a cheerleader all along. She gave me confidence when it seemed there was no reason to have any and for that I am grateful.

I would also like to thank Roberto Pieraccini, a brilliant author and bon vivant, who was kind enough to read every chapter as I generated them and who supported me in every business decision I made with this book. He also mixes a mean *Negroni*.

I very much appreciate the efforts of Jochen Hemmleb, co-author of the astounding *Ghosts of Everest*, who so kindly answered my emails even though they came from a stranger.

Thanks to Peter Krogh for helping me understand the history of mountaineering and the equipment that goes into it. Oh, and thank you for posing as Hoover for the pictures at the reading.

Speaking of which, thank you to Kirk Wood Bromley – untouchable playwright and dear friend – for believing in this project enough to hold a staged reading of it at his performance space in Brooklyn. It was that nudge that gave me the confidence to finally self-publish.

Thanks to Krishna Dayanidhi, Kelly Homolka, Alex Johnson, and Doug Zacker for being the first brave souls other than my wife to ascend Fumu (i.e. read the manuscript from start to finish). You were heroic to give it a shot without any precedent.

A second thank you to Doug for also taking the author photos. You are a master photographer, sir. The images are perfect. Which reminds me: Thanks to Jerry Sullivan for dressing up like Tersely for the chilly photo shoot. You look great, and you were splendid at regaling Doug and I with ripping tales of Kilimanjaro and South Mountain Reservation.

Thanks to Dr. Robert Ganji, Bill Webster, and Alex Hoguet, for providing minutiae like World War II boat speeds, mental health laws in the 1930's and 1940's, and the challenges of traversing the Presidentials in winter.

I would like to also thank the author of *The Ascent of Rum Doodle*, W.E. Bowman, posthumously. His hilarious climbing parody set the bar very high for me and provided the ultimate challenge: Mix mountain climbing and humor while not being *The Ascent of Rum Doodle*. I hope I have succeeded.

This section would be far from complete if I did not thank my children, Ruby and Jesse. Unbeknownst to them, many of the ideas contained in this book came from their imaginations. Don't worry, kids, you'll get a cut of the nickel I expect to net from this thing.

Finally, a special thank you to my mother and father, Nancy and David Bloom. My mom gave me the writer's bug and the proofreader's obsessive compulsive attention to details. And when I fan the black smoke at the top of Fumu for a moment and squint to see what is really at the core of this book, I see my father, sharing story after story with me about Amundsen, Scott, Hillary, Tensing, Mallory, Shackleton, and many other wealthy gentiles striking out to achieve the impossible and the ridiculous. Were they heroes or idiots? Maybe both? Without the foundation of my father's storytelling powers, I would have never been inspired to write this book. Thanks, Dad!

Bibliography

Ardito, S. (2000). *Tales of Mountaineering*. White Star. Vercelli, Italy.

Bowman, W.E. (1956). *The Ascent of Rum Doodle*. Pimlico:London.

Brown, D. (1970). *Bury My Heart at Wounded Knee: An Indian History of the American West*. Henry Holt & Company: New York.

Cox, S.M., Fulsaas. K. (Eds.) (1960). *Mountaineering: The Freedom of the Hills*. The Mountaineers Books: Seattle.

Dixon, D. (1992). *The Practical Geologist*. R.L. Bernor (Ed.). Simon & Schuster: New York.

Farwell, B. (1984). *The Gurkhas*. W.W. Norton & Company: London.

Hemmleb, J., Johnson, L.A., Simonson, E.R., Nothdurft, N.E. (1999). *Ghosts of Everest: The Search for Mallory & Irvine*. The Mountaineers Books: Seattle.

Herzog, M. (1952). *Annapurna: First Conquest of an 8000-meter Peak*. E.P. Dutton and Co., Inc: New York.

Hoyt, E.P. (1986). *Japan's War: The Great Pacific Conflict*. Cooper Square Press: New York.

Isserman, M., Weaver, S. (2008). *Fallen Giants: A History of Himalayan Mountaineering from the Age of Empire to the Age of Extremes*. Yale University Press: New Haven.

Keay, J. (2000). *The Great Arc: The Dramatic Tale of How India Was Mapped and Everest was Named*. Perennial: New York.

MacInnes, H. (Ed.) (2003). *The Mammoth Book of Mountain Disasters: True Accounts of Rescue from the Brink of Death*. Running Press: Philadelphia.

Neale, J. (2002). *Tigers of the Snow: How One Fateful Climb Made the Sherpas Mountaineering Legends*. Thomas Dunne Books: New York.

Parsons, M., Rose, M.B. (2003). *Invisible on Everest: Innovation and the Gear Makers*. Northern Liberties Press: Philadelphia.

About the Author

Lord Kenneth Tersely is a figment of Jonathan Bloom's poorly-digested lobster roll dreams.

Jonathan Bloom is an author from Maplewood, New Jersey. He writes everything from academic book chapters to phone menus. *Hell Is Above Us* is his first novel.

Connect with the author online:
www.jonathanebloom.com
http://twitter.com/jonfrmmaplewood

Made in the USA
Charleston, SC
03 June 2012